S0-BBM-801

# Vegetable Markets in the Western Hemisphere

# VEGETABLE MARKETS IN THE WESTERN HEMISPHERE

EDITED BY

*Rigoberto A. Lopez* AND *Leo C. Polopolus*

IOWA STATE UNIVERSITY PRESS/AMES

Manufactured in the United States of America

♾ This book is printed on acid-free paper.



First edition, 1992

---

Library of Congress Cataloging-in-Publication Data

Vegetable markets in the western hemisphere / edited by
Rigoberto A. Lopez and Leo C. Polopolus. — 1st ed.
p. cm.
Includes bibliographical references and index.
ISBN 0-8138-1052-3
1. Vegetable trade—Western Hemisphere. 2. Vegetable trade—United States. 3. Vegetable trade—Latin America. I. Lopez, Rigoberto A. II. Polopolus, Leo.
HD9220.W5V44 1992
380.1'415'091812—dc20 90-21777

---



Rigoberto Lopez is Associate Professor, Department of Agricultural and Resource Economics, University of Connecticut, Storrs.

Leo Polopolus is Professor, Food and Resource Economics Department, University of Florida, Gainesville.

# CONTENTS

## SECTION III: TRADE LINKAGES IN THE WESTERN HEMISPHERE



## SECTION IV: ISSUES IN VEGETABLE TRADE

# PREFACE

The papers contained in this volume grew out of a workshop entitled "The Markets for Vegetables in the Western Hemisphere: Trends, Policies and Linkages," held on September 6-7, 1988, at Cook College, Rutgers University, in New Brunswick, New Jersey. We are thankful to the International Agriculture and Food Program (IAFP) at Cook College and its director Dr. Reed Hertford for coordinating the logistics and financial aspects of the workshop. Special thanks go to Dr. Roberta Cook from the University of California at Davis for being the most valuable adviser in the planning of the workshop and of this volume.

The following institutions provided support and/or financing for the workshop: the Rockefeller Foundation, the Farm Foundation, the Interamerican Institute for Cooperation in Agriculture (Costa Rica), and the Florida and New Jersey Agricultural Experiment Stations. Much of the credit goes to the participants themselves who were described by Professor Bryan How from Cornell University as "the best in the field."

We are all aware of the importance of vegetables for well-balanced nutrition and as a potential generator of farm income, employment, and foreign exchange earnings. World vegetable trade has increased fourfold in the last two decades, paralleling the world grain trade. Yet, the Western Hemisphere has missed a lot of the action. In Latin America, exports of fresh vegetables declined by 20 percent while the U.S. exports increased only twofold in the same period. At present, there is a series of forces increasing the pressure for expansion of production and trade of vegetables in the Americas.

In the United States, there is a need to search for alternative crops to replace part of the low-priced grain crops. The movement toward decoupling of domestic policies (i.e., removing price support-type policies) and removing complementary import restrictions is accelerating in the face of large budget deficits and trade liberalization. The extent to which the new immigration reform will constrain the U.S. vegetable industry expansion is uncertain. Vegetables seem to be a plausible alternative, although fresh vegetable consumption has grown only 2 percent per year in the last decade and processed vegetable consumption is at best stationary.

In Latin America and the Caribbean, there is a pressing need to increase foreign exchange earnings to ameliorate the foreign debt crisis and to export alternative, high-value added crops. Again, in the minds of many, vegetables seem to be a sensible if not a plausible alternative. Recent performance of various countries in the hemisphere has been mixed, and even some optimism on foreign investment and export expansion of vegetables under the Caribbean Basin Initiative has dissipated. The danger of synchronized supply expansion in the Western Hemisphere is disorderly marketing of vegetables and producer losses. Some may argue that these markets may need a quasi-marketing order at the hemispheric level to ensure a smooth operation of these markets.

With the exception of a few commodities, why has the Western Hemisphere *not* increased vegetable production and trade to its potential? What are the constraints and opportunities? What are the trends, policies, and linkages? What are the key research and policy issues? To this point, there is a severe lack of information to answer these important questions. Thus, we would like to state two broad objectives pursued in this volume:

- to increase our understanding of trends, policies, and linkages of vegetable markets in the Western Hemisphere; and

- to assess the potential benefits, prospects, and strategies of increasing vegetable production and trade in the Western Hemisphere.

The degree of success or failure of this volume is measured by how well these objectives are met. Given the pool of authors in the forthcoming chapters, there is no doubt that these challenges will be met with the highest degree of knowledge in this relatively unexplored area.

Rigoberto A. Lopez
*University of Connecticut*

Leo C. Polopolus
*University of Florida*

# SECTION I: THE U.S. VEGETABLE MARKET

# 1

# THE U.S. SUPPLY OF VEGETABLES

Shannon Reid Hamm
*Economic Research Service, USDA*

## INTRODUCTION

The production of vegetables has trended upward between 1970 and 1987, growing 2 percent a year, in response to the rising demand for vegetables. Not only did the quantity of vegetables increase but also the variety and the availability. Sourcing of fresh and processing vegetables is big business in the United States. Cash receipts for vegetables (including potatoes) in the United States reached $9.2 billion in 1987, representing 14 percent of total agricultural crop receipts. The value for 1988 likely will fall slightly, due to lower potato and lettuce receipts plus the drought's negative impact on processed vegetable quantity and prices.

Even as more states supply vegetables, California, Florida, Wisconsin, Minnesota, and Texas still supply the majority of vegetables. The major fresh states have traditionally been California, Florida, Arizona, and Texas. The major processing states have traditionally been California, Wisconsin, Minnesota, and Oregon. However, in the face of increasing competition they are battling for shares of the U.S. vegetable market.

The importance of imports in vegetable supplies has increased over the years in the United States. Availability of vegetables, particularly fresh, increased within the season and over time. The majority of imports are from Mexico and recently the Caribbean Basin Initiative (CBI) countries for fresh vegetables and Spain and Taiwan for processing vegetables.

The objectives of this paper are to illustrate trends in supply of fresh and processed vegetables for key commodities at the national and regional levels and to discuss factors affecting the comparative advantage of producers within the United States. I conclude by addressing a few of the key issues which likely will affect the U.S. vegetable industry.

## TRENDS IN OUTPUT

Fresh and processing vegetable production grew at a steady 2 percent per year rate between 1970 and 1987 (Table 1.1). However, production for each category of vegetables grew at different rates. The majority of the increase was in fresh production, followed by frozen and then canned. It is noteworthy to point out that if processing tomato production were excluded from the analysis, production for canning would currently be trending down.

Table 1.1. Production of Fresh and Processing Vegetables, 1970-87

| | Production | | |
|---|---|---|---|
| Year | Fresh | Processing | Total |
| | Million pounds | | |
| 1970 | 15,218 | 16,914 | 32,132 |
| 1971 | 15,288 | 17,388 | 32,676 |
| 1972 | 15,774 | 18,105 | 33,879 |
| 1973 | 16,430 | 18,749 | 35,178 |
| 1974 | 16,973 | 20,822 | 37,794 |
| 1975 | 16,689 | 24,266 | 40,955 |
| 1976 | 17,610 | 19,618 | 37,228 |
| 1977 | 17,874 | 22,640 | 40,514 |
| 1978 | 18,442 | 19,960 | 38,403 |
| 1979 | 19,277 | 22,352 | 41,629 |
| 1980 | 19,190 | 19,114 | 38,304 |
| 1981 | 19,641 | 18,443 | 38,084 |
| 1982 | 20,792 | 22,359 | 43,152 |
| 1983 | 19,792 | 20,540 | 40,332 |
| 1984 | 21,713 | 22,790 | 44,503 |
| 1985 | 21,793 | 23,584 | 45,377 |
| 1986 | 21,627 | 23,233 | 44,860 |
| 1987 | 21,960 | 24,429 | 46,389 |
| | Percent | | |
| AAG[a] | 2 | 2 | 2 |

SOURCE: National Agricultural Statistics Service, USDA.

[a]AAG = The average annual growth rate.

## Fresh Market

Production of the 10 major fresh vegetables (asparagus, broccoli, carrots, cauliflower, celery, sweet corn, honeydews, lettuce, onions, and tomatoes) has grown steadily since 1970, reaching 22 billion pounds in 1987. The vegetables that showed the most rapid growth were the less traditional dual-use items, like broccoli and cauliflower. Output of broccoli rose a phenomenal 8 percent per year between 1970 and 1987, with an eightfold increase in market value to $239 million. Cauliflower production grew 7 percent per year during this period, while value increased ninefold to $188 million.

When production and value are broken down by type, fresh output for broccoli and cauliflower grew much faster than processing (Table 1.2). This

Table 1.2. Fresh and Processing Production for Broccoli and Cauliflower, 1970-87

| | Broccoli | | Cauliflower | |
|---|---|---|---|---|
| Year | Fresh | Processing | Fresh | Processing |
| | Million pounds | | | |
| 1970 | 98 | 216 | 135 | 94 |
| 1971 | 129 | 189 | 127 | 118 |
| 1972 | 138 | 227 | 161 | 138 |
| 1973 | 150 | 201 | 144 | 150 |
| 1974 | 159 | 234 | 155 | 148 |
| 1975 | 204 | 191 | 174 | 124 |
| 1976 | 223 | 206 | 199 | 108 |
| 1977 | 257 | 312 | 211 | 156 |
| 1978 | 265 | 275 | 182 | 199 |
| 1979 | 326 | 305 | 263 | 149 |
| 1980 | 380 | 295 | 280 | 145 |
| 1981 | 452 | 301 | 349 | 173 |
| 1982 | 542 | 340 | 342 | 195 |
| 1983 | 558 | 274 | 370 | 171 |
| 1984 | 674 | 355 | 482 | 187 |
| 1985 | 715 | 347 | 490 | 176 |
| 1986 | 844 | 309 | 591 | 162 |
| 1987 | 861 | 282 | 593 | 145 |
| | Percent | | | |
| AAG[a] | 13 | 2 | 9 | 3 |

SOURCE: National Agricultural Statistics Service, USDA.

[a]AAG = The average annual growth rate.

corresponds to changes in demand for fresh and processing. The relative importance of processing is reflected in the differences between the fresh and processing price. The price for fresh broccoli and cauliflower has traditionally been higher than for processing because the fresh market demands a higher quality product. These vegetables are thus grown primarily for the fresh market with the processing market taking residual supplies.

Even though carrots are also considered a dual-use vegetable like broccoli and cauliflower, they did not share the dramatic growth in production and value seen with broccoli and cauliflower. This is primarily a result of the carrot sector being a mature industry, with carrot production accounting for 12 percent of total fresh output in 1970 and 12 percent in 1987. Even though some states grow both fresh and processing carrots, a few states, like Arizona, grow only for the fresh market. As demand for fresh increases and that of canning declines, to only about 27 percent of the total processing crop, production likely will shift more into fresh. States growing for the fresh market continue to receive the highest output value per unit of input, while those growing for the processing market do not receive the same increase in revenues.

Production of the remaining fresh market vegetables (asparagus, celery, honeydews, lettuce, onions, and tomatoes) rose less rapidly. Moderate growth in these vegetables is understandable since they already capture the major share of the fresh vegetable market and product development has not inundated this group. While production of these vegetables continues to be concentrated in California, other states' share of total fresh output has increased.

## New Production Areas Emerging

Many states which traditionally have not been major players in commercial vegetable production are entering the arena. Much of the acreage has been devoted to vegetables like broccoli and cauliflower, as alternatives to traditional agricultural crops. Examples of this phenomenon are found in states like Virginia and Maine, which now are shippers of fresh broccoli. Other states like Alabama, Illinois, and Colorado are exploring the profitability of vegetable production and have themselves begun shipping broccoli. Producing a few acres of these high-valued vegetables has provided supplemental income to many small farmers in these and other states who were hurt in the early 1980s as crop prices plummeted and world markets dwindled.

Support for diversification into these and other more exotic and ethnic vegetables has been strong at the state level with help from groups such as county extension agents, and with the U.S. Department of Agriculture

(USDA) establishing a Small Farms Office. Estimates of the increased supply range, depending on how they are collected, because no official statistics exist. However, a consensus estimate puts the overall increase around 5 percent of the total U.S. supply.

The success of these states staying in the business of producing traditional commercial vegetables is contingent on several factors. First and most significant is that many of the growers are not experienced in vegetable production. They may not be able to efficiently compete with the traditional states that have the expertise and economies of scale, which help ensure their success, especially during periods of low prices. As prices of many traditional crops have recently strengthened, questions about appropriate resource allocations are being raised in these nontraditional states. Secondly, the need for labor to harvest vegetables places a huge burden on states not geographically close to major vegetable producing states which rely heavily on migrant labor. And thirdly, as supplies of vegetables increase, the newer, smaller states will find it hard to compete for a share of the U.S. vegetable market.

## Improved Technology Enhances Regional Specialization

Supplies regionalized as the technology in refrigerated transportation improved between 1970 and 1987, thus placing the source of fresh vegetables further from large urban areas. For example, broccoli sold in Eastern markets from 1970 through the early 1980s came predominately from California. California's favorable climate over other states allowed it to produce the largest quantities of broccoli and cauliflower, along with many other fresh vegetables. However, during the early 1980s producers in states such as Alabama and Virginia, identified and captured a small market window (Zwingli et al., O'Dell). By looking at the seasonal pattern of prices for broccoli, prices tended to be higher in the spring and fall months when California broccoli supplies drop. As broccoli grows favorably in the East during these months, Eastern markets can procure broccoli and cauliflower from closer states and receive a fresher product with lower associated transportation costs.

Despite the emergence of new producing areas selling in small market windows, the bulk of vegetable supplies will continue to come from states with the strongest comparative advantage, such as California and Florida. However, the long-term trend of expanding market niches for exotic, organic, greenhouse, and hydroponic vegetables from the less traditional States is likely to continue.

## Processing Market

Production of the four major processing vegetables (snap beans, sweet corn, green peas, and tomatoes) trended upward modestly during the 1970s and into the 1980s, as compared to fresh (Table 1.1). Total processing vegetable production grew 1.8 percent per year between 1970 and 1987. Sweet corn and tomatoes for canning in the early 1970s grew at the fastest pace due to strong demand and product diversification. Output for freezing snap beans, sweet corn, and green peas grew at a brisk 9 percent per year over the period.

The increase in production of canning vegetables over the period was due to stronger demand for processing tomatoes. Most of the growth in processing tomatoes is attributed to the expansion in the fast food industry and the increased availability of retail processed tomato products. Processed tomato output grew at an annual average of 2 percent and accounted for an average of 62 percent of total canning output. Canning snap bean, sweet corn, and green pea output remained fairly constant over the nearly two decades.

If processing vegetables are considered a distinct subsector of the vegetable industry, then the relative importance of the four major processing vegetables changed during the 1970-87 period. Processing tomatoes' share of the subsector's market peaked in 1975 at 70 percent. The market share since then has fallen as processing sweet corn's share grew from 20 to 25 percent. Even with the slight decline in share, tomatoes still account for the lion's share of the four major processing vegetables' output. Tomatoes accounted for about 62 percent of total 1987 production of the four major processing vegetables, down from 64 percent in 1986. This decline in share is likely to continue due to forces reducing supply such as imports.

Specialization of processing vegetable production resulted in production being heavily concentrated in the North Central states during the 1970s (See Appendix for definitions). As production technologies, packaging, and transportation favored canning during this period, the majority of processing output was in canned versus frozen form (Table 1.1). However with the development of refrigerated transportation, abundant water, and cheap hydrological power in the Pacific Northwest, freezing production increased and shifted to these states. The Pacific Northwestern states' comparative advantage has declined somewhat as new freezing technology, like Individually Quick Freezing technique (IQF), has lessened the need for water in processing and thus has lowered the cost of production. In turn, the North Central states have recaptured about 25 percent of freezing output.

The role that climate plays in each vegetable sector's relative importance changed the processing sector's share of 1988 production. The drought lowered production in the North Central states (Illinois, Wisconsin, Minnesota, Michigan, New York, and Ohio), which are the primary states for canning snap beans, sweet corn, and green peas. The drought's damage was most extensive on the processing green pea crop, with about 50 percent loss in those states. Green pea production likely will be at its lowest level since the earliest statistics were calculated. The canning snap bean and sweet corn crops will not be as severely devastated, due to the crops' ability to withstand more stress and because of last-minute rains. Sweet corn production for canning likely will fall 30 percent, while the decline in snap bean output likely will be about 22 percent from these states. The lower yields and quality from these three processing crops will reduce their value and thus their share of the total processing subsector's value in 1988.

## Specialization in Processing Tomatoes

The processing tomato industry is an example of the dynamics in comparative advantage. California's share of total processing tomato output has steadily increased between 1970 and 1987 to 88 percent in 1987 (Table 1.3). California accounted for 85 percent of the $448 million in 1987 processed tomato receipts. California's advanced production technology (e.g. mechanical harvesting) and controllable climate helped to boost its share of total production to more than 80 percent. The mechanical harvester, the ability to devote large segments of land to tomatoes, and high yields all contributed to California's becoming the major world supplier of processed tomatoes (Runsten and Moulton). California has a unique ability to control climate as the majority of rain falls within a 4-month period (December through March). This is combined with the extensive use of irrigation during the dry months to enhance yields and quality. However, some of these field-based advantages are being shared by other competing countries as world supplies steadily rise. California's world dominance is in paste, which consumes over half of its processing tomatoes.

California has benefited from increased demand in paste due to the growth in the fast food industry. The higher prices for paste brought about larger tonnages of California processing tomatoes. California's tomato pack became very concentrated in paste and a few others which experienced higher prices. This heavy reliance on paste recently outstripped demand, causing bulk paste supplies to burgeon. California's large paste supplies have resulted in lower prices of paste and other products. The industry has indirectly helped itself by slowing the growth in imports, though the victory did not come without a large price. California tomato processors and producers have consolidated in order to better withstand economic stresses.

Table 1.3. California's Share of U.S. Processing Tomato Production

| Year | Production | | California's Share of U.S. |
|---|---|---|---|
| | U.S. | California | |
| | Million pounds | | Percent |
| 1970 | 11,018 | 6,726 | 61 |
| 1971 | 11,031 | 7,759 | 70 |
| 1972 | 11,607 | 9,052 | 78 |
| 1973 | 11,869 | 9,723 | 82 |
| 1974 | 14,040 | 11,695 | 83 |
| 1975 | 17,008 | 14,541 | 85 |
| 1976 | 12,944 | 10,133 | 78 |
| 1977 | 15,558 | 13,339 | 86 |
| 1978 | 12,735 | 10,579 | 83 |
| 1979 | 14,659 | 12,700 | 87 |
| 1980 | 12,421 | 11,082 | 89 |
| 1981 | 11,432 | 9,806 | 86 |
| 1982 | 14,598 | 12,296 | 84 |
| 1983 | 14,060 | 11,946 | 85 |
| 1984 | 15,362 | 13,184 | 86 |
| 1985 | 14,354 | 12,204 | 85 |
| 1986 | 14,787 | 12,961 | 88 |
| 1987 | 15,204 | 13,405 | 88 |

SOURCE: National Agricultural Statistics Service, USDA.

## TRENDS IN IMPORTS

Competition for market share has increased not only from nontraditional vegetable producing states but also from other parts of the world. Overall, imports of vegetables accounted for 8 percent of total supply in 1987, up from 5 percent in 1970 (Table 1.4). Mexico is by far the most important supplier of imported fresh vegetables, while processed vegetable imports are more widespread from Western Europe and Asia (Table 1.5).

### Mexican Fresh Imports

Mexico has a favorable climate during the winter months when U.S. fresh vegetable supplies are lowest (Table 1.6). The winter vegetable competition

Table 1.4. Importance of Value of U.S. Vegetable Imports, 1970-87

| Year | Imports: Total Agricultural | Imports: Vegetables and Preparations | Vegetables as a Percent of Total |
|---|---|---|---|
| | Million Dollars | | Percent |
| 1970 | 5,770 | 296 | 5 |
| 1971 | 5,823 | 298 | 5 |
| 1972 | 6,467 | 365 | 6 |
| 1973 | 8,419 | 428 | 5 |
| 1974 | 10,221 | 408 | 4 |
| 1975 | 9,293 | 376 | 4 |
| 1976 | 10,966 | 455 | 4 |
| 1977 | 13,438 | 639 | 5 |
| 1978 | 14,805 | 796 | 5 |
| 1979 | 16,724 | 790 | 5 |
| 1980 | 17,366 | 864 | 5 |
| 1981 | 16,772 | 1,055 | 6 |
| 1982 | 15,389 | 1,127 | 7 |
| 1983 | 16,530 | 1,074 | 6 |
| 1984 | 19,334 | 1,331 | 7 |
| 1985 | 19,968 | 1,385 | 7 |
| 1986 | 21,440 | 1,603 | 7 |
| 1987 | 20,398 | 1,535 | 8 |

SOURCE: Foreign Agricultural Trade of the United States (FATUS), ERS, USDA.

is primarily between Florida and Mexico. Mexican supplies accounted for 36 percent of the 1987/88 winter fresh vegetable market (snap beans, cucumbers, eggplant, bell peppers, squash, and tomatoes). Imports from Mexico have increased significantly over the past few years.

Mexican imports have stabilized supplies of winter fresh vegetables by supplementing low domestic supplies. Mexican vegetable growers are in full production between December and April. Florida vegetables have been devastated by freezes during the coldest winter months in 4 out of the last 6 seasons. Thus Mexico's ability to capture a large share of the U.S. winter fresh vegetable market is due primarily to its favorable climate and close proximity to the United States but also to lower wage rates and land costs (Treichler).

Table 1.5. Major Sources of U.S. Vegetable Imports, by Value, 1987

| Country of Source | Value | As a percent of: Fresh and Frozen | Preparations and Preserves | Total United States | Leading Commodity Imported and Percent of U.S. Imports |
|---|---|---|---|---|---|
| | Million dollars | | Percent | | |
| Mexico | 544.7 | 90 | 10 | 35 | Tomatoes (96), Cucumbers (93), Onions (84) |
| Spain | 164.4 | 2 | 98 | 11 | P.[a] Olives (90), P. Artichokes (99), P. Tomatoes (19) |
| Taiwan | 128.9 | 13 | 87 | 8 | Peas (31), P. Mushrooms (43) P. Asparagus (29) |
| Canada | 123.1 | 75 | 25 | 8 | Carrots (68), Potatoes (99), Dry beans (18) |
| China | 68.8 | 3 | 97 | 4 | P. Mushrooms (33) |
| Japan | 42.5 | 2 | 98 | 3 | |
| Italy | 41.3 | 9 | 91 | 3 | P. Tomatoes (39) |
| Hong Kong | 38.4 | 1 | 99 | 3 | P. Mushrooms (13) |
| Germany | 32.8 | 0 | 100 | 2 | |
| Brazil | 29.4 | 4 | 96 | 2 | |
| Switzerland | 29.1 | 0 | 100 | 2 | |
| Thailand | 25.8 | 3 | 97 | 2 | |
| Dom. Rep. | 4.2 | 67 | 33 | 2 | Peas (12) |
| South Korea | 23.5 | 0 | 100 | 2 | |
| Guatemala | 20.3 | 93 | 7 | 1 | Peas (18) |
| Total U.S. | 1534.9 | 47 | 53 | 100 | |

SOURCE: FATUS, Calendar Year 1987 Supplement, USDA, ERS.
[a] P.= Processed

Mexican vegetable growers have entered the frozen vegetable business exporting more asparagus, broccoli, and cauliflower to the United States. The frozen imports flow into the U.S. market year-round and thus make total imports less seasonal. Mexican imports accounted for 84 and 95 percent of all the 1987 imported frozen broccoli and cauliflower in the United States, up from 83 percent, each, in 1983. Mexico appears to have a competitive advantage over California in the frozen broccoli and cauliflower market, because it has lower total labor and land costs (Cook). The recent U.S. immigration law, now being implemented, will likely force up agricultural wage rates in the United States and result in an even wider wage disadvantage.

Access to U.S. markets is further facilitated by the presence of large multinational companies in Mexico like Birdseye, Green Giant, and Campbells.

Table 1.6. Mexico's Import Share of Selected Fresh Vegetables

| Season | Mexican Import Share of | | | | | |
|---|---|---|---|---|---|---|
| | Snap Beans | Cucumbers | Eggplant | Bell Peppers | Squash | Tomatoes |
| | Percent | | | | | |
| 1970/71 | 13 | 59 | 51 | 51 | 41 | 55 |
| 1971/72 | 16 | 48 | 53 | 40 | 36 | 55 |
| 1972/73 | 15 | 51 | 62 | 40 | 33 | 52 |
| 1973/74 | 16 | 53 | 53 | 44 | 37 | 58 |
| 1974/75 | 9 | 36 | 41 | 29 | 29 | 53 |
| 1975/76 | 10 | 46 | 46 | 32 | 34 | 47 |
| 1976/77 | 18 | 50 | 46 | 38 | 37 | 47 |
| 1977/78 | 21 | 52 | 51 | 46 | 48 | 57 |
| 1978/79 | 24 | 68 | 48 | 42 | 43 | 54 |
| 1979/80 | 24 | 59 | 51 | 46 | 55 | 46 |
| 1980/81 | 19 | 57 | 42 | 38 | 30 | 36 |
| 1981/82 | 17 | 52 | 43 | 48 | 49 | 36 |
| 1982/83 | 18 | 54 | 45 | 39 | 53 | 39 |
| 1983/84 | 19 | 39 | 51 | 47 | 55 | 43 |
| 1984/85 | 24 | 54 | 44 | 47 | 42 | 35 |
| 1985/86 | 26 | 54 | 45 | 42 | 55 | 37 |
| 1986/87 | 23 | 58 | 43 | 44 | 63 | 38 |
| 1987/88 | 23 | 62 | 54 | 44 | 59 | 32 |
| AAG [a]/ | 4 | 0 | 0 | -1 | 2 | -3 |

SOURCE: Federal State Market News Service, Marketing Florida Vegetables Summary.
[a]AAG = The average annual growth rate.

Joint ventures between these companies and Mexican producers have provided a marketing channel for these products in the United States. However, some evidence exists that increased production in Mexico may soon reach a saturation point because Mexican laws prohibit foreigners from owning land and Mexican interest must hold the lion's share of the business (Treichler).

### CBI Countries' Fresh Imports

Imports of fresh vegetables have also risen from other smaller countries trying to compete for share of the U.S. fresh vegetable market. The Caribbean Basin Initiative (CBI) countries have increased imports of selected vegetables 82 percent between 1983 and 1987 (Table 1.7). However, it is not accurate to conclude that this increase was solely in response to the Act which provided duty-free access to U.S. markets for 12 years (Peters). Some of these vegetables under their former treatment in the Generalized System of Preferences (GSP) of the General Agreement on Tariffs and Trades (GATT) already were receiving duty-free status. The vegetables which did have tariffs often were imported with no tariffs levied primarily due to their winter shipping season. The winter vegetable period represents a seasonal low in U.S. fresh vegetable supplies and the most significant period for fresh vegetable imports.

The recent attention paid to imports from the CBI countries has stimulated economic activity in several of the Caribbean countries, though they still represent only about 5 percent of total fresh imports. Imports from CBI countries consist primarily of fresh melons, frozen broccoli, okra, and peas (Table 1.7).

Table 1.7. U.S. Imports of Vegetable Products from Caribbean Basin Beneficiary Countries

| Commodity | 1983 | 1985 | 1986 | 1987 Value | 1987 CBI as % of world | Top Ranking Suppliers |
|---|---|---|---|---|---|---|
| | Thousand dollars | | | | Percent | |
| **Dutiable** | | | | | | |
| Fast Track: | | | | | | |
| Melons, other | 1,606 | 3,359 | 7,813 | 12,982 | 50 | Guatemala, El Salvador, Panama, C.R. |
| Dasheens | 5,242 | 7,481 | 6,888 | 5,642 | 73 | Dominican Republic (D.R.) |
| Yucca | 1,807 | 2,392 | 3,105 | 3,135 | 96 | C.R. |
| Sweet potatoes | 1,387 | 1,804 | 1,733 | 1,945 | 99 | D.R. |
| Chayote | 1,498 | 1,580 | 1,362 | 1,311 | 51 | C.R. |
| Tomatoes | 339 | 542 | 2,077 | 1,097 | 1 | D.R., Jamaica |
| Peas, pidgeon | 634 | 478 | 569 | 322 | 90 | D.R. |
| Beans, green | 235 | 355 | 131 | 141 | 1 | Jamaica, D.R. |
| Non-Fast-Track: | | | | | | |
| Peas, pidgeon, fz | 1,220 | 1,205 | 1,267 | 1,978 | 95 | D.R. |
| Vegetables, other | 920 | 1,078 | 557 | 909 | 2 | Honduras, C.R. |
| Tomato paste | 0 | 278 | 410 | 111 | 3 | D.R. |
| **Non-Dutiable** [a] | | | | | | |
| Cantaloupes, fresh | 1,867 | 5,997 | 7,215 | 8,243 | 19 | Honduras, Guatemala, D.R. |
| Peas, prep/pres. | 6,058 | 4,897 | 5,935 | 7,054 | 81 | D.R., El Salvador, Guatemala |

(continued, next page)

Table 1.7 (continued)

| Commodity | 1983 | 1985 | 1986 | 1987 Value | 1987 CBI as % of world | Top Ranking Supplier |
|---|---|---|---|---|---|---|
| | Thousand Dollars | | | | Percent | |
| Broccoli, cut/slice, fz | 1,758 | 4,201 | 6,364 | 6,982 | 25 | Guatemala |
| Okra, cut/slice, fz | 6,482 | 5,223 | 4,093 | 4,848 | 99 | D.R., El Salvador, Guatemala |
| Peas, other | 2,237 | 3,058 | 3,865 | 4,663 | 45 | Guatemala, D.R. |
| Yams, fresh | 2,121 | 3,159 | 4,000 | 4,628 | 55 | Jamaica |
| Vegetable substances | 3,305 | 4,577 | 4,351 | 4,184 | 23 | D.R., other |
| Peppers, fresh | 1,349 | 3,381 | 3,299 | 1,745 | 3 | Jamaica, D.R. |
| Cucumbers, fresh | 1,022 | 2,212 | 1,470 | 1,498 | 3 | Jamaica, Bahamas, Honduras |
| Okra, fresh | 294 | 783 | 1,353 | 879 | 13 | Guatemala |
| Palm hearts | 105 | 458 | 311 | 869 | 12 | C.R., prep/pres. |
| Grand Total | 41,486 | 58,498 | 68,168 | 75,166 | – | |

SOURCE: Horticultural Circular, May 1988, Foreign Agricultural Service, USDA.
[a]GSP items plus MFN-free.

The largest quantity of vegetables exported to the United States from the CBI countries comes from the Dominican Republic (DR). Its share of U.S. fresh vegetable imports was 2 percent in 1987, a drop from 3 percent in 1986 (Table 1.5). The major fresh vegetable exported to the United States from the DR is dasheens, which accounted for 73 percent of the DR's agricultural exports to the United States (Table 1.7). Other vegetables exported to the United States from DR were peas, yams, cantaloupes, and tomatoes. Growth in market share from CBI countries likely will continue to increase as many of the vegetables imported are growing in demand, as multinational companies continue to invest in these countries, and as the United States pursues furthering trade liberalization.

The increase in CBI countries' share of the U.S. market does not, however, mean that the traditional vegetable producing states will be replaced. A recent study found that imports from the CBI countries were primarily competing with the winter fresh vegetable market (Peters). Florida, the primary producing state, and Mexico, the primary exporting country, likely will continue to dominate the winter fresh vegetable market as they both are geographically closer to the markets.

The primary finding indicated that simply comparing costs and revenues was insufficient to assess comparative advantage. The study looked at two winter fresh vegetables (cucumbers and peppers) primarily from Jamaica due to the country's strong economic need to diversify and increase exports.

The study found that the impact of these vegetables on Florida's winter fresh vegetable market was and will likely continue to be minimal because of Jamaica's higher production costs and strong trade controls. The continued use of export licensing requirements or papers for duty exemptions by the Jamaican government perpetuates time delays. These associated costs of exporting vegetables are not accounted for in the costs of production and further skew the competitive advantage towards Florida producers. Also, the ability to obtain adequate and timely transportation to the U.S. market severely limited their competitiveness.

## Processed Imports

U.S. imports of canned and frozen vegetables have increased 14 percent per year between 1978 and 1987 to 1 billion pounds. However, prior to 1978, the United States was not a major importer of processed vegetables, and much of the trade data are unavailable. In 1987, the leading regions exporting processed vegetables to the United States were Western Europe (primarily Italy and Spain) with about 13 percent of total processed imports and Asia (primarily Taiwan and Japan) with 11 percent (Buckley, et al.).

The recent increase (since about 1981) in processed imports was primarily in tomato paste and resulted from the overvalued U.S. dollar and expanded reprocessing capacity in the United States. The expanded processing capacity arose as huge tonnages of bulk paste were imported and adding value such as repackaging and/or processing became profitable (Runsten and Moulton). Processed tomato imports are by far the most important category of processed imports.

Imports of processed tomatoes were primarily in bulk paste, peaking in 1982 at 51 percent of total processed tomato imports. However, as domestic production of paste increased and prices dropped, imports of paste declined. The share of processed tomatoes accounted for by paste imports has fallen from an all time high of 198 million pounds in 1982 to 93 million pounds in 1987. By volume, the largest product imported was canned tomatoes, accounting for 59 percent of the 1987 total processed tomato imports. Overall, processed tomato imports have risen 8 percent per year between 1978 and 1987. This surge in import share has forced U.S. tomato processors to compete more aggressively for their share of the U.S. market.

The major exporting countries of processed tomatoes to the United States are Israel, Italy, Spain, Portugal, and Mexico. Their relative importance in the U.S. processed tomato industry have changed as they have become increasingly specialized. Israel, Italy, and Spain hold the lion's share of imported tomato products, while Portugal and Mexico dominate in paste exports to the United States (USDA).

## FURTHER CONSIDERATIONS

The vegetable industry is facing a rapidly changing environment. In order for the U.S. industry to remain competitive, it must address several major issues.

Trade liberalization is currently stimulating negotiation of free trade agreements between the United States and countries like Canada and Mexico. Freer trading of U.S. vegetables likely will expand U.S. producers' markets but at the same time make foreign vegetables more competitive in the United States. However, the U.S./Canada Free Trade Agreement contains a Snapback provision. The Snapback provision allows either country to reestablish the preexisting tariff levels within two weeks for a 60-day period if economic damage is found to the industry. The provision, however, requires both countries to maintain databases which include daily prices and imports and annual acreage.

The impact of Immigration Reform legislation on the vegetable industry is still uncertain. Assessment of impacts is difficult due partly to the lack of consistent cost of production budgets for vegetables from major producing states. No Congressional mandate currently exists for Cost of Production data on vegetables. The Reform's greatest impact will likely be to tighten labor supplies and raise wage rates that will in turn widen the labor cost disadvantage that now exists for vegetable growers in the United States relative to many foreign competitors.

Extending the Caribbean Basin Initiative likely will guarantee continuance of duty-free entry of produce beyond 1996. Some of the imports are in direct competition with domestically produced commodities and will force further adjustments in the U.S. vegetable industry.

Competition facing U.S. vegetable producers will increase from imports of vegetables, particularly frozen items. Competition will also originate from the less traditional states as the need and desire to diversify continues. Rising wage rates, freer trade policies, improved production and transportation technologies in nontraditional States, packaging, and marketing systems will all continue to exert pressure on traditional supply areas. Some of the vegetables which have been faced with heavy competition are currently looking at implementing various tools to reduce the competition. These range from Country/Region of Origin legislation to more enforcement of pesticide residue levels.

# APPENDIX

## Regional Distribution of States

| Region | States |
|---|---|
| Northeast | Maine, Vermont, New Hampshire, Massachusetts, Connecticut, New York, Pennsylvania, New Jersey |
| South | Delaware, Maryland, West Virginia, Virginia, Kentucky, Tennessee, North Carolina, Georgia, Florida, Alabama, Mississippi, Louisiana, Arkansas, Oklahoma, Texas |
| North Central | Ohio, Michigan, Indiana, Illinois, Wisconsin, Minnesota, Iowa, Missouri, North Dakota, South Dakota, Nebraska, Kansas |
| West | Montana, Wyoming, Colorado, New Mexico, Idaho, Utah, Arizona, Washington, Oregon, Nevada, California, Alaska, Hawaii |

## REFERENCES

Buckley, Kate C., Shannon Reid Hamm, Ben Huang, and Glenn Zepp. U.S. Fruit and Vegetable Processing Industries, USDA, ERS Staff Report No. AGES880216, August 1988.

Cook, Roberta. "California Broccoli and Cauliflower Growers Face Increasing Competition," *Vegetable Situation and Outlook Report*, USDA, ERS, TVS-244, February 1988.

Hoff, Frederic L. The Produce Industry: An Overview of Trends and Trade. A speech presented to the Joint Council on Food and Agricultural Sciences, Washington, D.C., April 14, 1988.

O'Dell, Charles R. Fall Broccoli Production Guide for Virginia. Virginia Cooperative Extension Service Publication 438-011, Virginia Tech University, 1984.

Peters, Mark A., and Timothy G. Taylor. "An Analysis of the Economic Potential for Export Vegetable Production in Jamaica." Unpublished M.S. thesis, University of Florida, Gainesville, Florida.

Runsten, David, and Kirby Moulton. "Competition in Processing Tomatoes." In Marketing California Specialty Crops: Worldwide Competition and Constraints. University of California Agricultural Issues Center, Spring 1988.

Treichler, Randy. Vegetables from Mexico: A Study of Fresh and Processed Imports. A paper for International Agricultural Development, University of California, Davis, California. January 1988.

U.S. Department of Agriculture. "Horticultural Products Review." Foreign Agricultural Service. FHORT 5-88, May 1988.

Zwingli, M.E., J.L. Adrian, W.E. Hardy, and W.J. Free. Wholesale Market Potential for Fresh Vegetables Grown in North Alabama. Alabama Agricultural Experiment Station Bulletin No. 586, Auburn University, July 1987.

# 2

# THE U.S. DEMAND FOR VEGETABLES

Vicki A. McCracken
*Washington State University*

## INTRODUCTION

Total consumption of vegetables and potatoes in the United States has increased over the last several decades. Per capita consumption of the major commercial fresh and processed vegetables increased over 20 percent since the early 1960s. Per capita potato consumption increased 6 percent over the same time period. By 1986, consumption of fresh vegetables had risen to 87.2 pounds per person. Fresh potato consumption increased to 51.9 pounds per person in 1986, up over the previous 8 years but considerably lower than in the years prior to 1970.

A number of changes have occurred in recent years which have affected the vegetable and potato industries. These include changes from within the industries themselves (e.g., technological advances in production, processing, and marketing), changes external to the industries in society which affect consumer demand for vegetables and potatoes (e.g., increased consumer income, changed household composition, indicated interest in diet, health, and fitness) and an interaction of these factors (Jones). The focus of this paper is on the second group of changes and their impact on vegetable and potato consumption.

The objective of this paper is to identify and explore the changes which have occurred in the consumption of fresh and processed vegetables and potatoes in the United States in recent years. First, changes in the structure of the U.S. population and trends in overall food and vegetable and potato consumption are discussed. Second, empirical studies on vegetable and potato consumption are reviewed and the importance of selected consumer characteristics in affecting future consumption are summarized. Finally, the relevance of this information for the vegetable and potato industries is discussed. The data sources and information needs for better understanding the demand side of the market are identified.

## BACKGROUND

Food consumption patterns are influenced by a number of factors. The functional or physiological value of a food is important. Food is purchased because of its nutritional contribution to health. Food is also valued for sociological and psychological reasons. Certain foods are demanded because they reflect the social status, religious beliefs, or aesthetic values of consumers or because they are consistent with consumers' life-styles. The level of consumption of a food is usually impacted by its economic value or price, as well as by its availability. In addition, consumers' knowledge and information (or possibly misinformation) about a food will influence their decision to consume the food. No single influence alone fully explains a society's or a specific consumer's food preferences. For example, U.S. consumers are concerned about nutrition but do not maximize the nutritive value of each dollar spent on food. They are health conscious but overeating is likely just as much of a problem as is insufficient food, and they are price conscious but do not always buy the least expensive foods. Regional, ethnic, and religious food preferences which were significant in the past appear to be breaking down with the mobile society. Consequently, in understanding food preference or food consumption patterns, a multitude of factors need to be considered.

The food consumer purchases a bundle of attributes, which include not only the farm value of the food, but also product form (e.g., fresh vs. processed), place (e.g., for consumption at home vs. away from home), and time utilities (e.g., at harvest only vs. all year round). For example, potatoes can be consumed as frozen fries at a fast food facility, as potato salad purchased from the delicatessen at the local supermarket, or as baked potatoes prepared from the fresh product at home. Thus, consideration of the entire product bundle (not just the farm component) is necessary for understanding and predicting food consumption, and hence in order to decide what to produce, how to produce it, and how to market it.

The previously mentioned factors affect an individual consumer's food preferences. Food is typically produced for groups of consumers. Hence, information about general health concerns, the socioeconomic and demographic structure, and food consumption trends of the entire population is important.

## TRENDS IN CONSUMPTION

Americans have become increasingly aware of and concerned about the amounts of fat, cholesterol, sugar, sodium, and fiber in their diets. Also of concern is the availability of certain vitamins and minerals in the foods they consume. Coupled with these changing nutritional concerns are other socioeconomic and demographic trends which directly or indirectly impact the diet of the U.S. population. Changes have occurred with respect to the size and age-sex composition of households, the number of households with multiple wage earners, the urbanization and geographical location of residences, the racial mix of the population, and the per capita income. Those 65 and over are an increasing share of the total population, and the average household size has declined. There has been a steady growth in the number of married female wage earners. The percent of white households has declined. Population growth has shifted to the South and West, away from urban areas, and per capita income has been rising.

These changes have been accompanied by alterations in food eating patterns, including what is eaten (meat vs. vegetables), when it is eaten (meals vs. snacks), where it is eaten (at home vs. away from home), and in what form it is eaten (fresh vs. processed). Per capita expenditures for food consumed at home (FAH) as a proportion of total per capita food expenditures for food has decreased since at least 1960 (Figure 2.1). The proportion spent

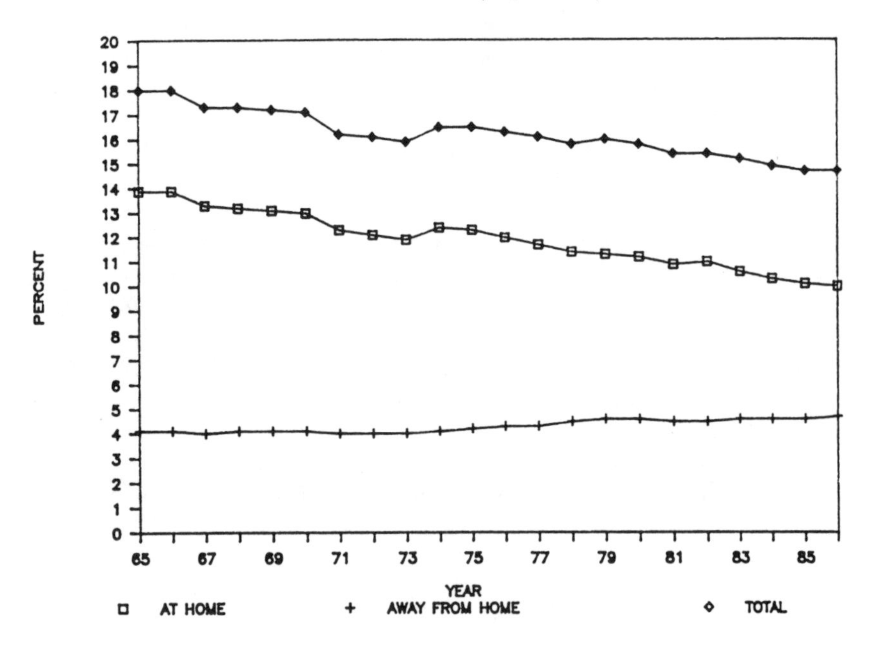


Figure 2.1. Expenditures for Food (Percent of Disposable Income)

SOURCE: Karen L. Bunch. *Food Consumption, Prices, and Expenditures.* USDA, ERS Statistical Bulletin No. 749, January 1987 (Table 92). Data are from the U.S. Department of Commerce, Bureau of Economic Analysis.

on food away from home (FAFH) has increased slightly. Within the total FAFH market, consumption has shifted from conventional full-service restaurants to fast-food establishments (Figure 2.2). The fast-food establishment's share of the away-from-home food dollar grew from less than 10 percent in the early 1960s to 31 percent in 1986 (Manchester).

This shift of expenditures from FAH to FAFH reflects an increased demand for marketing services and directly affects the marketing channels and institutions with which producers, food processors, shippers, and other commodity specialists must deal (O'Rourke). Traditionally, a small number of food items accounted for the majority of food purchases away from home. In recent years, this has changed towards more variety in the foods obtained from the FAFH sector. FAFH markets have increasingly become important interpreters of consumer demand, with their product specifications influencing what is grown and how it is produced and packaged. Within the FAH market a large number of convenience foods such as pre-cut vegetables, microwavable vegetable dishes, and ready-to-eat delicatessen salads have appeared. Hence, certain households may be substituting consumption of convenience foods at home for eating out.

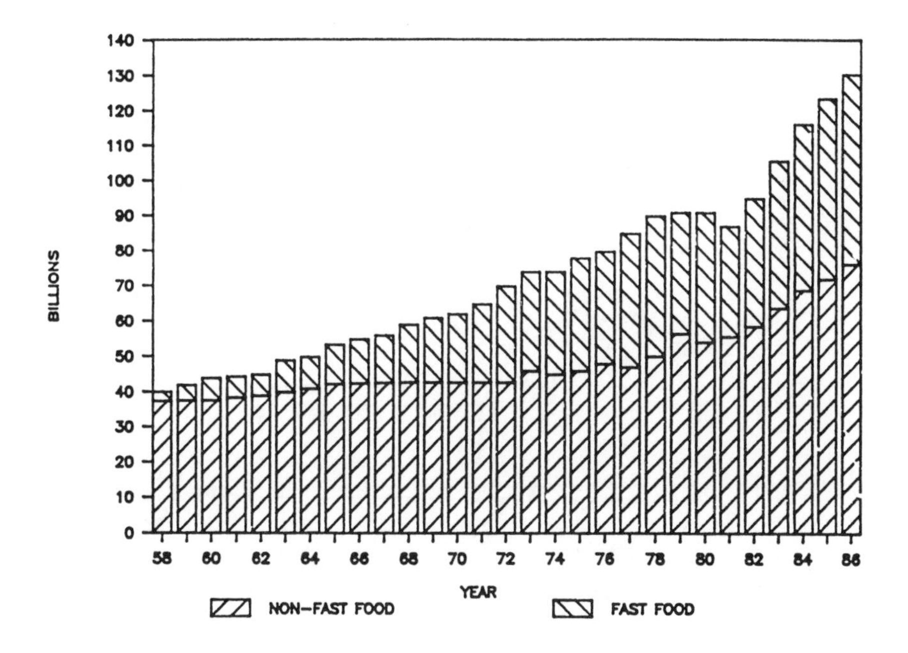


Figure 2.2. Away From Home Food Expenditures (Billions of Dollars)

SOURCE: U.S. Department of Agriculture, National Agricultural Statistics Service. *Agricultural Statistics*, 1987.

The mix of foods consumed in the United States has changed considerably since the mid-1960s. Relative to 1967 consumption levels, the average American is consuming more food, but the increase in crop products is almost three times greater than that of animal products (Figure 2.3). Within the group of crop products, consumption of sugars and sweeteners and vegetables has increased more (relative to their respective 1967 level) than fruits and cereals (Figure 2.4). Despite the rather steady upward trend in total vegetable consumption, there have been important changes in the product form consumed (i.e., fresh vs. processed) and in the specific vegetables consumed. Some of the major changes in vegetables and potato consumption are discussed below.

Total consumption of fresh and processed vegetables (excluding potatoes) increased to about 190 pounds per person per year in 1985. Fresh vegetable consumption constituted about 48 percent of the total, or 91 pounds. Canned

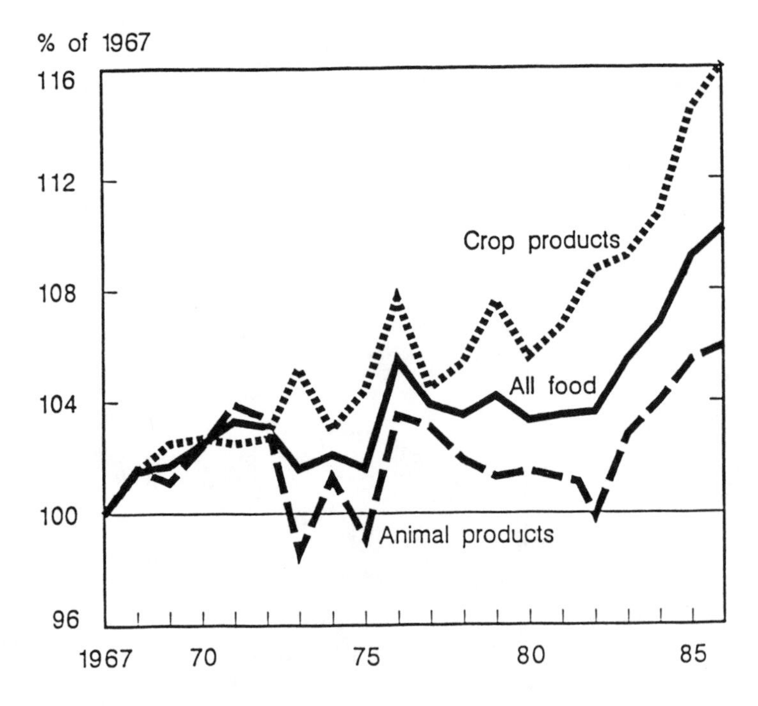


Figure 2.3 Per Capita Consumption of Food (Percent of 1967)

SOURCE: *1988 Agricultural Chartbook.* USDA Agriculture Handbook No. 673, April 1988 (Chart 124).

and frozen vegetable consumption accounted for 43 percent and 9 percent of total consumption, respectively. Over the last 15 years, the trend in vegetable consumption has been toward fresh and frozen products and away from canned products (Figure 2.5). Over this time period fresh and frozen vegetable consumption increased 21 percent and 20 percent, respectively, while canned vegetable consumption declined about 8 percent (Love). Some vegetables have followed these general trends while others have not (Table 2.1).

Tomatoes continue to be America's second favorite vegetable, with only potatoes being consumed in larger quantities. Per capita consumption of tomatoes increased during the 1960s and 1970s, peaked in the mid-1970s at about 75 pounds, then leveled off at a slightly lower level in the late 1970s and early 1980s. However, by the mid-1980s consumption was again on the rise, possibly related to the trend towards eating away from home and the growing popularity of tomato-based ethnic foods (Love).

The largest percentage increases in vegetable consumption have been for

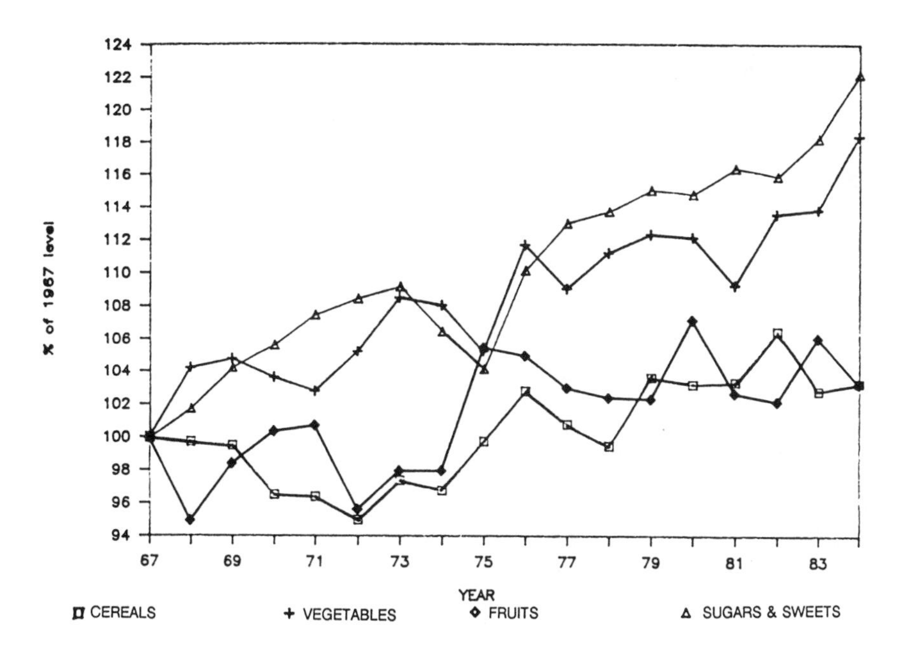


Figure 2.4. Selected Crop Products (Per Capita Consumption)

SOURCE: Karen L. Bunch. *Food Consumption, Prices, and Expenditures.* USDA, ERS Statistical Bulletin No. 749, January 1987 (Table 23).

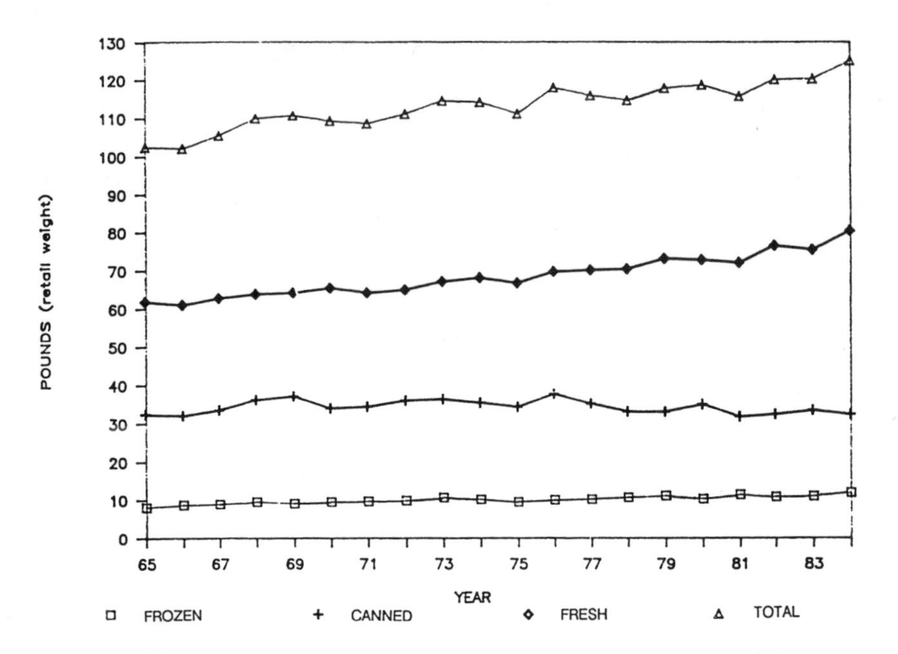


Figure 2.5. Per Capita Consumption of Vegetables (Pounds [Retail Weight])

SOURCE: U.S. Department of Agriculture. Economic Research Service. *Agricultural Outlook Yearbook.* March 1987 (Table 32C).

broccoli and cauliflower. It is speculated that these vegetables have been increasingly popular among consumers who are seeking to increase their consumption of foods that are high in vitamins and fiber (Love). Consumption of broccoli and cauliflower in both the fresh and frozen form has increased, but there has been a greater push towards the fresh product. Per capita consumption of fresh broccoli and cauliflower increased 175 percent and 123 percent between the 1974-76 and 1983-85 periods, respectively. Consumption of both reached record highs in the 1980s, increasing over 20 percent between 1985 and 1986.

Salad bars in restaurants and fast-food establishments grew in popularity in the 1970s, and they continue to be popular as they are installed in supermarkets and other retail stores. Lettuce and other salad vegetables benefited from the increased away-from-home eating in the 1960s and 1970s. Per capita lettuce consumption increased about 1.5 percent per year from 1962-77, leveled off at about 26 pounds during the late 1970s and early 1980s, and declined slightly in the mid-1980s. This decline has increased interest in new types of lettuce such as Butterhead and varieties from new technologies (Love). Celery consumption has followed a growth and decline pattern similar to that of lettuce since the late 1960s. Trends in the consumption of other vegetables can be determined from Table 2.1, and are generally consistent with the movement towards the fresh and frozen products and away from the canned product.

Table 2.1. Per Capita Consumption of Selected Vegetables and Potatoes–Fresh and Processed (Farm-Weight Basis)

| Commodity | 1974-76 | 1977-79 | 1980-82 | 1983-85 | 1986 | 1987[a] |
|---|---|---|---|---|---|---|
| | Pounds per Person | | | | | |
| **Asparagus** | | | | | | |
| Fresh | .41 | .30 | .33 | .42 | .65 | .60 |
| Canned | .54 | .38 | .35 | .30 | .29 | .30 |
| Frozen | .22 | .19 | .12 | .09 | .09 | .10 |
| **Broccoli** | | | | | | |
| Fresh | .95 | 1.24 | 1.87 | 2.62 | 3.46 | 3.60 |
| Frozen | 1.05 | 1.30 | 1.39 | 1.44 | 1.64 | 2.20 |
| **Carrots** | | | | | | |
| Fresh | 6.59 | 5.69 | 7.15 | 7.69 | 7.80 | 8.50 |
| Canned | .98 | 1.05 | .88 | .90 | .91 | .90 |
| Frozen | 2.65 | 2.61 | 2.39 | 2.50 | 2.32 | 2.40 |
| **Cauliflower** | | | | | | |
| Fresh | .91 | 1.08 | 1.52 | 2.03 | 2.68 | 2.70 |
| Frozen | .62 | .70 | .86 | .91 | .92 | .90 |
| **Celery** | | | | | | |
| Fresh | 7.20 | 7.24 | 7.71 | 7.42 | 7.10 | 7.10 |
| **Corn[b]** | | | | | | |
| Fresh | 7.88 | 7.50 | 7.29 | 7.60 | 7.11 | 7.30 |
| Canned | 12.88 | 13.34 | 11.66 | 11.10 | 11.89 | 10.50 |
| Frozen | 5.87 | 7.02 | 7.38 | 8.60 | 9.02 | 7.90 |
| **Green Beans** | | | | | | |
| Canned | 4.73 | 5.30 | 3.68 | 4.27 | 3.79 | 3.70 |
| Frozen | 1.43 | 1.40 | 1.49 | 1.68 | 1.75 | 2.00 |
| **Green Peas[c]** | | | | | | |
| Canned | 2.85 | 2.84 | 2.61 | 2.15 | 2.16 | 2.00 |
| Frozen | 1.93 | 1.81 | 1.69 | 1.93 | 1.88 | 1.70 |
| **Lettuce** | | | | | | |
| Fresh | 23.75 | 25.78 | 26.00 | 25.70 | 23.21 | 22.70 |
| **Onions** | | | | | | |
| Fresh | 15.00 | 16.10 | 15.50 | 18.19 | 19.02 | 16.30 |

(continued, next page)

Table 2.1 (continued)

| Commodity | 1974-76 | 1977-79 | 1980-82 | 1983-85 | 1986 | 1987[a] |
|---|---|---|---|---|---|---|
| | | | Pounds per Person | | | |
| **Tomatoes** | | | | | | |
| Fresh | 12.13 | 12.80 | 13.33 | 14.91 | 17.17 | 16.80 |
| Canned | 62.96 | 61.94 | 60.98 | 64.10 | 63.40 | 64.60 |
| **Total Fresh Reported** | 73.20 | 75.57 | 82.40 | 84.43 | 87.00 | 85.60 |
| **Potatoes** | | | | | | |
| Fresh | 50.60 | 50.52 | 47.09 | 47.41 | 49.60 | 44.00 |
| Canned | 2.08 | 2.19 | 1.87 | 1.79 | 1.10 | 1.80 |
| Frozen | 36.96 | 41.88 | 38.02 | 41.00 | 44.30 | 44.30 |
| Other Process | 30.80 | 27.89 | 26.90 | 28.19 | 28.60 | 28.60 |

SOURCE: USDA, ERS

[a]1987 figures are preliminary and are rounded up to one decimal point.

[b]"On-COB" basis.

[c]"In-Shell" basis.

Potato consumption deviates from the general shift towards fresh vegetable consumption (Table 2.1 and Figure 2.6). In 1965, 64 percent of potatoes (on a farm-weight basis) were consumed in the fresh form. By 1985, less than 42 percent were consumed in the fresh form. Over this time period, total potato consumption trended upward slowly. The growth in the processed has been mainly due to an increased popularity of frozen products in the fast-food market with consumption increasing almost 200 percent (from 14.3 to 42.4 pounds).

Since the early 1970s, the variety of vegetables offered by retail food stores has grown considerably. A 1986 study conducted by the Produce Marketing Association and the Food Marketing Institute found that the number of produce items carried by the average retail grocery store increased from about 65 in 1970 to over 200 in 1986 (Greenberg). Food service operations have also followed the trend of increased product diversity and have added a number of specialty produce items to their menus. Hence in future years, it is expected that there will continue to be changes in consumption of vegetables.

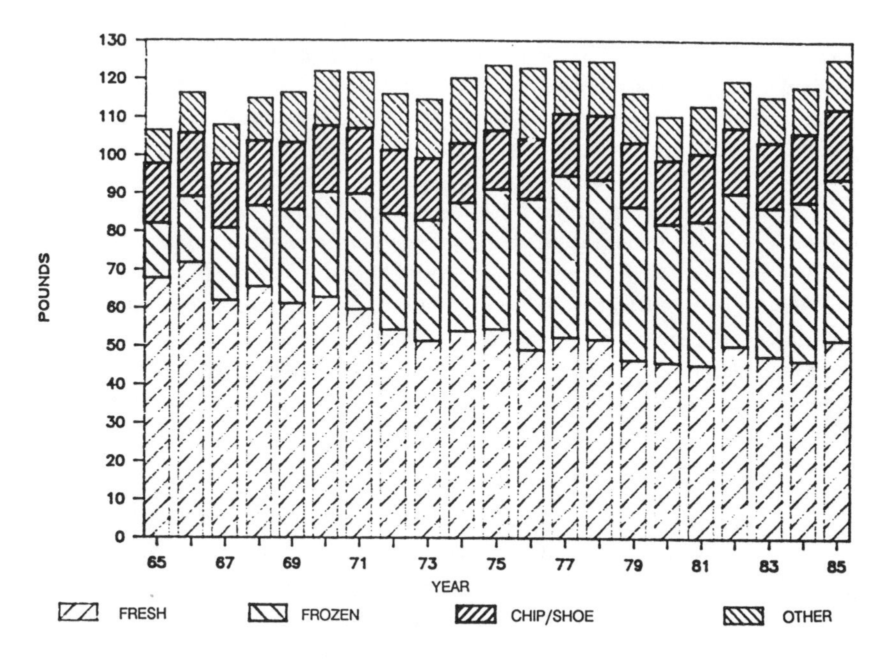


Figure 2.6. Per Capita Consumption of Potatoes (Pounds)

SOURCE: Karen L. Bunch. *Food Consumption, Prices, and Expenditures.* USDA, ERS Statistical Bulletin No. 749, January 1987 (Table 23).

## CONSUMPTION PATTERNS BASED ON CROSS-SECTION DATA

The above discussion of food consumption trends is based on per capita figures obtained from United States Department of Agriculture's (USDA's) food supply historical series which measures national aggregate "consumption" of several hundred foods. This concept of food consumption is based on a commodity-flow concept, and is the residual of total supply (production, imports, and beginning stocks) after subtracting off other uses (exports, shipments to U.S. territories, seed requirements, nonfood industrial use, livestock feed, year-end stocks, and waste). This is not a measure of actual food consumption but of food disappearance. Nevertheless, the two concepts are highly associated for perishable products like food and hence either measure provides a fairly reasonable indicator of trends over time (Bunch).

Data on actual ingestion of and expenditures on food are available only from periodic surveys of households and individuals. The USDA conducts a national survey of household food consumption (NFCS) approximately every 10 years. Since 1985, continuous surveys of food consumption for subgroups of U.S. individual households have been conducted on a more frequent basis (e.g., CSFII-1985). These surveys provide individual product detail on foods available for consumption by the households, as well as household socioeconomic and demographic data. These cross-sectional data provide a detailed snapshot of food use by individuals and households and allow researchers to sort out some of the important food consumption determinants (e.g., household size and age-sex composition, income, and location of residence) which are concealed in aggregate time series data. The most recent of these comprehensive surveys, for which data are available, was conducted in 1977 (a survey is currently being conducted and data will soon be available for analysis).

Another group of household surveys with national coverage is the Bureau of Labor Statistics (BLS) Consumer Expenditure Surveys (CES), which were conducted at about 10-year intervals between 1888 and 1979. Since 1979, Continuous Consumer Expenditure Surveys (CCES) have been initiated on a smaller group of households, with provision for summary reports on a quarterly basis. The main purpose of the CES and CCES is to provide comprehensive data on spending (food and nonfood) in American households. These surveys do not provide as much detail for individual food products as does the USDA survey, and their focus is on expenditure rather than quantity used.

Despite the limitations of the USDA and BLS household survey data, they do provide food consumption and expenditure detail at various points in time and for selected market segments. The following discussion is based on data from these surveys.

The finding of an increased importance of the away from home market over time is also obvious from BLS Expenditure Survey (Table 2.2). In 1972-73, 26.8 percent of the food budget was spent away from home. By 1980-81, this figure had increased to 32.4 percent. This trend was also evident in the USDA Survey Data, although the magnitude of the numbers differs because of differences in the surveys (Table 2.2). The BLS survey also shows an increase in expenditures for fresh vegetables for consumption at home and a decrease in processed vegetable expenditures between 1972-73 and 1980-81, consistent with previously reported findings based on time series quantity data.

Large changes occurred in the at-home consumption of selected vegetables and potato products between the 1965-66 and 1977-78 USDA household survey periods (Table 2.3). Consumption increases were recorded for many

Table 2.2. Allocation of Food Expenditures, 1972-73, 1977-78, and 1980-81

| | 1980-81 | 1972-73 | % Change in CPI, 1972-73 to 1980-81 | 1977-78 | 1965-66 |
|---|---|---|---|---|---|
| | | | % | | |
| Total Food | 100.0 | 100.0 | 87.1 | 100.0 | 100.0 |
| Food Away From Home | 32.4 | 26.8 | 95.7 | 22.6 | 17.9 |
| Food At Home | 67.6 | 73.2 | 84.6 | 77.4 | 82.1 |
| Food At Home | 100.0 | 100.0 | 84.6 | 100.0 | NA |
| Vegetables | 7.4 | 7.9 | 95.3 | 7.3 | NA |
| Fresh | 4.6 | 4.5 | 81.3 | 3.9 | NA |
| Processed | 2.8 | 3.4 | 104.4 | 3.4 | NA |

SOURCE: J.R. Blaylock and D.M. Smallwood. U.S. Demand for Food: Household Expenditures, Demographics and Projections. USDA, ERS Technical Bulletin No. 1713, February 1986. 1972-73 and 1980-81 figures are based on BLS 1972-73 CES and 1980-81 CCES. 1977-78 figures are from 1977-78 USDA Nationwide Food Consumption Survey.
NOTE(S): NA indicates Not Available.

Table 2.3. Quantity of Vegetables and Potatoes Used per Person in One Week, 1965-66 and 1977-78

| | 1965-66 | 1977-78 | % Change 1965-66 to 1977-78 |
|---|---|---|---|
| Fresh Vegetables | 2.450 | 2.693 | +10 |
| Dark Green, Leafy | 0.104 | 0.110 | + 6 |
| Carrots | 0.143 | 0.158 | +10 |
| Tomatoes | 0.426 | 0.422 | - 1 |
| Cabbage | 0.202 | 0.269 | +33 |
| Lettuce | 0.390 | 0.428 | +10 |
| Corn | 0.262 | 0.211 | -19 |
| Onions | 0.247 | 0.215 | -13 |
| Commercial Canned Vegetables | 0.864 | 0.903 | + 5 |
| Commercial Frozen Vegetables | 0.180 | 0.192 | + 7 |
| Juice–Canned Vegetables | 0.169 | 0.160 | - 5 |
| Dried Vegetables | 0.106 | 0.094 | -11 |
| Sweet Potatoes | 1.740 | 1.386 | -20 |
| Fresh White | 1.487 | 1.160 | -22 |
| Fresh Sweet Potatoes | 0.094 | 0.061 | -35 |
| Commercial Frozen | 0.050 | 0.054 | + 8 |
| Chips, Sticks, Salad | 0.071 | 0.078 | +10 |

SOURCE: USDA Human Nutrition Information Service, Consumer Nutrition Division, NFCS 1977-78 Report No. H-6, June 1983 (Table 26). Data are from the 1965-66 and 1977-78 USDA Nationwide Food Consumption Survey.

fresh vegetables. Cabbage consumption increased 33 percent while corn consumption decreased 19 percent. Home use of commercially canned and frozen vegetables also increased, while canned juice and dried vegetable consumption decreased. These figures are not entirely consistent with those previously reported based on time series data partially because of the different food consumption measures used (i.e., food disappearance vs. food availability) and inclusion of foods consumed away from home (in the time series data). Fresh potato consumption decreased rather dramatically (22 percent) while commercially processed potato product consumption increased between the two survey periods, a finding which is fairly consistent with the time series data.

Regional differences in household vegetable and potato consumption and expenditure can be seen in a tabulation of the 1977-78 USDA survey data (Tables 2.4 and 2.5). The regional differences varied depending upon how consumption was measured–quantities vs. expenditures–and whether food consumed away from home was included. Differences in expenditures for a

Table 2.4. Average Intake of Vegetables and Potatoes of Individuals Using At Least Once in 3 Days by Region, 1977-78

| Food Group | Northeast | North Central | South | West |
|---|---|---|---|---|
| All food: | | | | |
| Total Vegetables | 192 | 201 | 203 | 195 |
| White Potatoes | 57 | 71 | 62 | 53 |
| Tomatoes | 28 | 24 | 24 | 27 |
| Dark Green Vegetables | 8 | 6 | 11 | 8 |
| Deep Yellow Vegetables | 9 | 8 | 8 | 9 |
| Other Vegetables | 90 | 92 | 99 | 98 |
| Food Away from Home: | | | | |
| Total Vegetables | 29 | 32 | 32 | 33 |
| White Potatoes | 10 | 13 | 11 | 12 |
| Tomatoes | 4 | 3 | 3 | 3 |
| Dark Green Vegetables | 1 | 1 | 1 | 1 |
| Deep Yellow Vegetables | 1 | 1 | 1 | 1 |
| Other Vegetables | 14 | 14 | 15 | 16 |

SOURCE: USDA Human Nutrition Information Service, Nutrition Monitoring Division, NFCS 1977-78 Report No. I-3, July 1985. Data are from the 1977-78 USDA Nationwide Food Consumption Survey.
NOTE(S): Figures are in grams per day.

Table 2.5. Weekly per Person Expenditures for Vegetables and Potatoes by Region, 1977-78

| Item | Region | | | | |
|---|---|---|---|---|---|
| | All | Northeast | North | South Central | West |
| Vegetables and potatoes | 1.37 | 1.58 | 1.22 | 1.31 | 1.43 |
| Vegetables | 1.11 | 1.30 | .94 | 1.05 | 1.21 |
| Fresh | .60 | .73 | .49 | .54 | .71 |
| Dark Green | .07 | .10 | .05 | .06 | .07 |
| Deep yellow | .04 | .05 | .04 | .03 | .05 |
| Light green | .20 | .22 | .17 | .20 | .22 |
| Tomatoes | .10 | .12 | .07 | .09 | .13 |
| Other | .20 | .25 | .17 | .16 | .24 |
| Canned | .32 | .35 | .30 | .33 | .30 |
| Frozen | .12 | .15 | .10 | .10 | .12 |
| Juice | .03 | .03 | .03 | .03 | .03 |
| Dried | .04 | .03 | .02 | .05 | .04 |
| Potatoes, including sweet | .26 | .27 | .28 | .26 | .22 |
| Fresh | .14 | .14 | .14 | .16 | .11 |
| Canned | .01 | .01 | .01 | .01 | .01 |
| Frozen | .02 | .03 | .03 | .01 | .02 |
| Dehydrated | .01 | .01 | .01 | .01 | .01 |
| Chips, sticks, and salads | .09 | .09 | .10 | .07 | .08 |

SOURCE: D.M. Smallwood and J.R. Blaylock. Household Expenditures for Fruits, Vegetables, and Potatoes, USDA, ERS, Technical Bulletin No. 1690, May 1984. Data are from the 1977-78 USDA Nationwide Food Consumption Survey.

NOTE(S): Group and subgroup totals may not be equal due to rounding.

given physical quantity of food could be reflecting differences in the quality (and hence price) of the food consumed.

Table 2.4 shows regional vegetable intake differences (aggregating over method of processing) and Table 2.5 shows regional expenditure differences by method of processing and vegetable (for the fresh form). Average per capita total intake of vegetables (at and away from home) was highest in the South (203g/day) and lowest in the Northeast (192g/day). In contrast, in terms of total at-home vegetable expenditures, per capita weekly expenditures were highest in the Northeast ($1.58/week) and lowest in the North Central Region ($1.22/week).

White potato intake (total of at and away from home) was highest in the North Central Region (71g/day) and lowest in the West (53g/day). Total at-home potato expenditures were also highest (slightly) in the North Central Region ($.28/week) and lowest in the West ($.22/week). Only small regional differences were observed in deep yellow vegetable consumption. Dark green vegetable intake was highest in the South (11g/day) and lowest in the North Central Region (6g/day). Expenditures on dark green vegetables were highest in the Northeast ($.10/week) and lowest in the North Central Region ($.05/week).

Per capita vegetable and potato expenditures also differed by household income level (Table 2.6), household size (Table 2.7), and race of household

Table 2.6. Weekly per Person Expenditures for Vegetables and Potatoes by Income Quintile, 1977-78

| | Income Quintile | | | | | |
|---|---|---|---|---|---|---|
| Item | I(lowest) | II | III(middle) | IV | V(highest) | Not Reported |
| Vegetables and potatoes | 1.48 | 1.39 | 1.29 | 1.30 | 1.45 | 1.36 |
| Vegetables | 1.23 | 1.14 | 1.03 | 1.03 | 1.19 | 1.10 |
| Fresh | .64 | .60 | .54 | .56 | .68 | .61 |
| Dark green | .09 | .07 | .06 | .05 | .07 | .07 |
| Deep yellow | .04 | .04 | .04 | .04 | .05 | .04 |
| Light green | .22 | .19 | .18 | .18 | .23 | .20 |
| Tomatoes | .11 | .11 | .09 | .09 | .11 | .09 |
| Other | .18 | .19 | .17 | .19 | .23 | .20 |
| Canned | .38 | .36 | .32 | .30 | .30 | .31 |
| Frozen | .10 | .10 | .11 | .12 | .15 | .11 |
| Juice | .03 | .02 | .03 | .04 | .04 | .03 |
| Dried | .07 | .06 | .03 | .02 | .02 | .04 |
| Potatoes, including sweet | .25 | .25 | .26 | .28 | .26 | .26 |
| Fresh | .17 | .16 | .13 | .12 | .12 | .14 |
| Canned | .01 | .01 | .01 | .01 | .01 | .01 |
| Frozen | .01 | .02 | .02 | .03 | .03 | .02 |
| Dehydrated | .01 | .01 | .01 | .01 | .01 | .01 |
| Chips, sticks, and salads | .06 | .07 | .09 | .11 | .10 | .08 |

SOURCE: D.M. Smallwood and J.R. Blaylock. Household Expenditures for Fruits, Vegetables, and Potatoes, USDA, ERS, Technical Bulletin No. 1690, May 1984. Data are from the 1977-78 USDA Nationwide Food Consumption Survey.
NOTE(S): Annual income after taxes for income quintiles: I(lowest)–$3,385; II–$7,020; III–$10,469; IV–$14,567; and V(highest)–$23,168. Group and subgroup totals may not be equal due to rounding.

Table 2.7. Weekly per Person Expenditures for Vegetables and Potatoes by Household Size, 1977-78

| | Household Size (number of members) | | | | | | |
|---|---|---|---|---|---|---|---|
| Item | All | 1 | 2 | 3 | 4 | 5 | 6 or more |
| Vegetables and potatoes | 1.37 | 1.94 | 1.67 | 1.46 | 1.28 | 1.15 | 1.04 |
| Vegetables | 1.11 | 1.68 | 1.40 | 1.18 | 1.01 | .90 | .80 |
| Fresh | .60 | .99 | .82 | .64 | .53 | .46 | .40 |
| Dark green | .07 | .12 | .09 | .07 | .06 | .05 | .05 |
| Deep yellow | .04 | .07 | .06 | .04 | .04 | .03 | .03 |
| Light green | .20 | .32 | .27 | .20 | .18 | .15 | .14 |
| Tomatoes | .10 | .17 | .13 | .10 | .08 | .08 | .07 |
| Other | .20 | .31 | .27 | .22 | .18 | .14 | .12 |
| Canned | .32 | .40 | .35 | .35 | .31 | .29 | .27 |
| Frozen | .12 | .19 | .15 | .13 | .11 | .10 | .07 |
| Juice | .03 | .06 | .05 | .04 | .03 | .02 | .02 |
| Dried | .04 | .04 | .04 | .04 | .03 | .03 | .04 |
| Potatoes, including sweet | .26 | .27 | .27 | .27 | .27 | .25 | .24 |
| Fresh | .14 | .16 | .16 | .14 | .13 | .12 | .12 |
| Canned | .01 | .01 | .01 | .01 | .01 | .01 | .01 |
| Frozen | .02 | .02 | .02 | .02 | .03 | .02 | .02 |
| Dehydrated | .01 | .01 | .01 | .01 | .01 | .00 | .01 |
| Chips, sticks, and salads | .09 | .08 | .07 | .09 | .10 | .09 | .08 |

SOURCE: D.M. Smallwood and J.R. Blaylock. Household Expenditures for Fruits, Vegetables, and Potatoes, USDA, ERS, Technical Bulletin No. 1690, May 1984. Data are from the 1977-78 USDA Nationwide Food Consumption Survey.

head (Table 2.8). Households in the lowest income group spent the most on vegetables and potatoes ($1.48/week) and the middle income group spent the least ($1.29/week). This finding for the lowest income group is probably related to lower spending on more expensive food groups and reflects that low income level is not independent of other factors (e.g., small household size and age of household head) which influence spending. Per capita spending on vegetables and potatoes decreased steadily as household size increased (from $1.94/week for a one-person household to $1.04/week for households with more than six members). Greater expenditures by smaller households may be due to economies of scale in purchasing vegetables and potatoes by larger households, differing nutritional needs of some individuals in larger households (e.g., younger children), and greater tastes and preferences for higher quality products by smaller households. While there were only small differences in expenditures between white and black households, nonwhite/nonblack households spent substantially more on vegetables and less on potatoes. Greater vegetable expenditures may be due to this group's preference for vegetables over other foods.

Table 2.8. Weekly per Person Expenditures for Vegetables and Potatoes by Race, 1977-78

| | Race | | | |
|---|---|---|---|---|
| Item | All | White | Black | Nonwhite/Nonblack |
| Vegetables and potatoes | 1.37 | 1.36 | 1.39 | 1.58 |
| Vegetables | 1.11 | 1.09 | 1.14 | 1.38 |
| Fresh | .60 | .60 | .61 | .75 |
| Dark green | .07 | .05 | .14 | .10 |
| Deep yellow | .04 | .04 | .02 | .04 |
| Light green | .20 | .20 | .21 | .21 |
| Tomatoes | .10 | .10 | .08 | .16 |
| Other | .20 | .20 | .15 | .24 |
| Canned | .32 | .32 | .31 | .43 |
| Frozen | .12 | .12 | .13 | .06 |
| Juice | .03 | .03 | .02 | .03 |
| Dried | .04 | .03 | .07 | .10 |
| Potatoes | .26 | .27 | .25 | .20 |
| Fresh | .14 | .13 | .17 | .13 |
| Canned | .01 | .01 | .01 | .00 |
| Frozen | .02 | .02 | .01 | .01 |
| Dehydrated | .01 | .01 | .00 | .00 |
| Chips, sticks, and salads | .09 | .09 | .05 | .05 |

SOURCE: D.M. Smallwood and J.R. Blaylock. Household Expenditures for Fruits, Vegetables, and Potatoes, USDA, ERS, Technical Bulletin No. 1690, May 1984. Data are from the 1977-78 USDA Nationwide Food Consumption Survey.

NOTE(S): Group and subgroup totals may not be equal due to rounding.

## REVIEW OF EMPIRICAL RESEARCH

Many factors, internal and external to the produce industry, have been postulated as causing the changes that have been occurring in vegetable and potato consumption over time and the differences that exist across population subgroups. External factors include economic influences such as relative price changes, increases in the overall purchasing power of the consumer, changes in household demographics, and changes in tastes and preferences as influenced by information and exposure to different technologies and lifestyles (Kinsey). One can speculate on what has been affecting consumption (as was done in the previous section of this paper), but it is useful to consider what factors empirical research has found to have important and significant effects on vegetable and potato consumption. Basically, this research involves statistically analyzing the relationship between household vegetable consumption and factors such as the price of vegetable products, household income, household size and composition, and other demographic factors. The influence of specified variables as indicated in the works of Smallwood and Blaylock, Blaylock and Smallwood, Cox and Wohlgnant, McCracken (1984, 1988), and others is summarized briefly. These studies are based mainly on the cross-sectional data collected in the USDA household and BLS expenditure surveys.

### Price

Cox and Wohlgenant found that the demand for fresh vegetables, canned vegetables, and frozen vegetables was significantly and negatively affected by own-prices. This indicates that consumers decrease consumption of a vegetable form if its (own) price increases (other things unchanged). The study also found significant and positive cross-price effects for frozen vegetables, indicating that canned vegetables substitute for the frozen form. In contrast, fresh potato prices are not so important in determining fresh potato consumption over time (Jones), but the price of processed potatoes has an important negative impact on consumption of processed potatoes and positive impact on consumption of fresh potatoes. Hence, while prices may not be so important in determining total vegetable and potato consumption, they do affect the composition of consumption.

### Income

Most studies indicate that income is a significant determinant of expenditures on and intake of vegetables and potatoes–total, fresh, processed, and by specific product. For example, Smallwood and Blaylock found that if a household's income increased by 10 percent, it would increase its expenditures on vegetables and potatoes by 0.89 percent (on vegetables by 1.08 percent and potatoes by 0.04 percent). A 10 percent income increase would result in disaggregate expenditure changes as follows (Smallwood and Blaylock):

| | |
|---|---|
| Vegetable and Potato Expenditures | 0.89% |
| Vegetables | 1.08 |
| Fresh | 1.51 |
| Canned | - 0.41 |
| Frozen | 4.75 |
| Juice | 2.70 |
| Dried | - 3.30 |
| Potatoes | 0.04 |
| Fresh | - 0.62 |
| Canned | - 1.24 |
| Frozen | 1.35 |
| Dehydrated | - 0.51 |
| Chips, sticks, and salad | 1.70 |

McCracken (1984) found that income had a positive impact on total vegetable intake away from home. McCracken (1988) also found that income had a negative impact on fresh potato intake at home and a positive impact on potato chip consumption at home and fried potato consumption away from home. These results support the speculation that income affects vegetable and potato consumption, but that the effect differs among products.

## Household Size and Age-Sex Composition

Households of differing size and composition differ in terms of their consumption of vegetables and potatoes. Blaylock and Smallwood found that older household members tend to spend more on a food item than do younger members (with exceptions for FAFH). For vegetables, teens had a smaller impact than other age groups on at-home household expenditures for both fresh and processed vegetables. The changing age distribution of the U.S. population and the large variations in expenditures for households of different age composition suggest that food consumption patterns are likely to be altered in years to come. Projections by Blaylock and Smallwood indicated that the aging of the population will increase household vegetable expenditures over their 1980 levels (by 6.7 percent), with fresh expenditures increasing more than processed expenditures (7.8 percent and 5.2 percent, respectively). Mc-

Cracken (1984, 1988) found household size and composition to be important determinants of vegetable and potato consumption away from home.

## Region

Regional differences in vegetable and potato consumption were consistently found in the various studies reviewed. Per capita vegetable expenditures tended to be higher in the Northeast and West relative to the South and Northeast, but varied by product and particular study. For example, on the basis of the 1977-78 USDA household data Smallwood and Blaylock estimated expenditures for most vegetables were highest in the Northeast (Table 2.9), but the 1980-81 BLS expenditure data (Blaylock and Smallwood) indicate that they were highest in the West (Table 2.10). Regional differences

Table 2.9. Simulated Weekly per Person Expenditures for Vegetables and Potatoes by Region, 1977-78

| | REGION | | | |
|---|---|---|---|---|
| | | Percent Change from Base | | |
| | Northeast (base) | North Central | South | West |
| | $ | | % | |
| Vegetables and Potatoes | 1.80 | -16 | -11 | - 8 |
| Vegetables | 1.47 | -21 | -12 | - 7 |
| Fresh | .85 | -25 | -18 | - 2 |
| Canned | .39 | - 2 | .5 | -.4 |
| Frozen | .17 | -33 | -29 | -11 |
| Juice | .04 | 7 | - 2 | -16 |
| Dried | .02 | 23 | 123 | 73 |
| Potatoes | .28 | 9 | 2 | -12 |
| Fresh | .16 | - 6 | 7 | -20 |
| Canned | .01 | 13 | 6 | - 1 |
| Frozen | .02 | 17 | -40 | -26 |
| Dehydrated | .01 | 39 | -34 | 15 |
| Chips, Sticks, and Salad | .07 | 45 | 2 | 5 |

SOURCE: D.M. Smallwood and J.R. Blaylock. Household Expenditure for Fruits, Vegetables, and Potatoes. USDA, ERS Technical Bulletin No. 1690, May 1984. Data are from the 1977-78 USDA Nationwide Food Consumption Survey.

Table 2.10. Simulated Weekly per Person Expenditures for Total Food and Vegetables, by Region, 1980-81

| | | REGION | | | |
|---|---|---|---|---|---|
| | Mean (base) | Northeast | North Central | South | West |
| | $ | % | | | |
| Total Food | 23.47 | 103.4 | 96.6 | 97.6 | 103.2 |
| Food Away From Home | 8.63 | 98.7 | 98.6 | 100.0 | 102.7 |
| Food At Home | 15.26 | 105.9 | 96.2 | 96.2 | 103.0 |
| Vegetables | 1.21 | 102.9 | 91.6 | 100.7 | 106.0 |
| Fresh | .77 | 103.3 | 91.6 | 95.7 | 111.3 |
| Processed | .46 | 102.9 | 91.9 | 107.5 | 98.7 |

SOURCE: J.R. Blaylock and D.M. Smallwood. U.S. Demand for Food: Household Expenditures, Demographics, and Projections. USDA, ERS Technical Bulletin No. 1713, February 1986. Data are from the 1980-81 BLS Continuing Consumer Expenditure Survey (CCES).

in away-from-home vegetable consumption were not so strong (McCracken, 1984), but regionality did affect the type of potato product eaten out (McCracken, 1988). While these differences are due to differences in the data sets and time periods, they do suggest that there are regional differences in consumption and hence that marketing strategies may be more effective if regionalized.

### Race

Nonblack households tend to spend more on vegetables and potatoes for use at home than do their black counterparts (Blaylock and Smallwood, and McCracken, 1988). However, per capita consumption patterns vary by product and by whether nonblack households are further subdivided into nonwhite/nonblack and white (Smallwood and Blaylock). In the away from home market racial differences were stronger–black households were less likely to consume vegetables and potatoes than similar nonblack households (McCracken, 1984, 1988). These results suggest the need to focus marketing efforts by race (and ethnic group).

## SUMMARY

U.S. consumption of vegetables and potatoes has increased over the last decade. There has been a tendency towards the consumption of fresh and frozen products, and away from the consumption of canned products. Potatoes are a major exception to this general trend. The magnitude of consumption changes differed by vegetable–tomatoes continued to be America's favorite vegetable (excluding potatoes), but broccoli and cauliflower experienced larger percentage consumption increases. The variety of vegetables available in food stores and in food service outlets has increased and will likely continue to increase. It is expected that there will continue to be changes in consumption of vegetables and potatoes.

The empirical research reviewed supports the hypothesis that vegetable and potato consumption patterns have been influenced by changes in society which are external to the produce industry. An increasing per capita income, aging population with smaller households, and increasing nonwhite/nonblack segment of the population will all tend to further increase vegetable and potato consumption. These changes will have differential effects, however, on different vegetables and product forms. Movement of the population away from the Northeast and into the South and West will only have a minor effect on vegetable and potato consumption.

This paper provides an overview of current knowledge base of vegetable and potato consumption. More and better data are needed, nevertheless, in order to more accurately identify past trends in vegetable and potato consumption, determine what factors have been influencing consumption trends, isolate market segments for particular vegetables and potato products, and assess the future market for vegetables and potatoes. Specific data needs or improvements include consistent information on total vegetable consumption (fresh, frozen, and canned) over time. This is possible only if there is consistent information on the major, traditional vegetables over time. Information on consumption over time of the less traditional, exotic items is also needed. Information on the flow of vegetables and potatoes in the food service sector and consumption is critical. More frequent surveys of households' vegetable and potato consumption and expenditure would be useful in order to determine whether there are changes in the structure of demand over time and to incorporate changes in supply into the consumption analyses. Finally, detailed information on consumers' attitudes towards diet and health and towards vegetables and potatoes over time will enable researchers to more completely assess consumption behavior.

This paper has focused mainly on the traditional factors that affect vegetable and potato demand. Areas of future research interest include measuring the impact of advertising generic and specific campaigns and food safety concerns on vegetable consumption. Such research should provide the vegetable industry with information useful in developing effective marketing and promotion strategies.

## REFERENCES

Blaylock, J.R., and D.M. Smallwood. U.S. Demand for Food: Household Expenditures, Demographics, and Projections. USDA, ERS Technical Bulletin No. 1713, 1986.

Bunch, Karen L. Food Consumption, Prices, and Expenditures, 1985. USDA, ERS Statistical Bulletin No. 749, 1987.

Cox, Thomas L., and Michael K. Wohlgenant. "Prices and Quality Effects in Cross-Sectional Demand Analysis." *Amer. J. Ag. Econ.*, 68(4):908-919, 1986.

Greenberg, Laurence. "Popularity of Fresh Produce Transforms Marketplace." *Restaurants*, USA, pp. 43-44, May, 1987.

Jones, Eugene. An Economic Analysis of the U.S. Potato Industry. Proceedings from a Symposium on Fruit and Vegetable Marketing, New Orleans, LA, November, 1985.

Kinsey, Jean. Demographic and Lifestyle Trends that Impact Food Consumption Patterns. North Central Regional Research Publication No. 311, pp. 32-43, 1986.

Love, John. "U.S. Vegetable Industry in the 1980s." *National Food Review*, NFR-31, 1986.

McCracken, Vicki A. "An Economic Analysis of the Away From Home Food Market." Ph.D. thesis, Purdue University, 1984.

McCracken, Vicki A. Consumer Demand for Potatoes: At Home and Away From Home. Washington State University, College of Agriculture and Home Economics, Ag. Research Bulletin XB 1000, 1988.

Manchester, Alden. Developing an Integrated Information System for the Food Sector. USDA, ERS Ag. Econ. Rept. No. 575, August, 1987.

O'Rourke, A. Desmond. The Changing Market for Food Away From Home and Its Implications for Washington Producers and Processors. Washington State University, College of Agriculture and Home Economics, Ag. Research Bulletin 0984, 1981.

Smallwood, D.M., and J.R. Blaylock. Household Expenditures for Fruits, Vegetables, and Potatoes. USDA, ERS Technical Bulletin No. 1690, 1984.

U.S. Department of Agriculture. Food Consumption, Prices, and Expenditures. ERS, Statistical Bulletin No. 749. Washington, D.C., 1985.

U.S. Department of Agriculture. Vegetables and Specialties–Situation and Outlook Report. ERS, TVS-245 and previous issues. Washington, D.C., 1988.

# THE U.S. VEGETABLE MARKET: DISCUSSION

Glenn A. Zepp
*U.S. Department of Agriculture*

Shannon Hamm points out that both fresh and processing vegetable output is rising and that production is becoming more concentrated in specialized areas (California, Florida, Arizona, and Texas for fresh vegetables; California, Wisconsin, Minnesota, and Oregon for processing). She also points out that there are exceptions to the predominant pattern of greater regional specialization, exemplified by the emergence of new broccoli production centers in Maine, Virginia, Arkansas, Illinois, and Colorado. Her concern that this reverse specialization may be short-lived if prices for traditional crops rise and growth in the fresh broccoli market levels off seems justified.

The Hamm paper identifies several factors causing shifts in regional specialization which merit highlighting:

1. Improved refrigerated transportation and storage. This has lowered costs for delivering quality product to consumption centers, thereby shifting comparative advantage in favor of farmers in a few specialized areas. Lettuce production, for example, is concentrated (90 percent of total output in 1987) in California and Arizona. Celery is similarly concentrated in California and Florida.

2. New production and harvesting technology. This is exemplified by mechanized harvesting for processing tomatoes which appears to have shifted comparative advantage in favor of California growers. Because of the drier climate during the harvest period, California farmers bear less risk of crop loss due to wet weather when letting mature fruit sit on the vine. Some ripe tomatoes must wait on the vine while slower maturing fruit develops in order to recover a high proportion of the crop with once-over mechanical harvesting.

   Another example is the use of full-bed plastic mulch in Florida's winter vegetable production. Florida and Mexico compete head-to-head during the December-May marketing period. In the early and mid-1970s, Florida growers adopted the practice of planting vegetables through a plastic film mulch. In addition to boosting yields because of better control over the plant's root zone, the practice provided a measure of protection against damage from cold weather. Florida producers appeared to benefit more from the new technology than growers in Mexico because of the extra cold protection and because controlling the root environment helped vegetable plants more on the sandy soils in Florida than on the heavier clay-loam soil in Mexico.

3. Changing product price relationships. Falling prices for the traditional field crops in southern Virginia apparently altered farmers' comparative advantage in broccoli.

4. Changing input price relationships. Higher labor costs in the United States may alter comparative advantage, leading to more production in low-cost foreign production areas and less in the United States.

5. Governmental subsidies. These include Federal and State programs which benefit producers in one production area over those in another. Federally subsidized irrigation probably helped concentrate much of the country's fruit and vegetable production in the Western areas.

I have a comment about criteria for judging comparative advantage which relates to the Hamm paper. Several frameworks are available to assess comparative advantage. They range in complexity from cost of production comparisons to spatial allocation models relying on mathematical programming. All require a lot of data. The Economic Research Service has periodically updated studies assessing competition between the United States and Western Mexico in supplying winter fresh vegetables to U.S. markets. Several economic criteria have been used in these studies to judge comparative advantage. The one in the most recent study used interregional comparison of residual returns to management and risk per unit of production. Residual returns were estimated by budgeting typical (or average) enterprise cost and revenue in each production area. The area with the highest residual return for a particular commodity was judged to have a comparative advantage. Noneconomic criteria, such as the availability of a marketing infrastructure, also have to be considered in judging comparative advantage for new production areas.

Vicki McCracken's paper methodologically traces vegetable utilization trends and reviews consumption studies, and concludes that we are eating more vegetables and potatoes, particularly in the fresh and frozen forms. In fact, she reports that consumption of canned vegetables is on the decline.

Vickie classifies demand shifters into two types: (1) internal industry changes such as improved potato freezing techniques that created new potato products thereby shifting the demand for potatoes, and (2) external changes such as in income, household composition, and health awareness. Her paper deals with this latter category. She concludes that future changes in these shifters will raise overall vegetable and potato consumption, although not necessarily that of all items or product forms.

There are several additional developments on the horizon which merit consideration in evaluating future consumption of vegetables and potatoes:

1. Federal and State policies. A consistent policy of disseminating health information that promotes consumption of vegetables at the expense of other food categories would likely strengthen demand. Several nationally respected organizations (the National Academy of Science and the U.S. Surgeon General) have recently released information which suggests raising the fresh fruit and vegetable content of the U.S. diet at the expense of animal products could improve health prospects. Regular dissemination of information by the Federal government about the apparent unhealthful effects of smoking appears to have weakened cigarette demand. Dissemination of information favorable to fresh product consumption would likely boost demand for vegetables.

2. Clean food. By clean I refer to freedom from pesticide residues. The news media are currently focusing on consumers' demands in wanting assurance of the safety of their food and their turning to foods that are certified pesticide residue free. There always has been a demand for organic foods–presumably free of pesticide residues. If properly handled, clean-food promotion may boost total vegetable demand. But, there is a chance it raises general concern about pesticide residue risks in vegetables and weakens demand.

# THE U.S. VEGETABLE MARKET: DISCUSSION

John R. Brooker
*University of Tennessee*

Analysis of the demand and supply of food products in the United States is certainly dependent upon the availability of data. Hamm and McCracken have commented on the various aspects of the information available to researchers. After securing price and quantity data, researchers can, and undoubtedly will, generate quantitative estimates of demand and supply functions. Progress in the development of methodologies that can be used to quantitatively estimate these relationships have perhaps even exceeded the impressive growth in the U.S. consumption of broccoli. However, the development of appropriate data series to support these methodologies has fallen behind. A major issue regarding current and future analysis of the demand and supply of vegetables in the United States is the data base available to examine industry problems.

The paper presented by McCracken capably addresses the recent changes in per capita consumption of vegetables and potatoes. The fact that these per capita consumption changes have occurred is not debatable. What may be debatable is the motivating force behind these adjustments in food consumption. One of the points in McCracken's background comments is that the "consumers' knowledge and information (or possible misinformation) about a food will influence their decision to consume the food." Considerable data were presented to reveal recent changes in food eating patterns, i.e., what is eaten, when it is eaten, where it is eaten, and in what form it is eaten. Comprehension of the driving forces behind these changes is important to researchers and government policymakers concerned with the economic efficiency of the system and the nutritional well-being of the general public. The problem of understanding why consumers eat what they do, where and when, has been the subject of much research.

The agricultural economics profession has a rich history in the area of demand analysis (Nuckton). Beginning with the partial demand analysis work in the 1930s, much of the empirical investigation of demand has been based on the traditional economic analysis of consumer choice. Recent work by some demand economists has focused on the development of a methodology for estimation of a complete demand system from time-series data (Huang).

Another approach used to analyze consumer demand is referred to as the characteristics approach (Ladd and Suvannunt; Terry et al.). The characteristics approach has appealed to some economists because it assumes the demand for a consumer good is derived from the consumer's demand for the attributes that the food contains.

As McCracken points out, the consumer purchases a bundle of attributes, not just the farm product itself. These attributes are nutrition, satisfaction, status, service, and any other "characteristic" of the product that can be defined. Attempts to place a value, called the marginal implicit price, on each attribute has been successful to a point, but unsuccessful in solving an old problem confronting economists working on demand analysis, namely, how to account for changes in preferences. The absence of a good, quantifiable variable that can explain why consumers ignore some considerations about nutrition, continue to overeat in the light of health awareness, and do not always adhere to their personal price conscience, certainly complicates the estimation of an ideal explanatory demand equation. Demographic information has be used to account for some differences in eating habits.

As pointed out in the consumption data, from 1967 to 1986 per capita consumption of all food increased about 10 percent (McCracken, Figure 2.3). Crops increased more than animal products in per capita consumption, which sends a pleasant signal to vegetable producers and handlers, but may possibly send a red flag signal to the animal industry. And, this does appear to be the response of the pork, beef, poultry, and dairy sectors, since they each have engaged in expensive promotional campaigns. While much of this advertising is self-cancelling, each commodity subsector expects to gain market share at the expense of the others. So the only beneficiary may be the advertising agencies.

Examining the per capita consumption of four crop products–cereal, vegetables, fruits, and sugar and sweets (McCracken, Figure 2.4)–revealed that the cereals and fruits were both about 3 percent higher in per capita consumption in 1984 than in 1967. Per capita vegetable consumption increased an impressive 18 percent, but sugars and sweets increased an even more impressive 22 percent. This really emphasizes the conflict in our society between the so-called health and fitness movement and the high level of per capita consumption of sweets. Of course, this is on an aggregate consumption basis. The dietary habits of consumers vary in response to the usual listing of social and demographic variables.

Per capita consumption values should be viewed with caution. The value for any one particular year may be substantially higher or lower than the previous year because of a change in overall supply, not because of an adjustment in the demand curve. Karl Fox noted that per capita consumption closely follows supply. As noted in McCracken's paper, the increase in per capita consumption of broccoli and cauliflower has been phenomenal. For most other vegetables the increase in fresh consumption has been at least partially at the expense of the canned and frozen forms.

Another problem with per capita consumption values is that they may disguise the amount of food thrown away. McCracken notes that per capita figures are based on the residual of total supply (production, imports, and beginning stocks) after subtracting off other uses. So, it is a measure of food disappearance, not consumption. The nutritionists working in some of our public school lunch programs may take pride in the placement of spinach, green beans, broccoli, etc., on the plate lunches of the school children. Unfortunately, an alarming proportion of this food may be thrown away. Similarly, the percentage of away-from-home expenditures has increased "from less than 10 percent in the early 1960s to 31 percent in 1986." (McCracken) Sitting in our fast food restaurants, especially those with salad bars, and watching the customers will impress most observers with the volume of food, including vegetables, that is thrown away. I have not examined any studies that measured the amount of food thrown away at home and/or at restaurants, but my guess would be that on a relative basis more food is thrown away at food service outlets than at home. If this is true, could part of the increased per capita consumption in the last few years be attributed to the increase in food purchased away from home? The movement of the product off the farm may be positively affected, but the use of such aggregate data to evaluate nutritional programs could result in findings that might be seriously misleading.

The continued development of the microwaveable entrees in the retail food stores may significantly impact the distribution of sales of many food products in the fresh or processed form. In a 1974 study in North Carolina regarding an analysis of the shifts in the demand and supply of U.S. vegetables, Mathia and Schrimper noted the impressive shift in per capita consumption between 1960 and 1971 towards canned and frozen and away from fresh. One reason cited was "the typical consumer is more affluent, and as such, demands vegetables prepared for immediate cooking or consuming." Another reason cited was that the technological innovations associated with the processing sector shifted the comparative advantage in favor of production for processing. If the life-styles and affluence of the U.S. consumers continue to boost built-in services and taste variation, then perhaps the consumption of fresh will again yield to the new (microwave) processing technology. On the fresh side, irradiation of fresh vegetables may affect consumers' demand for some products and the source of these products (Morrison).

Consideration of the consumer's desire for "taste variation" combines the earlier discussion about measuring consumer preference with the influence of advertising. The term "taste variation" refers to the consumers' desire for new, unique, or different taste experiences. The produce departments of the major retailers provide visual testimony to the consumers' desire for variety. From the vegetable processor's perspective, variety is revealed through product proliferation. An article by Connor defined product proliferation as products that are minor variants of existing products. An example could be a package of frozen green beans with mushrooms; green beans with mushrooms and onions; green beans with mushrooms, onions, and almonds; and so on. This proliferation of products provides manufacturers with the opportunity to saturate markets in an effort to supply all consumer segments and to differentiate their products through advertising, which in turn may permit them to follow a pricing strategy designed to extract consumer surplus by engaging in price discrimination.

Perhaps the marketing behavior of the food manufacturers and retailers, which are occasionally combined in one conglomerate organization, will have more influence on per capita consumption by controlling what's available at fast-food outlets than the consumers choosing what they want to eat. In other words, people may consume larger quantities of a certain food because the food service outlets make it available and entice the public to buy the product versus the notion of the consumer making a choice based on a rational decision to maximize a personal utility function that includes all food products. Will it be possible for the product development strategy and advertising program of food outlets to "control" the consumer? Is the consumer choosing the food product, or is the manufacturer "leading" the consumer to make the purchase because of the influence of advertising? The power of television advertising has some researchers concerned about the potential for causing people to buy what they perhaps would not buy otherwise.

The efforts of manufacturers to effectively compete with fresh vegetable consumption will unquestionably entail expensive advertising programs in the future. Large food companies and grower-shippers are also striving to further develop consumer interest in brand identification of fresh vegetables. These efforts may have more long-run impact on the location of production than on total U.S. consumption. McCracken notes that "consumption patterns have been influenced by changes in society which are external to the produce industry." Among the list of causal factors, advertising is missing. In an article by Parker and Connor, television advertising is noted as a major causal force in changing food habits of the consumers. O'Rourke and Greig countered with the contention that changes in demographics, labor force participation by women, growth of the leisure industry, and other phenomena are just as likely to have altered food consumption habits. Surely, the past changes and future changes in consumption habits, which we often call tastes and preferences, are the cumulative, net result of all these factors. For vegetables and potatoes to continue to hold current market shares and/or expand market shares, the industry may need to engage in substantial advertising expenditures. Since the consumer's stomach, at least in the short run, is fixed in capacity, there will probably continue to be adjustments in consumption among products and product groups (Buse). Mass media advertising will play an important role in influencing U.S. consumers' demand for fresh vegetables.

The sources of vegetable supplies for the U.S. consumers are presented in a comprehensive manner in the paper by Hamm. The supply trends obviously coincide with the consumption trends discussed by McCracken. A recent sequence of events in Tennessee coincides with the first of three factors noted by Hamm as limiting the development of commercial vegetable markets in nonmajor production states. These three factors are inexperienced growers, labor for harvest, and overall increase in the total supply of vegetables.

A large vegetable processor operates a freezing plant in west Tennessee. Over the past two decades the company has gradually shifted its source of strawberries, squash, and a few other vegetables to Texas and Mexico. The company also processes broccoli in a California plant. A decision was made a few years back to shift some of the production and processing of broccoli to Tennessee. Processing several thousand acres of broccoli in an Eastern state would greatly reduce their expense of shipping processed broccoli from California to Eastern markets. The plan was to begin in the spring with broccoli produced in Mississippi, followed by broccoli from Tennessee in the late spring and early summer, continuing with Kentucky broccoli during the summer. Then the pattern would be reversed for the late summer and fall crops. Unfortunately, growers could not obtain the yields anticipated. The per pound cost of production exceeded the per pound price the processor was willing to pay the grower. The processor has closed the broccoli line in its west Tennessee plant. Good soybean producers may not be good broccoli growers–at least not without some transition time.

The entrance of new producing areas searching for alternatives to traditional crops will add pressure to the total supply of vegetables, which may possibly intensify the dynamic nature of the vegetable industry. This is because the new suppliers will be striving to replace existing suppliers. Market window studies may identify time periods in the past when supplies have been lower than at other times of the year, with the anticipated inverse relationship with price. If we accept the constant stomach capacity concept, the consumer will still be in the position of reducing the consumption of one food product to increase the consumption of another food product. In the short run the wholesaler is in the same predicament. If a wholesaler switches to a new supplier he must reduce purchases from his old supplier. Of course, an expanded population of consumers would help to absorb new suppliers. In either case, with new suppliers both inside and outside the United States, market window analysis based on past shipment and price data may be invalid.

As noted by Hamm, the origin-labeling legislation efforts and enforcement of pesticide residue levels are possible tools for reducing competition. Consumer safety is a valid concern, and consumer protection programs may occasionally help certain groups of producers. On the other hand, consumer and environmental activists could dramatically impact overall supplies if they successfully impose a zero-tolerance regulation on carcinogenic chemical additives in produce. The pesticide residue issue could also have an adverse effect on demand. An interesting point regarding the activists is that they seem to ignore the fact that scientists have discovered natural toxins in many foods (Hazlett).

Research efforts to examine the competitive position of vegetable producers in various production areas within the United States as well as assessment of the importing nations will be limited by the availability of adequate data. As Hamm noted, consistent production cost data from competing states are not available. Of course, cost of production data must be used with great caution. A region's competitive position involves much more than comparison of production-marketing cost data. Opportunity cost is perhaps the most important factor to consider.

McCracken's closing paragraph regarding the need for "more and better data" is strongly supported. In the minor supply areas, and for many minor vegetables, price-quantity data on a time series basis are not available. More data on individual crops are needed at the state or at least the regional level, as well as the national level. Data are needed for many so-called minor vegetables to support estimation of price and income elasticities. In the past decade there have been several reductions in the data collection efforts of state and federal agencies. There has been a reduction in the number of fresh and processed crops reported in Agricultural Statistics. The number of destinations reported in the unload data (USDA) has been reduced to the point of being useless to many locations. Researchers need more data regarding the origins of production and distribution to destinations. Work on interregional competition and competitive position analysis is severely limited by the absence of adequate data to permit useful empirical analysis.

## REFERENCES

Buse, Rueben C., "What is America Eating and What is Happening to Meat Consumption." Paper presented at BOA/S-165 Symposium, Charleston, S.C., Oct. 20-21, 1986.

Connor, John M., "Food Product Proliferation: A Market Structure Analysis," *Amer. Jour. Agri. Econ.*, 63(4):1981. Nov. 1981.

Fox, Karl A., *The Analysis of Demand for Farm Products*, USDA Technical Bulletin No. 1081, 1953.

Hamm, S.R., "The U.S. Supply of Vegetables." Paper presented at The Market for Vegetables in the Western Hemisphere: Trends, policies, and Trade Linkages Conference, Rutgers University, Sept. 6-7, 1988.

Hazlett, Thomas W., "Ingredients of a Food Phobia," *The Wall Street Journal*, August 5, 1988.

Huang, Kyo S., *U.S. Demand for Food: A Complete System of Price and Income Effects*, USDA, ERS, Technical Bulletin No. 1714.

Ladd, George W., and Veraphol Suvannunt, "A Model of Consumer Goods Characteristics," *Amer. Jour. Agri. Econ.*, AAEA, Vol. 58, 1976.

Mathia, Gene A., and Ronald A. Schrimper, *Analysis of Shifts in Demand and Supply Affecting U.S. and N.C. Vegetable Production and Price Patterns*, Econ. Info. Rpt. No. 35, Dept. of Econ., N.C. State Univ., Jan. 1974.

McCracken, V.A., "The U.S. Demand for Vegetables." Paper presented at The Market for Vegetables in the Western Hemisphere: Trends, Policies, and Trade Linkages Conference, Rutgers University, Sept. 6-7, 1988.

Morrison, R.M., "Irradiating Fresh Vegetables: Checklist for Commercial Viability," *Vegetable Situation and Outlook*, USDA, ERS, TVS-241, Washington, D.C., Feb. 1987.

Nuckton, Carole F., *Demand Relationships for Vegetables: A Review of Past Studies*, Giannini Foundation Special Report 80-1, Calif. Agri. Exp. Sta., Univ. of Calif., Davis, Aug. 1978.

O'Rourke, A. Desmond, and W. Smith Greig, "Estimates of Consumer Loss Due to Monopoly in the U.S. Food-Manufacturing Industries," *Amer. Jour. Agri. Econ.*, Vol. 63, No. 2, May 1981.

Parker, Russell C., and John C. Connor, "Estimates of Consumer Loss Due to Monopoly in the U.S. Food-Manufacturing Industries," *Amer. Jour. Agri. Econ.*, Vol. 61, No. 4, Nov. 1979.

Schultz, H., *The Theory and Measurement of Demand*, Chicago: Univ. of Chicago Press, 1938.

Terry, Danny E., John R. Brooker, and David B. Eastwood, *Characteristics Theory and Household Demand for Food Nutrients*, Bull. 639, Univ. of Tenn. Agri. Exp. Sta., Knoxville, Oct. 1985.

U.S. Department of Agriculture, *Fresh Fruit and Vegetable Unload Totals for 23 Cities*, AMS, Fruit and Vegetable Division: Washington, D.C., various years.

# SECTION II: POLICIES AND INSTITUTIONS

# 3

# THE PRODUCE INDUSTRY IN TRANSITION: FOCUS ON MARKETING

Thomas R. Pierson and John W. Allen
*Michigan State University*

## INTRODUCTION

Marketing efforts are becoming increasingly important for profitable sales across the entire food industry. Produce is no exception as traditionalism declines and more effective marketing comes of age. Consumers, retailers and wholesalers, as well as growers, packers and shippers are changing their attitudes and behaviors with respect to produce. Improved marketing strategies are emerging at all levels. These strategies and associated practices are closely linked to the following basic components of the marketing process:

1. Knowledge and understanding of customers' wants, needs and perceptions.

2. Developing and positioning products and services to match customers' wants, needs and perceptions.

3. Communicating positive product and service responses to target customers.

Although these basic components understate the substantial complexity and great need for creativity inherent in the marketing process, they are indicative of the fundamental marketing approach increasingly applicable and necessary for success in today's produce industry.

On broad and aggregate commodity bases, U.S. total and per capita produce consumption is up; for some commodities, dramatically so. However, in many highly competitive produce markets, supplies of relatively undifferentiated commodities of *ordinary quality* in *traditional packs* chronically overwhelm relatively static or declining demand for these kinds of products, frequently forcing shipping point prices below profitable levels. Unfortunately, this situation is likely to persist. On the positive side, there are opportunities to reduce the pitfalls of the production/commodity approach. These opportunities, which are available to "market driven" product organizations, reside in emerging consumer trends and preferences which in turn create potentially profitable situations throughout the produce production and distribution channels.

The purpose of this paper is to describe and analyze the positive changes occurring in the U.S. produce system. Emphasis will be given to the ongoing transition within the produce industry. Growers, packers, shippers, wholesalers and retailers are moving away from their traditional production/commodity orientation toward a contemporary marketing approach.

## CONSUMERS: THE DRIVING FORCE FOR CHANGE

Changing consumer demographics, life-styles and preferences continuously present produce marketers with challenges, but also with opportunities. A few of these often cited changes are as follows:

1. Two-income families are rapidly rising. They constitute 26% of all families in the early 1960s and 44% of all families today. it is estimated that over 50% of all families will earn two incomes by 1990.

2. Family income is rising. Currently, 26% of all families have an annual income of $35,000 or more. By 1990 it is estimated that 31% of all families will earn $35,000 or more (in real dollars).

3. The nature of families is changing. Increasingly, households are headed by Single adults (Allen and Pierson). Traditional families (husband employed, with children) are approximately 28% of all families in which the wife is 18-44 years old. This group declined by 25% between 1976 and 1987. Dual-income families with no kids–DINKS–make up 14% of families in which the wife is 18 to 44 years old and increased 31% between 1976 and 1987. Dual-employed families with children–DEWKS–constitute 46% of these families and increased by 61% during the same period (Allen).

4. Lifestyles are changing. "For growing···(B2. Week, 4/87)"

5. There is a growing availability of new technology in food preparation. Microwave oven ownership and use is rising. In 1985 microwave ownership was at 44%, and present ownership is at about 66%.

These kinds of societal changes have led, in turn, to four important dimensions of changing consumer preferences as well as directions of response by today's market-oriented produce operators.

## Desires for More Convenient Food and Produce Continue

The long-term trend toward greater convenience appears as a frequent topic of discussion among virtually all involved in food marketing. Though convenience is often viewed in the context of preparation time reductions, in a broader sense, perhaps it is having food that is wanted, when it is wanted, with relatively little effort. With respect to produce, even though some items and uses are the ultimate of convenience, such as eating an apple out of hand, many items and uses are highly inconvenient; apples for a Waldorf salad for example. Clearly, today's produce offers numerous opportunities for increased convenience to ultimate consumers, as well as customers throughout the distribution system.

## Quality Produce: Standards are Rising

It is apparent that interpretations of quality differ greatly among consumers as well as among produce marketers. In many instances, quality serves as an all-encompassing concept relating to perceptions of appearance, consistency, freshness, nutrition, safety, taste and understanding. Thus, quality, as the term is most frequently used, connotes a broader meaning than any of the above individual attributes. Expectations of improved quality produce, perhaps more than any other food category, have been rising over the past decade and will continue to do so in the years ahead.

## Nutrition, Safety and Health: Issues of Increasing Importance

Many produce marketers view the past 15 years as an era of growing consumer awareness and concern with respect to health, diet, nutrition, and safety. What was thought by many to be a fad in the 1970s has become a series of on-going complex and important issues in the 1980s. The produce industry has benefited significantly from the growing health-nutrition awareness of the past decade but now faces damaging consequences as concerns over the effects of pesticide residues on human health have surfaced.

## Produce Variety and Excitement: Key Growth Strategy

Growth strategies of produce marketers are increasingly focusing on variety and excitement for shopper appeal. Growers, shippers and retailers are proliferating products with new and different tastes and flavors. At the same time, retail produce department decors and merchandising approaches are emphasizing more interesting and pleasurable shopping experiences. It may seem that opportunities for new types of produce, new tastes and flavors, as well as new approaches to merchandising, are virtually limitless; however, achieving marketplace success with new foods and merchandising requires a balance between "newness" and sufficient consumer familiarity and understanding to foster acceptance.

## Consumers and Produce: Today's Agenda

Consumers judge the benefits of all food, including produce, not only on the above four broad factors, but in many instances on a fluid set of criteria which changes over time and which differs among individuals. The following list, though not intended as definitive, is reflective of the words and phrases being used in today's marketplace by consumers to assess and describe produce.

- Appearance
- Consistency
- Convenience
- Excitement
- Freshness
- Nutrition
- Quality
- Safety
- Taste
- Understanding
- Uniqueness
- Variety
- Price/Value

With the above consumer produce criteria in mind, a marketing litmus test for produce products is suggested: *Does the product respond to a perceived consumer desire*–one or more of the above criteria? No produce product can succeed unless it meets this fundamental test of true marketing. That it meets a desire will not, of course, in itself insure profit or success; however, unless it does meet these criteria, the product cannot succeed over time. Moreover, in today's highly competitive arena, products, if they are to succeed, will likely meet *several* important consumer desires.

One means of determining whether a produce product meets this litmus test of serving consumers' desires is to consider the following consumer purchase decision criterion that applies to all food products:

$$\begin{array}{c}\textbf{Consumer}\\\textbf{Purchase}\\\textbf{Decision}\end{array} \longrightarrow \begin{array}{c}\textbf{Consumer}\\\textbf{Value}\\\textbf{Perception}\end{array} = \frac{\textbf{Perceived Benefits}}{\textbf{Price}} = \frac{\begin{array}{ll}\textbf{Appearance} & \textbf{Quality}\\\textbf{Consistency} & \textbf{Safety}\\\textbf{Convenience} & \textbf{Taste}\\\textbf{Excitement} & \textbf{Understanding}\\\textbf{Freshness} & \textbf{Uniqueness}\\\textbf{Nutrition} & \textbf{Variety}\end{array}}{\textbf{Price}}$$

A shopper of food products formulates decisions based upon analytical and/or emotional processes that ultimately result in acceptance or rejection of products. This decision process involves an evaluation of the perceived worth or benefits of the product in comparison to the price charged. Picture a shopper in a supermarket considering the purchase of a given produce item. What goes through the shopper's mind as the product is examined/handled? What are the shopper's perceptions of benefits, in comparison to the price? This comparison translates into a value perception of the product, which, in turn, converts to the purchase or rejection decision. It is recognized, however, that consumers respond in very different ways. Consumers from different demographic/life-style segments, possessing varying wants and needs, will place different emphases on the benefits criteria as well as the price.

If the perceived benefits of the item exceed the price charged, and if the benefit-to-price comparison is more favorable than other perceived purchase alternatives, the shopper will likely purchase the item; otherwise, the product will be rejected. Given this as the nature of purchase decisions, the process of marketing, including but not limited to the branding of products, plays a vital role in heightening consumers' value perceptions of fresh fruits and vegetables. Indeed, heightening consumers' value perceptions is the basic challenge confronting produce marketers in their efforts to improve consumer demand and achieve profitable operations (Allen and Pierson).

Based upon aggregate statistics, the produce industry has fared well in recent years. U.S. consumption of fresh fruits and vegetables has increased steadily since 1975; per capita consumption is up 15-20% and total consumption is up 20-30% (Brown and Suarez). However, some believe that major total consumption increases may be more difficult to achieve in the future, thus the role of marketing, as described above, assumes an even larger role. Over time, all foods are competing against an ever longer list of alternative products, each positioned to gain its "share of stomach."

## SUPERMARKET PRODUCE OPERATIONS: RESPONDING TO CONSUMERS

As indicated in the previous section, consumers have been and remain the primary force for change in the produce business. However, since the mid-1970s, supermarket operators have been effectively responding to consumers' increasing interest in produce and have helped the business to grow. As early as 1981, a nationwide survey by *Chain Store Age Supermarkets* showed that consumers ranked quality produce as the most important among 13 factors in selecting a supermarket. At that time, "quality produce" ranked higher than quality meat, low prices or cleanliness (McLaughlin and Pierson,

1983). It is interesting that the *1987 Trends Update* by the Food Marketing Institute reports that 98% of shoppers surveyed cited "quality produce" as a key reason for selecting a supermarket. Thus, produce remains as the leading shopper draw (Linsen).

As consumer interest has grown so has produce department performance. *Progressive Grocer's* 1988 Sales Manual reports produce sales at 8.4% of overall store sales, and it is not uncommon to have produce sales in the 12-15% range and even higher. These figures are up from 5-6% or lower in the early 1970s. Gross margins are also up from 18% in the 1960s to 32.4% in 1987 (Linsen). Perhaps most importantly from retailers' perspectives, produce is estimated to contribute 21% of store profits (Scheringer), making produce perhaps the most profitable of all major store departments.

The number of important ways in which retailers have stimulated produce growth over the past decade is instructive. It should be noted that many of the following improvements, while recognized and responded to by shoppers in supermarkets, are truly joint efforts of the produce industry–growers, packers, shippers, wholesalers and retailers.

## Improved Quality of Produce

Improved quality has been a major industrywide initiative. Improved quality produce has resulted from better varieties, improved cultural and harvesting practices, as well as better packing and handling throughout the distribution system including more refrigeration and humidity controls such as misters at the retail level. Improvements in quality have not resulted from "silver bullet" solutions, but instead hard work and numerous small improvements from production to retail.

## Increased Variety and Depth of Selection

Growth in the number of items in the average supermarket is shown below:

**Produce Items in Supermarkets**

| Year | Items |
|---|---|
| 1975 | 65 |
| 1981 | 133 |
| 1983 | 173 |
| 1984 | 216 |
| 1988 | 250-300 est. |

Although the average number of items today is in the range of 250-300, it is not uncommon to encounter stores with as many as 400 or more produce items. The number of items has quadrupled and is accounted for by: rapid increases in specialty and exotic items; new, as well as repositioned older varieties; and increasing depth of selection, i.e., new sizes of products and packs, as well as new qualities which are almost always superior to those existing or at least are merchandised as such.

### Greater Selling Space for Produce

Selling space devoted to produce now accounts for an average of 15% of supermarket floor space (Linsen) up from 3-4% in smaller older stores of the 1970s and 11-13% of store space in the early 1980s (McLaughlin and Pierson, 1983).

### Extended Marketing Season

Increasingly, produce knows no season. Consumers are not aware of traditional produce seasonality. More importantly, many desire quality produce on a year-round basis. Retailers and other produce marketers are learning of this desire and are endeavoring to supply many formerly seasonal items on year-round bases.

### More Merchandising Flair and Shopper Appeal

Industrywide, bulk produce displays account for slightly over 80% of all sales. Contemporary produce departments feature dazzling bulk displays on tables and fixtures creatively designed to establish specific images; contemporary or farmers market, for instance. Such produce departments are often highlighted by track lighting and neon signage. These kinds of retail environments seek to present quality produce at its finest in distinctive ways. For retail operators, this has been a major means of achieving needed differentiation in markets usually characterized by overstoring and slow growth.

### More Effort to Create Shopper Understanding

The produce industry has come to realize that shopper understanding has a highly positive impact on sales and consumption. As a consequence, produce marketers in recent years have been providing much more information to shoppers. Often such information takes the form of in-store demonstrations, videos, display signage, recipe cards, etc. Common messages often relate to nutritional information, produce safety, home handling techniques, as well as recipes and product usage information.

## Convenience Produce Gaining Acceptance

Increasingly, busy, on-the-go customers want their fruits and vegetables fresh and they want them easy, without fuss. Convenience-oriented produce items are serving this need. Several examples are as follows:

- Precut vegetables for snacks and salads
- Salad bars in supermarkets often accounting for 1% of total store sales
- Premade, packaged salads, as at McDonalds (for shoppers trying to avoid the "inconvenience" of the salad bar)
- Fresh fruit and dessert bars
- Baked potato bars with a variety of toppings
- Juice bars and fresh-squeezed juice operations
- In-store pineapple peeling and coring operations
- Vegetables in microwave trays, ready for cooking.

## DPP Will Facilitate More Precise Retail Produce Decisions

A model direct product profit (DPP) program has been developed for retail produce operations. This computerized system brings a level of precision to produce operations that previously was not practical. The system will incorporate store door produce costs, with additional costs for virtually all in-store activities, as well as on-line sales data to provide better information for a whole range of decisions: make or buy decisions for value-added produce, determinations of optimum handling practices, merchandising and promotion decisions, information useful in controlling labor costs as well as shrink, etc. (The Packer, July 2, 1988).

## Changing Retailer and Supplier Relationships

Given the above changes in retail supermarket produce operations, changes are also occurring between wholesale/retail buyers and shipping-point sellers. Retailers want new, higher quality, longer shelf-life products to meet changing consumer preferences and to reduce wholesale and retail labor requirements, as well as products to provide distinctive competitive advantages. Buyers are also seeking dependable services to facilitate the buying function and marketing support to help insure that newly introduced, as well as traditional products, succeed in the marketplace.

These emerging changes in wholesale/retail buyers' purchasing behavior can be described in much the same manner as consumer purchasing behavior, except the perceived benefits component of the model relates to this audience rather than to consumers.

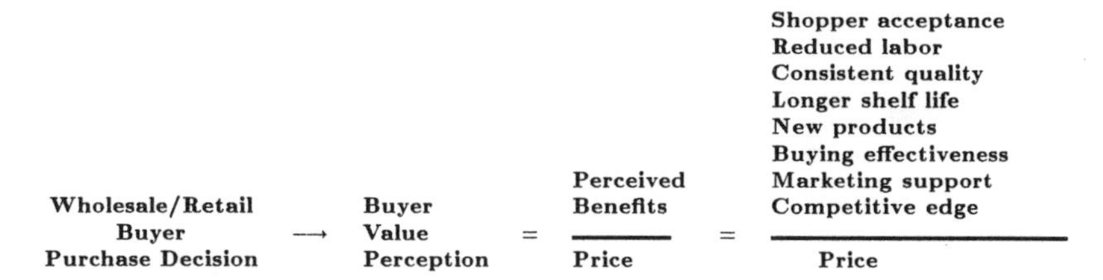


Consumers' benefits criteria are considered under "shopper acceptance." In fact, this equation reflects buyers' perceptions of consumers' desired benefits. The remainder of the criteria are more buyer specific. To provide some historical perspective and reality, most sellers would say that, traditionally, the only relevant part of the model has been price; however, the willingness of buyers to pay for improved and consistent quality, as well as other factors, has increased dramatically during the 1980s. Today, more than ever before wholesale/retail buyers will pay higher prices *when they believe* the products and services are truly superior to other offerings.

Another aspect of buyers' purchasing behavior is an increasingly close relationship with consumer interests. There has been a subtle shift over time of buyers moving to the role as consumers' purchasing agents versus their more traditional role as suppliers' selling agents at the retail level (McLaughlin; McLaughlin and Pierson, 1984).

## SHIPPING-POINT FIRMS: MARKETING COMES OF AGE

Produce firms and organizations, especially those at the shipping point have tended to be production-, sales- and source-oriented. That is, energies and efforts in these organizations have been directed almost exclusively at *producing* and *selling* products. This is in contrast with *marketing* efforts to determine what product attributes and services wholesale/retail buyer customers and ultimate shopper/consumer customers want and are willing to pay for. In fact, the complex of customers confronting shipping-point firms is far more diverse than simply wholesale/retail buyers and consumers. The customer environment often includes brokers, and terminal market operators as well. Additionally, each of these types of participants consists of different groups, or segments, thus creating an extremely complex and often confusing customer environment. Though the basic customer-oriented marketing process presented in the introduction to this paper may appear to be simple in concept, its successful implementation requires tremendous commitment, skill and creativity (McLaughlin and Pierson, 1984).

### Motivation for Change

Increasingly, shipping-point sellers are facing markets with burdensome supplies of commonplace products, most often of ordinary quality and sold in traditional packs. These undifferentiated products usually yield low profits. At the same time, many suppliers are beginning to realize the survival and higher profit opportunities presented by changing consumers and changing retailer customers, especially their willingness to pay more for products perceived to possess superior benefits or attributes. Of course, the key issues are: *Which customers and consumers will pay more? How much more will they pay? What kinds of new or improved products will they want? How can such products be produced and distributed?* The remainder of this section will focus on a number of industrywide, marketing-oriented initiatives by shipping-point firms followed by several examples of marketing-oriented efforts by leading firms.

### Industrywide Marketing Initiatives

During the 1980s, significant broad-based change has occurred in many shipping-point organizations. Among the most important changes are:

1. Improved Quality. In recent years there has been no more important or pervasive change in the produce industry than improved quality products. Of course, such improvements must begin at the production level.

2. More Value-added Products and Services. Value-added products and services provided by suppliers are many. They include mixed-load capabilities, supplier-initiated transportation scheduling, and more consumer packaging performed at the source level rather than at wholesale or retail levels. As more services and functions shift to the shipping point, tighter coordination of grower, packer and shipper activities becomes paramount.

3. Multicommodity and Multinational Operations. Increasingly, shipping-point firms are realizing the marketing advantages of multicommodity, multiregional and multinational operations. This constitutes a major step toward reducing the excessive fragmentation characteristic of the produce industry. Multicommodity and multinational operations help to establish extended seasons and year-round customer contact so vitally important in rapidly changing produce markets. Clearly, there are also advertising and promotion advantages, as well as greater flexibility and objectivity in production decisions (McLaughlin).

## Marketing Initiatives by Leading Firms

Beyond industrywide changes cited above, it is becoming clear that numerous produce firms are increasingly embracing a contemporary marketing orientation. A few firms and their leading-edge marketing approaches are highlighted as examples of this emerging change in the produce industry.

1. **Sun World International of Indio, California**. Sun World is a $200 million produce marketer with a solid base in the "commodity" produce business and with efforts under way to establish a number of superior marketplace positions. The following comments are edited excerpts from an insightful *Produce Business* interview with James R. Rinella, President, and David Marguleas, Manager of Merchandising and Corporate Relations at Sun World.

   Sun World's marketing process begins with analyses of the marketplace to identify niches that Sun World might have opportunities to fill. The process then works from the customer back toward the production level using research when appropriate to identify production, handling and distribution approaches to successfully meet the marketplace need.

   - Quality Assurance. Quality assurance is a key aspect of Sun World's strong marketing program. The program involves written specifications for each phase and step in the production and distribution system. The program extends from initiatives in the fields of Sun World's growers, through harvest and postharvest handling until delivery to wholesaler customers. It is an integrated program which keeps production, marketing and sales personnel abreast of what is happening. The program is evolving and improving; for example, when a troubled load is identified in the market, a person is dispatched to check on the problem and to make it right with the customer. Additionally, steps are taken to understand what went wrong and to alter practices to avoid repeat problems in the future.

- Branding of Proprietary Products. Proprietary products are ones in which Sun World has a proprietary interest in the variety. This is an approach to gain product differentiation which is so beneficial to successful branding. The approach has thus far been taken with products such as Sun World's DiVine Ripe tomatoes, LeRouge Royale peppers and the Sun World Seedless watermelon.

  The DiVine Ripe tomato was first brought to market in 1986 and has had an orderly, controlled and successful expansion of production and marketing since. In the marketplace with other tomatoes that retail from $.39 to $.89 per pound, the DiVine Ripe retails for $1.29 to $1.89 per pound. Sun World is now striving for a 12-month supply of consistent quality DiVine Ripe tomatoes to match demand at profitable prices.

  Another branded/proprietary program is the LeRouge Royale pepper accompanied by a family of Royale peppers: LeJaune, LeVert and L'Orange. The letter items are color variations of LeRouge and possess its super eating, size and wall-thickness characteristics. Sun World has also introduced a nectarine–MayGlo–which will be marketed 2-4 weeks ahead of the competition from San Joaquin. Also, a mango will be marketed from October through December, when there are no other mangos in season.

- Convenience Products. In addition to high quality and unique products, Sun World is moving to capitalize on consumer desires for convenience. They are currently market-testing a pack of multicolored peppers using smaller sizes from the Royale line. This approach takes advantage of production realities as well as consumer desires.

  Bagged avocados with guacamole mix is another convenience item which calls attention to this specific product use of avocados. Recipes are also included in the package, once again as a convenience for shoppers. These products are positioned as values for consumers and are seen by retail customers as aids helping sell more avocados (Drum).

2. **Frieda's Finest Produce Specialities, Inc.** Frieda's markets over 200 different types of branded specialty produce items including: kiwis, macadamia nuts, sunchokes, tofu, ginger and shallots. Located on the Los Angeles wholesale produce market, Frieda's began operations in the early 1960s with the belief that the retail market for fresh mushrooms

was largely untapped. Today, Frieda's sales are over $10 million per year. The organization played a role in expanding the market for fresh mushrooms and has moved on to literally hundreds of other products with the same market driven philosophy–to help customers by better serving their wants and needs. Frieda is sensitized to consumers by up to one thousand letters per week providing suggestions for recipes, as well as questions and comments about the produce Frieda is selling, as well as other items consumers are looking for.

In order to serve consumers, Frieda must convince distributors and retailers to handle the products. Frieda's consumer letters help to accomplish this, and so does the highly identifiable brand and characteristic purple packaging. Consumer packages are relatively small in size matching consumer needs for many specialty items, as well as keeping unit prices reasonable. Additionally, the packaging helps many items remain fresher longer, again benefiting retailers as well as consumers. Finally, use information, including recipes, is enclosed with products to help insure consumer satisfaction (Schnack).

Freida's Finest Produce Specialities is an excellent example of affirmative marketing: find out what is needed, find ways to provide it and then communicate improved products and services to customers.

3. **Babe Farms of Santa Maria, California**. As recently reported in *The Packer*, Babe Farms began operations 2-1/2 years ago with 175 acres producing about 65 baby and specialty items. Today, the list includes nearly 80 items on 525 acres.

   The key to Babe's success lies in its ongoing search for new items–as items become staples they find new ones. Babe's is currently investigating market opportunities for microwaveable combination packs of small specialty and baby items to save customers' preparation time. The organization is also constantly working to improve consistency of its products for its customers (The Packer, April 23, 1988).

Many other marketing examples could be cited. In fairness to the numerous firms and produce organizations which are embracing the marketing orientation, more examples should be cited; however, the above examples clearly illustrate the increasing importance of the marketing orientation to the produce industry.

## CONCLUSION

Adoption and application of the marketing process is the most important positive development taking place in today's produce industry. This development is characterized by a new philosophy among produce industry leaders from a traditional production/commodity orientation toward one of marketing. These two widely differing philosophies are characterized by the two following business approaches.

### Production/Commodity Orientation

With respect to the production/commodity orientation, production and sales of existing products are maximized often overlooking customer needs and related profit opportunities. Customers are usually viewed as being alike. The marketplace is seen as static, or at least sellers' behaviors imply a static marketplace. And finally, appeals to customers are based primarily upon *prices* and *quantities* of traditional products.

### The Marketing Orientation

Within the marketing orientation, customer satisfaction is maximized with products and services based upon their wants and needs. Customers are viewed as different from one another with differing and identifiable wants and needs. The marketplace is seen to be dynamic, requiring new products and services over time. And finally, appeal to customers is based upon their ever-changing perceptions of value and quality.

Simply stated, the fresh produce industry has crossed the threshold of contemporary food marketing. It is beginning to move away from the tradition of *selling* commodity fruits and vegetables in favor of *marketing* products targeted to the wants and needs of specific customer groups and consumer segments.

A basic conclusion is that the produce industry–growers, packers, shippers, wholesalers and retailers–is increasingly a market-driven system. That is, each participant is responding to its customers; shoppers in the case of supermarket operators, and shoppers, as well as wholesale/retail buyers, in the case of shipping point organizations.

The new wave of "marketed" produce is upon us; but it has only begun. There are many challenges and opportunities confronting contemporary produce marketers in their efforts to fully develop and expand the marketing approach. These marketers are necessarily in a learning and experimenting mode, open to new ideas and responsive to the challenges. Although the marketing process is new to the produce industry, commodity sellers ought to beware; the new wave of "marketed" produce will become increasingly tough competition and ultimately will be invincible.

## REFERENCES

Allen, John W., and Thomas R. Pierson, The Expanding World of Fresh Prepared Foods: Packaging and Distribution Challenges, Food Industry Institute, Michigan State University, East Lansing, Mich. 48824, November 1987, pp. 1-26.

Brown, Richard N. Jr., and Nydia R. Suarez, *Fresh Fruits and Vegetables: Some Characteristics of the U.S. Market for Nine Selected Imports, 1975-85,* Agriculture and Trade Analysis Division, Economic Research Service, U.S. Department of Agriculture, Washington, D.C. 20005-4788, June 1988, p. 10.

*Business Week*, April 27, 1987.

Drum, David, "Produce Business Interview: James Rinella, President and C.E.O. Sun World International," *Produce Business*, May 1988, pp. 19-25.

Linsen, Mary Ann, "And The Produce Beat Goes On," *Progressive Grocer*, June 1988, p. 131-137.

McLaughlin, Edward W., Buying and Selling Practices in the Fresh Fruit and Vegetable Industry: Implications for Vertical Coordination, Ph.D. Dissertation, Department of Agricultural Economics, Michigan State University, East Lansing, Mich. 48824, 1983.

McLaughlin, Edward W., and Thomas R. Pierson, *The Fresh Fruit and Vegetable Marketing System: A Research Summary*, Department of Agricultural Economics, Michigan State University, East Lansing, Mich. 48824, August 1983, pp. 1-30.

McLaughlin, Edward W., and Thomas R. Pierson, The Fresh Produce Industry in Transition: Strategic Questions for Produce Marketers, Staff paper No. 84-6, Department of Agricultural Economics, Cornell University, Ithaca, N.Y. 14853, 1984.

Otten, Alan L., "People Patterns," *The Wall Street Journal*, July 21, 1988, p. 17.

Scheringer, Joe, "Off-the-Shelf: Hot Product Categories," *Grocery Marketing*, November 1987, p. 30.

Schnack, Marg, "Creative Thinking: Designer Food," *Continental Magazine* (carried aboard Continental Airlines), 1983.

*The Packer*, "Eyes, Hands on DPP Model During Introductory Session," July 2, 1988, p. 2A.

*The Packer*, "Babe Farms Keeps on Growing," April 23, 1988, p. 4C.

# 4

# THE ROLE OF PUBLIC POLICIES IN U.S. VEGETABLE PRODUCTION AND MARKETING

Leo C. Polopolus
*University of Florida*

## INTRODUCTION

Because of the absence of a federal price and income support program for vegetable growers, the casual observer may conclude that producers and marketers of vegetables in the United States operate in a business environment with minimal or no government involvement. The reality is, of course, that the visible hand of government is omnipresent, either to restrain vegetable producers and marketers from bad conduct, to promote orderly marketing, or to improve the safety, well-being, and quality of people and their environment.

While this paper intends to briefly review a lengthy list of government programs and policies affecting vegetable producers and marketers, it should be noted at the outset that very few, if any, federal statutes have been enacted solely for the vegetable trade. This is not to deny the impact, however, of federal programs on vegetable growers and marketers.

Vegetables, for purposes of this paper, are defined to include those vegetables sold in both fresh and processed product markets. Since the focus of this book is upon fresh vegetable markets in hemispheric trade, however, the major focus will be upon the production and marketing of vegetables for produce markets in the United States.

Admittedly, several of the policies and programs of the United States Department of Agriculture (USDA) are of considerable importance to vegetable growers and marketers. However, vegetable businesses are often more heavily impacted by policies and programs of other federal agencies, as well as state and/or local programs. This paper intends to highlight the major public policies, irrespective of their administrative origin.

Overall, the purpose of this paper is to present an overview and cursory assessment of federal intervention in vegetable markets in the United States. Major policy issues will be surfaced from the point of view of producers, marketers, and consumers. International trade policy issues, however, will not be given much attention in view of their coverage in other papers in this volume.

Wherever possible and appropriate, an effort will be made to relate the United States policy agenda to the prospect of increased hemispheric trade in vegetables. There is no doubt about the recent increased demand for fresh vegetables by consumers. Concomitantly, there is increased interest by producers in finding profitable alternative crops, particularly vegetables. These two forces of increased consumer demand and new supply sources beg the problem of coordination of demand and supplies of vegetables on a hemispheric basis. The combination of highly perishable products, easy market entry, and constrained aggregate market size for fresh vegetables could lead to increased market inefficiency and excessive resource commitments to vegetable production in the Western Hemisphere. Imaginative Pan American public policies could be developed to better communicate and coordinate production and marketing decisions to avoid or minimize inappropriate resource use and red ink to growers and/or marketers.

## WHY PUBLIC INTERVENTION?

Even though the invisible hand of unfettered competition normally does an adequate job of providing for efficient resource use and fairness in market transactions, the national public interest is adversely affected by occasional market failure, unfair dealings, and intentional abuse of public health, food and occupational safety, and the natural environment. Stated in economic jargon, government intervention in private markets occurs because of the inability of competitive markets to achieve socially efficient resource allocation. Government intervention is thus intended to correct observed market failure (Archibald and Dahl).

Federal laws and related regulations and enforcement procedures become necessary because voluntary approaches to promoting competition, health, safety and environmental quality in vegetable and other product markets break down from a propensity of market participants to cheat or take a "free ride" on the back of those other market participants. Federal programs, therefore, can establish mandatory standards of performance to eliminate or lessen "free rider" problems.

Thus, federal policies and programs become important to promoting effective competition, orderly marketing, public health and safety, as well as environmental quality. Historically, these types of policies began in the nineteenth century with programs to improve transportation (canals, roads, and railroads) and regulate monopolies. Many other policies affecting vegetable trade were established before the New Deal era began in 1933, such as laws regarding food safety, cooperatives, market news, and commodity grading. Marketing orders for fruits and vegetables were introduced with the New Deal legislation of 1933 and refined with the passage of the Agricultural Marketing Agreement Act of 1937. While the 1930s is generally thought of as the heyday era of agricultural legislation, each decade since then has witnessed new federal legislation or major amendments to existing legislation. For example, even though the Food and Drug Act was enacted in 1906, major supplemental legislation concerning food health and safety was added in 1938, 1947, 1958, 1966, 1970, and 1976. Food processors, including vegetable canners and freezers, have been particularly subject to considerable health and safety regulation because of the clear relationship between food and human health (Archibald and Dahl).

There are, of course, negative aspects to federal intervention in vegetable markets. Regulations have the tendency to reduce labor productivity growth, increase costs of production/processing/marketing, escalate government expenditures, and restrain the development of new technology (Archibald and Dahl). It has been estimated (by Denison) that one-fourth of productivity growth is lost in the United States to meet government regulations. Sometimes regulations impose trade barriers or serve to restrict supplies with higher consumer prices as a result. In other cases, e.g., transportation and communications, the high costs of regulation and/or ineffective regulation has led to deregulation.

For purposes of this paper, public policies affecting the vegetable sector have been grouped into eight categories. Although the groups are not uniquely separate or independent, some classification scheme of the public policies was deemed necessary to expedite the presentation. The eight types of public policies affecting vegetable growers and marketers are as follows:

- Orderly Marketing;
- Fair Trading/Competition;
- Food Safety and Health;
- International Trade;
- Farm Labor;

- Transportation;
- Environmental Quality; and
- State and Local Policies.

## ORDERLY MARKETING

At the producer level, vegetable markets are dramatically affected by inherent perishability and seasonality factors. Also because vegetables are annual crops, there is relative ease of entry over relatively large geographic zones. Except for vegetables produced for processing (which commonly involve grower-processor contracts), vegetable markets display erratic or quite unstable price patterns over seasons and within given seasons.

If there had been an absence of market price information, grades, market support, and occasional volume management programs, vegetable growers would have experienced even more chaotic price variability, as well as frequent periods of negative profits. Thus, federal programs involving orderly marketing seek to address problems created from a lack of market information, grades and standards, market support, and stable and/or reasonable prices.

### Market Information

With the explosion in the type, number, variety, and geographic origin of fresh vegetables marketed in the United States in recent years, the federal price reporting system has been generally overwhelmed. The proliferation of exotic, ethnic, miniature, organic, and/or vine-ripe vegetables accentuates the growth and popularity of fresh vegetables, but it also underscores the problems of inadequate or nonexistent public market information on these new market developments.

Historically, public price reporting by the USDA began while central wholesale markets dominated trade in farm products (Henderson, Schrader, and Rhodes). We all know about the decline in these market institutions over time, although central wholesale markets for vegetables have stabilized and remain vital in major metropolitan areas. Price reporting for major vegetables and vegetable products occurs at the farm gate, f.o.b. shipping point or f.o.b. processing point, and at the wholesale level.

From an economist's perspective, the available price data on vegetables from the USDA often does not have corresponding quantity data. Also decreases in federal expenditures for vegetable market information have yielded piecemeal data. Changes in the vegetable marketing system and/or structure have left the available published data somewhat unrepresentative of actual market conditions. Many vegetable markets have also become "thin" in terms of numbers of buyers and sellers, creating problems of access to market information by government agencies.

There are several alternative solutions to the market information problem. First, the government could expand and modernize the scope of its coverage. This would require considerable public expenditures and/or user fees. Secondly, scanning data at retail store level could be utilized for providing retail price/quantity data on the full mix of vegetables sold in fresh and processed form. The question here is who would pay for these data services and who would benefit from their disclosure. Thirdly, computer assisted marketing programs, if they become utilized by the trade, could furnish price and other data as a by-product of private negotiations. Unfortunately, none of these alternatives appear likely to cope with the data reporting problems at hand.

## Grading

The Agricultural Marketing Act of 1946 established the broad authority of the USDA to conduct standardization and grading. The Agricultural Marketing Service of the USDA has responsibility for most of the vegetable grading programs. (The USDA, however, was in the vegetable grading business much earlier than 1946.)

Vegetable grades serve to protect market participants from abuse, enhance economic efficiency, and increase product competitiveness in domestic and international trade. The USDA vegetable grading services give assurance to buyers and sellers that products meet specific grade or contract requirements. Use of official grade standards is voluntary and the cost of vegetable grading services are usually borne by users. Grading may occur at shipping points or destinations. The USDA grading services are available throughout the 50 states and Puerto Rico via cooperative agreements with state departments of agriculture and other state agencies. Grading services can be somewhat tailor-made for a variety of market participants, such as shippers, receivers, institutional buyers, government agencies, and processors.

The introduction of high speed refrigerated transportation has altered the quality requirement for some vegetables. Also, the introduction of varying processes for drying, canning, freezing, and dehydrating vegetables has changed the meaningfulness of many vegetable grades and standards.

In effect, some of the historical approaches to grades and standards for fresh vegetables have been rendered somewhat impotent by new marketing developments. For example, the trend toward specification buying has sometimes altered the need for and usefulness of vegetable grades and standards (Nichols, Hill, and Nelson). Also, the use of shipper, processor, and/or wholesale brand names to specify product quality characteristics reduces the reliance on grades and standards.

## Marketing Orders

The Agricultural Marketing Agreement Act of 1937, as amended, provides enabling legislation for redress of the marketing problems of fruit and vegetable growers. Three basic weapons may be utilized by growers to deal with their marketing problems–volume management, minimum quality standards, and market support activities. Specific programs are initiated by growers, with program approval required by the United States Secretary of Agriculture. Once the necessary referenda and approval processes are completed, all growers and handlers are required to comply with the regulatory provisions covered by the marketing order. Thus, federal marketing orders permit marketing programs to be developed uniquely for each vegetable product for the specified geographic areas. Programs are essentially self-financed from assessments on handlers, greatly minimizing government expenditures.

In actual practice most federal vegetable marketing orders have involved potatoes and onions in various parts of the nation (Armbruster and Jesse). Other federal marketing orders are currently in operation for tomatoes, celery, and melons. Under consideration are possible new marketing orders for strawberries, Vidalia onions, and greenhouse cucumbers. State marketing orders are also in effect for several other vegetable products, particularly in California.

What is striking about federal marketing orders for vegetables is the almost unanimous use of grade and size regulations as the tool to deal with disorderly marketing. There is no evidence of volume management programs, except possibly for shipping holiday provisions for some onion orders and the authority for production allotments for the Florida celery order. Most vegetable orders, however, permit pack and container standardization. Generic advertising is not popular among the federal vegetable orders.

Of particular significance for hemispheric trade in vegetables is Section 8e of the Agricultural Marketing Agreement Act. This provision requires that imports meet the identical minimum quality, size, and maturity standards of vegetable products covered by the marketing order. The Act applies this import restriction to a specified subset of covered commodities. In effect, Section 8e prevents "dumping" of low quality imported vegetables into domestic markets (Polopolus et al.). Over a period of years, Section 8e provisions have been an important policy issue of the Florida tomato order (Armbruster and Jesse).

## FAIR TRADING/COMPETITION

While enforcement has not been uniform and/or effective over time, the United States has an arsenal of laws and regulations to promote competition and deter unfair trading practices. These programs can be grouped into two categories–those that provide a general framework for economic regulation and those that deal more specifically with agricultural issues and concerns.

### General Economic Regulation

The antitrust policies of the United States are embodied primarily in the Sherman Act of 1890, the Clayton Act of 1914, the Robinson Patman Act of 1936, and the Federal Trade Commission Act of 1914. Overall, these statutes seek to maintain workable competition by regulating market conduct and specific anticompetitive acts or practices. More specifically, these programs are designed to

- prohibit contracts in restraint of trade;
- prohibit monopolization and conspiracy to monopolize;
- prohibit price discrimination, tie-in sales, mergers and acquisitions, interlocking directorates;
- regulate price discrimination by restricting concentrated buying power; and
- prohibit unfair or deceptive practices, false or misleading product claims.

It does not appear that vegetable producers and marketers have been among the lead violators of federal antitrust laws. In fact a review of CCH Trade Cases for the 1967-1977 period revealed that less than 6% of all food related price fixing and price discrimination cases involved fruit and vegetable firms. In contrast dairy product firms accounted for roughly 30% and bakery firms represented almost 20% of the total number of reported cases (Polopolus and Wershow). These results support the notion that vegetable markets are indeed competitive throughout the grower to retailer marketing chain.

### Agricultural Fair Trading/Competition Programs

Because of some unique characteristics of agriculture and agricultural institutions, the United States has developed a set of specialized laws.

1. Cooperatives. While the Clayton Act offered limited antitrust exemption to agricultural cooperatives, the Capper-Volstead Act of 1922 clarified and broadened the protection. Because of excessive competition in agricultural markets, cooperatives were given a legal framework for increasing the market power of producers. Cooperatives were, however, prohibited from restraining trade and unduly enhancing prices.

   In 1926 the Cooperatives Marketing Act was enacted to further support the Capper-Volstead Act. Under this 1926 Act, cooperatives were permitted to exchange market information between producer associations. Sanctions were applied to certain forms of behavior between processors and producers.

   In 1980 it was estimated that there were 379 fruit and vegetable marketing cooperatives in the United States representing average sales of $15 million. These cooperatives were estimated to account for a one-fourth share of the total market (Harris et al.). While vegetables are less likely to be involved with cooperatives, as compared with fruit products, cooperatives are nevertheless an important marketing alternative for vegetable growers.

2. PACA. The Perishable Agricultural Commodities Act (PACA) was passed in 1930 to eliminate unfair trading practices and assure producers of prompt and full payment for products marketed. The program, administered by the USDA, is highly relevant to fresh and frozen vegetable markets.

   The PACA program assumes that producers are not in a position to protect themselves from unfair practices of buyers, such as arbitrary rejection of shipments or nonpayment for delivered goods. PACA also protects buyers from short product weights and quality misrepresentation (Knutson, Geyer, and Helmuth). Most disputes between shippers and receivers involve failure of buyers to pay promptly or disputes over product quality. The program is self-financed from licensing fees. The USDA enforces compliance through revocation of licenses and in some instances bonding requirements of licensees.

   Overall, the PACA program has been very effective in solving disputes in the produce trade without costly litigation in state and/or federal courts. A large increase in filings under PACA since 1984, however, has led to a projected deficit in the user fund pool. Increased fees from $300 to $500 per licensee have been proposed to deal with proposed deficits.

3. Bargaining Cooperatives. The Agricultural Fair Practices Act of 1967 reaffirmed producers rights to organize for marketing or bargaining purposes. The Act sets standards and fair practices for handlers and processors. The Act has been ineffective in achieving its stated objectives, however. This is due in large measure to the Act's disclaimers which give handlers (processors) the right to select producers for any reason other than cooperative membership. Moreover, the Act does not require that the handler (processor) deal with cooperatives (Knutson, Geyer, and Helmuth).

   Cooperative bargaining associations involved with vegetables have become less important in recent years. The share of total cash receipts of vegetables for processing negotiated by bargaining associations declined between 1978 and 1982 for tomatoes, potatoes, carrots, green peas, sweet corn, and cauliflower. Typically, bargaining associations negotiate only with private proprietary processors, as distinct from marketing cooperatives (Carman and French).

## FOOD SAFETY AND HEALTH

There is now intense national interest regarding the safety of foods consumed in the American diet. Both fresh and processed vegetables are under considerable scrutiny by existing federal programs. The difficulty and complexity with our federal programs in this area have to do with the multiplicity of federal agencies involved, numerous pieces of legislation, and several (sometimes overlapping) federal agencies vying for leadership roles.

Processed vegetable products come under the authority of the Food Act of 1906 and the Food, Drug, and Cosmetic Act of 1938, as amended. Our federal policies prohibit the sale and manufacture of adulterated and misbranded products. Standards on filth and contaminants are established. Also, these programs prescribe tolerances on pesticide residues and food additives. Since the passage of the Delaney clause in 1958, food additives are screened for health risk, additives are licensed, and the use of carcinogenic additives is prohibited.

For fresh vegetables, the United States Food and Drug Administration enforces pesticide tolerance, while the United States Environmental Protection

Agency (EPA) sets standards on pesticide tolerance. Under the Insecticide, Fumigate, and Rodenticide Act of 1947, pesticides are classified by the EPA and the USDA for their degree of risk (restricted or unrestricted). Pesticides are licensed for specific uses and applicator licenses are required for restricted pesticides. Worker safety standards are established under the Occupational Health and Safety Act of 1970.

To protect consumers from fraud and deceit in packaging and labeling, the Fair Packaging and Labeling Act of 1966 specifies standards for label information under the enforcement authority of the FDA, FTC, and the Commerce Department. The Consumer Products Safety Commission establishes packaging standards for hazardous products under the Poison Prevention Packaging Act of 1976. Moreover, the United States Department of Defense is responsible for the food safety of all military personnel (Sporleder, Kramer, Epp).

Given this complex web of programs and federal enforcement agencies, several experts have recommended that a single federal regulatory agency be established for food. A USDA workshop on Processed Fruits and Vegetables has further recommended that federal regulations concerning chemical residues override state regulations (The Packer). Debate is now extant on whether or not private laboratories should be testing fresh produce for product safety, as opposed to traditional public testing units within the FDA and/or the USDA.

Another major issue arises from the disparity between analytical measurement capability of pesticides versus the much slower advances in toxicology. For example, contaminants can be measured in minute parts per billion, whereas their potential risks to human health and the environment may be unknown or measured only crudely (Archibald and Dahl).

There is also concern about the no-risk framework of the Delaney Clause on food additives. It has been proposed elsewhere that any new food safety framework:

1. provide guidelines for explicit risk, benefit assessment of food additives and technology;

2. allow scientific review of the regulatory decision process; and

3. provide regulatory flexibility consistent with other health and safety policies (Archibald and Dahl).

With regard to fresh produce, a USDA Workshop on Fresh Fruits and Vegetables concluded that food safety represents one of the biggest challenges for the industry. Fresh vegetables were deemed safe in U.S. markets under current monitoring, inspection, and grading systems. It was recommended that imported fresh vegetables must meet the same standards as domestically grown vegetables (The Packer).

## INTERNATIONAL TRADE

While several other papers in this volume will discuss trade policies as related to vegetables, it should be noted here that international trade policies are important to marketing both fresh and processed vegetable products.

For fresh vegetable trade, tariff barriers for entry into U.S. markets have been lessened substantially from a series of events. The Kennedy Round of the General Agreement on Tariff and Trade (GATT) in the 1960s led to a 50% reduction in import tariffs. More significantly, the 1974 United States Trade Act established the Generalized System of Preferences (GSP). The GSP granted to the President the authority to provide duty-free treatment on imported products from developing countries. Since most imported fresh vegetables are from beneficiary developing countries, tariff barriers on fresh vegetable imports are minimal.

The duty-free status of a large class of products was reinforced with the passage of the Caribbean Basin Economic Recovery Act of 1983, commonly known as the Caribbean Basin Initiative (CBI). The centerpiece of the CBI program is one-way free trade for potentially 28 CBI countries (Polopolus, 1985). Even though tariffs were already zero for fresh vegetable imports from the CBI region, the program sends a signal that imports of vegetables are welcome in U.S. markets. Thus, economic factors, such as packaging, marketing, and transportation costs, become important to penetration of U.S. markets rather than tariff rates.

Sensitivity to the problem of pesticide residues from imported food products is reflected in the recent passage of the Omnibus Trade and Competitiveness Act of 1988. Among many other provisions, the Act calls for an evaluation and monitoring of pesticide residues in domestic and imported food products.

## FARM LABOR

For fresh vegetables particularly, labor is a major cost component of production. Federal labor policies, which in earlier years tended to exempt agricultural producers and/or workers, have moved in the direction of closing coverage gaps between farm and nonfarm sectors for such major program areas as minimum wages and unemployment insurance. In addition, numerous specialized programs have been created over the years to protect the health and safety of farm workers, such as programs involving child labor, labor contractors/crew leaders, farm labor camps, field sanitation/drinking water, and education for migrants. In many instances parallel or slightly divergent state programs have been developed. In other exceptional situations, states have developed unique programs that have departed from federal philosophy, e.g., California's special statute regarding collective bargaining for farm workers.

Over the past decade the public debate regarding farm labor has shifted somewhat from collective bargaining issues to concerns about the environment surrounding farm workers. Environmental concerns have been highlighted by the passage of a federal program establishing standards for field sanitation and drinking water on relatively large farms.

Since a major paper at this workshop will address the relationship between vegetable trade and the role of labor, emphasis here will be to highlight only a selected number of public policy areas.

## Minimum Wages

The Fair Labor Standards Act is a federal law that establishes the criteria for minimum wages for all workers, including farm workers. Farm employers who use fewer than 500 man-days of labor during any calendar quarter of the proceeding calendar year are exempt. This means that farm employers with roughly seven or more full-time employees working five days a week must pay minimum wages to their farm employees. The current federal minimum wage is $3.35 per hour. Farm work is exempt from the overtime provisions of the Fair Labor Standards Act.

Considerable debate is presently occurring in the United States Congress regarding amendment of the Fair Labor Standards Act to not only raise the minimum wage standard, but to require "indexation" in the minimum wage by 50% of average hourly earnings after 1991. There appears to be some support in the Congress for raising the minimum wage to some level, but more serious opposition to any indexation provision (Polopolus).

## Unemployment Insurance

Since 1978, federal standards have been applied to covered farm employers for unemployment insurance of farm workers who became unemployed through no fault of their own. The federal standard for coverage is at least a payroll of $20,000 in any calendar quarter or 10 or more employees employed for 20 or more weeks during a year (Covey). Individual states may and some do have more stringent (broader) eligibility requirements. Individual states also have quite variable benefit provisions for unemployed workers eligible for benefits.

For farm workers, unemployment insurance is a source of income protection. For the regional economy, it is said that unemployment insurance provides some stability to the economy. The program also tends to maintain a permanent work force by reducing the propensity to migration, encourages employers to stabilize their employment practices, and preserves job skills of workers by permitting them to search for jobs which utilize their skills (Polopolus).

### Labor Contractors/Crew Leaders

Both state and federal laws have been enacted to protect migrant and seasonal workers from abuse and unfair treatment of labor contractors or crew leaders. The federal program was amended recently under the Migrant and Seasonal Agricultural Worker Protection Act (MSPA). The program seeks to register labor contractors/crew leaders and require these farm employers to meet certain standards.

Agricultural employers, even though not ordinarily regarded as a labor contractors, are required to register under the federal program if they recruit, solicit, hire, employ, furnish transport of migrant and/or seasonal agricultural workers, or house migrant agricultural workers. There are several groups exempted from the program, including the following: family businesses, small businesses, common carriers, labor organizations, nonprofit organizations, and employees of exempt employers.

The federal program requires that farm labor contractors or covered agricultural employers must disclose certain information to migrant agricultural workers at the time of recruitment.

### Field Sanitation and Drinking Water

A somewhat recent federal program has been introduced to require employers of 11 or more agricultural field workers to provide toilets, handwashing facilities, and drinking water at no cost to employees. The handwashing facility must include either a basin, container, or outlet with an adequate supply of potable water, soap, and single use towels. Potable water must meet local or state standards or those standards prescribed by the United States Environmental Protection Agency. Toilet facilities may include either biological, chemical, flush, and combustion toilets and sanitary privies.

The federal regulations regarding field sanitation and drinking water define the number of such facilities required in relation to the field work force, the location of these facilities in relation to work location, temperature and dispensing method of drinking water, waste disposal standards, and the employers' responsibilities for promoting good hygiene among farm workers.

## Immigration Reform

Passage of the Immigration Reform and Control Act (IRCA) of 1986 redefined U.S. policy regarding aliens. Without discussing the new Act's many provisions, it goes without saying that the Act now affects every employer and every worker in the nation, even where no alien workers are involved (Polopolus).

IRCA makes it mandatory that all employers examine documentation of all prospective employees before hiring them. Employers must also keep records of the documents examined. Employers must examine documents which establish both employment authorization and identity. Each employer must also fill out a form, known as an I-9, for each new hire and maintain it on file for at least three years.

## Overall Farm Labor Policy

The difficulty with labor policy issues is the maintenance of a balance between equity for workers and competitiveness for the industry of agriculture. Historically, farmers have been able to remain viable through biological and mechanical innovations. The adoption of new agricultural technology has tended to lower real costs of production and real prices to consumers. The next decade is expected to witness the increasing impact of biotechnology research applied to agricultural production from public and private sources.

There is now such a bewildering array of labor programs affecting farm employers that the costs of paperwork are becoming substantial. This is not to deny the importance or benefits of the programs in effect. A federal study group is needed to suggest innovative ways to simplify the statutes and programs without adversely affecting their beneficial attributes (Polopolus).

The serious question about IRCA is the impact that this law will have upon wage rates for seasonal and perishable crop workers. Will the imposition of civil and criminal sanctions (fines) on vegetable growers who knowingly hire illegal aliens affect wage rates? Will those vegetable workers recently given amnesty or temporary resident alien status via the Seasonal Agricultural Workers program abandon agricultural employment for less seasonal employment? Will the revised H-2 program become flexible enough for application to vegetable producers throughout the nation? And finally, is it conceivable that enforcement of IRCA will be adequate to stem the tide of new flows of alien workers seeking employment in vegetable and other farms in America? Stay tuned.

## TRANSPORTATION

Transportation is a critical factor in the vegetable marketing system. Except for canned and dehydrated vegetable products, refrigerated transportation services are required for most vegetables.

Transportation policy in the United States took a sharp turn a few years ago from intense regulation to much milder forms of regulations. Even before this change in policy direction, however, the bulk of fresh vegetables were being shipped by the truck mode of transfer, as rail shipments of perishables had become fraught with slow service, misdirected cars, and breakdowns in equipment, among other problems. Air transport of vegetable products has historically been of minor importance, except for a few specialty or early season fresh vegetable products of high per unit value.

The primary federal regulatory agency for rail and truck transportation services is the Interstate Commerce Commission (ICC) which was created in 1887. The Railroad Revitalization and Regulatory Reform Act of 1977 and later legislation were enacted to relax the regulatory climate for railroads and permit the railroad industry to regain some of its lost traffic.

Processed vegetable products transported by trucks are regulated by the ICC. However, fresh vegetables transported in trucks are exempt from freight rate determination by the ICC.

In 1980 both rail and motor truck transportation services were deregulated significantly. The Staggers Rail Act of 1980 gave railroad companies greater flexibility to compete for traffic. The Act permitted railroads to offer short term discounts to shippers and to offer special freight rates for large volume contracts. The Act also permitted railroads to purchase and operate motor and water carriers. The Staggers Act also made it somewhat easier for railroads to abandon unprofitable branch lines.

The Motor Carrier Act of 1980 deregulated trucking. The Act facilitated entry of new carriers and reduced regulations influencing truck rates and routes.

While truck transport services dominate vegetable product shipments, there are two major factors that could increase the rail's share of traffic in the future. For long distance hauls, well designed and managed unit trains can reduce transit time at competitive rates. Secondly, a surge in energy prices could lead to much higher truck rates. There is no doubt that simply on an energy per ton mile basis, rail transport is more energy efficient.

## ENVIRONMENTAL QUALITY

Laws and regulations dealing with environmental quality arise because the market system often fails to incorporate production externalities into prices of products. Production externalities in vegetable production and processing occur whenever the actions of one producer affect the utilities or production possibilities of another, either positively or negatively, in a way that is not reflected in the market. In the absence of government intervention, producers rarely have incentives to consider their external effects and to internalize them by eliminating harmful wastes, residues, and chemicals voluntarily. The objective of environmental regulation is to ensure that harmful external effects are reduced or eliminated (Archibald and Dahl). Without elaboration or full description, a list of some of the federal environmental programs, enforced mostly by EPA, are included in Table 4.1.

Table 4.1. Selected Federal Environmental Programs Affecting Food Markets

| Program | Purpose |
|---|---|
| Solid Waste Disposal Act of 1965 | Subsidies for new waste treatment facilities |
| National Environmental Policy Act of 1967 | Environmental Impact Reports; prohibits environmentally risky projects |
| Water Pollution Control Act of 1972 (as amended) | Sets maximum effluent standards for point source pollution |
| Clean Air Act of 1970 (as amended) | Sets ambient standards and emission levels |
| Federal Environmental Pesticide Control Act of 1972 | Licenses processing and manufacturing facilities; prohibits and/or restricts use of risky materials |
| Resource Conservation and Recovery Act of 1976 | Issues permits to handle and dispose of hazardous substances |
| Toxic Substances Control Act of 1976 | Prohibits manufacture or sale of substances which pose unreasonable risk to public health or environment |

In addition to the above federal programs, most states have their own set of programs dealing with the environment. In some cases these state programs are more restrictive than federal programs.

## STATE AND LOCAL POLICIES

State and/or local governments throughout the nation have responsibility for land use planning, zoning, water allocation, water quality, and public health and safety. State water laws and land use regulations are of particular importance to vegetable producers and marketers.

## CONCLUDING REMARKS

For a subsector of the food system that is purported to be relatively free of government intervention, domestic vegetable trade is surprisingly involved in a network of U.S. policies and programs. However, very few, if any, of these federal programs have been designed solely for vegetable production and/or marketing.

The pertinent question at this point has to do with the relevance of all these federal policies and programs for vegetable trade in the Western Hemisphere. Specifically, what are the critical program areas for future development?

In my view the major policy areas that require increased attention in the hemisphere involve common and acceptable standards of food safety, minimum quality standards, and improved market information.

For U.S. consumers, pesticide residues on or in vegetable products will command increasing concern and attention. Domestic vegetable producers complain that, in some instances, foreign produce enters U.S. markets with pesticides currently banned from use by U.S. growers. The heightened interest in the safety of vegetables will likely lead to additional regulations and tighter enforcement at national borders and entry ports.

Establishing and/or improving minimum quality standards for vegetable products marketed in the United States would result in mostly positive benefits to producers. Minimum quality standards via marketing order type programs can provide these benefits:

1. increase the retail demand for a product resulting in higher prices and/or increased quantities sold;

2. reduce marketing margins with benefits accruing to both consumers and producers; and

3. reduce supply which, with inelastic demand at the farm level, will result in increased total returns to producers for a given crop.

Moreover, minimum quality standards can address vegetable marketing problems such as excessive shrinkage, poor product image, failure to match product characteristic to consumer demand, free riders, and inefficiency in long distance transactions (Polopolus et al.).

Finally, improved and expanded public market information on vegetable markets is needed at all stages of the fresh and processed vegetable marketing chain. It may be that we need to experiment with user fees for agricultural price and other market information. Fresh vegetable markets particularly are well known for their dramatic and often erratic price swings within and over seasons. Poor market information for vegetables in the United States and throughout the Western Hemisphere leads to inefficient resource use, lagged resource adjustment, and poor coordination between consumers' wants and producers' expectations.

## REFERENCES

Archibald, Sandra O., and Dale C. Dahl, "Regulating United States Food Processing Industries", Chapter 5 in *Economics of Food Processing in the United States*, edited by Chester O. McCorkle, Jr., San Diego: Academic Press, 1988.

Armbruster, Walter J., and Edward V. Jesse, "Fruit and Vegetable Marketing Orders", Chapter 5 in *Federal Marketing Programs in Agriculture*, edited by Walter J. Armbruster, Dennis R. Henderson, and Ronald D. Knutson, Danville, Illinois: Interstate, 1983.

Carman, Hoy F., and Ben C. French, "Economics of Fruit and Vegetable Processing in the United States", Chapter 6 in *Economics of Food Processing in the United States*, edited by Chester O. McCorkle, Jr., San Diego: Academic Press, 1988.

Covey, C.D., Handbook of Regulations Affecting Florida Farm Employers and Employees, Circular 699, Gainesville: Florida Cooperative Extension Service, January 1986.

Denison, E.F., *Accounting for Slower Economic Growth: The United States in the 1970s*, Washington, D.C.: The Brookings Institution, 1979.

Harris, Harold M., Jr., Edward V. Jesse, Randall E. Torgerson, James D. Shaffer, and Leon Garoyan, "Cooperatives and Bargaining", Chapter 7 in *Federal Marketing Programs in Agriculture*, edited by Walter J. Armbruster, Dennis R. Henderson, and Ronald D. Knutson, Danville, Illinois: Interstate, 1983.

Henderson, Dennis R., Lee F. Schrader, and V. James Rhodes, "Public Price Reporting", Chapter 2 in *Federal Marketing Programs in Agriculture*, edited by Walter J. Armbruster, Dennis R. Henderson, and Ronald D. Knutson, Danville, Illinois: Interstate, 1983.

Knutson, Ronald D., L. Leon Geyer, and John W. Helmuth, "Trade Practice Regulation", Chapter 8 in *Federal Marketing Programs in Agriculture*, edited by Walter J. Armbruster, Dennis R. Henderson, and Ronald D. Knutson, Danville, Illinois: Interstate, 1983.

Nichols, John P., Lowell D. Hill, and Kenneth E. Nelson, "Food and Agricultural Commodity Grading", Chapter 3 in *Federal Marketing Programs in Agriculture*, edited by Walter J. Armbruster, Dennis R. Henderson, and Ronald D. Knutson, Danville, Illinois: Interstate, 1983.

Polopolus, Leo C., The Caribbean Basin Initiative and Its Potential Impact Upon Agriculture in South Florida, Staff Paper 285, Gainesville: Food and Resource Economics Department, University of Florida, August 1985.

Polopolus, Leo C., "The 1986 Immigration Reform Act and Florida Agriculture", Florida Food and Resource Economics, No. 76, May-June, 1987.

Polopolus, Leo C., "Farm Labor in Florida–An Update", Gainesville: Food and Resource Economics Department, University of Florida, April 15, 1988.

Polopolus, Leo C., Hoy F. Carman, Edward V. Jesse, and James D. Shaffer, *Criteria for Evaluating Federal Marketing Orders: Fruits, Vegetables, Nuts, and Specialty Commodities*, Washington, D.C.: Economic Research Service of the United States Department of Agriculture, December 1986.

Polopolus, Leo, and James S. Wershow, "The Incidence, Nature, and Implications of Price-Fixing Litigation in United States Food Industries", *Southern Journal of Agricultural Economics*, 10(1978):1-7.

Sporleder, Thomas L., Carol S. Kramer, and Donald J. Epp, "Food Safety", Chapter 9 in *Federal Marketing Programs in Agriculture*, edited by Walter J. Armbruster, Dennis R. Henderson, and Ronald D. Knutson, Danville, Illinois: Interstate, 1983.

*The Packer*, "Food Safety Proposals Take Federal Focus", July 9, 1988. (USDA Processed Fruit and Vegetable Workshop.)

*The Packer*, "Common Agenda for Food Safety Issues Urged", July 9, 1988. (USDA Fresh Fruit and Vegetable Workshop.)

# 5

# POLICIES AND INSTITUTIONS IN VEGETABLE MARKETING IN THE WESTERN HEMISPHERE: THE MEXICAN EXPERIENCE

S. Kenneth Shwedel
*Asociación Americana de Soya-Mexico*

## INTRODUCTION

Churchman defined a system as "a set of parts coordinated to accomplish a set of goals." Vegetable marketing systems are those activities which involve the production, assembly, wholesaling, retailing, and consumption of vegetables. Coordination takes place through both formal and informal institutions.

Institutions function by delineating "sets of ordered relations among people which define their rights, exposure to the rights of others, privileges and responsibilities" (Schmid). They identify rules and consensus (Powelson). When institutions are formal, rules are set forth as operating procedures, codes, or laws. Informal institutions operate through consensus formation, pressure rewards, and exclusion. Formal system goals are set forth through policymaking processes.

Riggs describes bureaucratic institutions by the number of functions they perform. In developed societies, the administrative structure performs a wide range of specific functions, while in traditional societies formal institutions undertake a very limited number of functions. Most developing countries are between the two. Furthermore, while bureaucrats are not value neutral, in developing societies they are much more personally involved in determining goals. Political and administrative functions are fused (Riggs).

Riggs' description can be applied to the institutional environment for vegetable marketing in the Western Hemisphere. Informal and nongovernment institutions play an important role since formal institutions frequently do not adequately perform all of the necessary market facilitating functions. The lines between policy formation and administrative functions are not clearly drawn. Political concerns outweigh administrative efficiency even at relatively low levels in the bureaucracy. Policy conflict and contradiction are frequent occurrences as different agencies responsible for similar and complementary functions will often respond to different clientele groups. Stated policy often gives way to other concerns reflecting interest group power. The policy focus for vegetable marketing in Latin America has not centered on one set of objectives, but rather on both development as well as export (foreign exchange earnings) objectives.

The literature on the role of food marketing systems in economic development is extensive. Improvements in food marketing systems promote favorable economic and social performance by:

1. reducing risks through better information;
2. rewarding economies in production and distribution;
3. making demand for products more elastic by stimulating new processes, storage, etc.;
4. developing the administrative capacity by providing opportunities for efficient organization to better coordinate production with demand; and
5. incorporating marginal groups into society by providing them access to economic and social opportunities (Moyer).

Likewise, an inefficient marketing system can create barriers to development. Performance failures of the agricultural marketing system in coordination and physical distribution can retard the transition from a traditional to a highly productive economy. Uncertainty and unrewarding farm product prices, unreliable and expensive farm inputs, high prices and uncertain supplies of food to urban consumers all encourage the maintenance of low-productivity subsistence farming (Harrison et al., 1975).

Vegetable market improvements have been the object of a number of projects throughout Latin America. Production frequently takes place on small farms and is labor intensive. Total consumer purchases of these products represent an important part of their total monetary expenditures. Michigan State's LAMP research showed "total fruit and vegetable purchases approach 25% of consumer expenditures" (Harrison et al., 1974). Furthermore, LAMP pointed out that many of these products are often dietary staples, e.g., yams, potatoes, manioc, onions, and tomatoes (Harrison et al., 1974).

To the extent that market performance is improved, it is felt that producer and consumer welfare can also be improved. However the benefits may not be equally distributed since more than one marketing system for the same crop often exist (Shwedel). In fact, if special care is not taken in the design of marketing programs, producer and consumer welfare may actually deteriorate for some groups–particularly small farmers.

In spite of the stated development concerns for improving vegetable marketing systems, many infrastructure improvements are initiated as a response to "urban blithe." Central wholesale markets located in and near the downtown areas cause traffic and sanitation problems. The real concern is to relocate the wholesale market to solve these urban problems. Projects will go forward without necessarily addressing the effects on market system performance.

Vegetable exports have become an import source of foreign exchange earnings for some countries. In 1987 fresh vegetable exports equaled 3.4% of Mexico's total nonpetroleum exports. Excluding oil, they were the fourth most important export product. As a result of the CBI there has been renewed interest in stimulating vegetable exports in Central America. Being labor intensive, there is the added advantage coming from employment creation. The processed vegetable export industry in Latin America has also been growing.

While its potential for generating foreign exchange and creating employment cannot be denied, there are a number of concerns in Latin America regarding vegetable exporting: commercial problems with the United States, especially in light of the growing protectionism in that country; the fact that the presence of foreign investment raises questions about overall development effects and net outcome on foreign exchange balances; and domestic food priorities versus trade balance considerations.

The dual focus on the role of vegetable marketing has often resulted in a dual set of policies and institutions regulating and guiding the industry. Export goals and development objectives need not be contradictory. Problems arise when the set of policies and institutions respond to other pressures that are inherently contradictory. This is especially the case as programs are operationalized and a larger number of institutions become involved. Additionally, vegetable policy may be contradictory to other food policy goals. When this occurs, system performance is often determined by informal negotiations and power relationships.

The Mexican experience offers a unique opportunity to examine the nature of vegetable marketing *vis à vis* the different policy goals as managed by a wide range of institutions. The vegetable marketing system in Mexico is made up of three distinct, although overlapping, components: the domestic fresh vegetable market; the fresh and essentially winter vegetable export market; and the processed vegetable market, which is now also aggressively moving into the export market (serving both the ethnic or Hispanic and "Anglo" markets in the United States). Food policy in Mexico has focused on staple consumer items. Vegetables have never, as such, been a major focus of food policy decisions, yet they have affected all three areas of the industry from production to marketing in different ways and magnitudes.

The different policies and institutional effects on the vegetable industry are identified and analyzed in the next three sections of this paper. Vegetable production and exportation are then dealt with in the following two sections.

## THE POLICYMAKERS

The design, control, and implementation of food policy are fragmented among different Secretariats, government institutions, and state enterprises. A recent study by the IICA (Inter-American Institute for Cooperation on Agriculture), for example, identifies 33 key agencies located in four different sectors performing 295 different marketing functions (IICA).

Most of the activities and functions relating to agricultural production are concentrated within the Secretary of Agriculture and Water Resources (SARH), while those actually relating to marketing correspond to the Secretary of Commerce and Industrial Promotion (SECOFI). The Secretary of the Treasury (SHCP) is responsible for policies and functions relating to financing and taxation. Major exceptions are those activities which relate to ejidos and ejidatarios. They tend to be centralized within the Secretary of Agrarian Reform (SRA).

There exist specialized cabinets (permanently staffed working groups) under the direct authority of the Presidency and made up of representatives of key government agencies. Their function is to coordinate policy. The Agricultural Cabinet is the one most directly related to the food sector, however the Foreign Trade Cabinet has an impact on trade policy. The SARH complains that decisions regarding agricultural trade have been made without their input. Important economic decisions including those affecting agriculture end up being made by the Economic Cabinet.

There are a number of state enterprises with a narrow focus but very important for specific products involved in activities such as exporting coffee (IMECAFE) and producing cigarettes (TABAMEX) and sugar (AZUCAR). Others produce input or provide sectorwide services; among others, for example, ALBAMEX makes balanced feed, FERTIMEX produces fertilizers, and

ANDSA operates warehouses. Probably the most important agency, however, is CONASUPO, which through its affiliates is involved in all different phases of marketing: purchasing raw agricultural commodities, warehousing, food processing, wholesale and retail distribution, and even, in some cases, exporting. There are no government companies which are now primarily involved in vegetable production or distribution. CONASUPO, however, through its wholesaling and retailing activities does handle both fresh and processed vegetables.

Financial support comes through a series of trust funds. Both FIRA and FIDEC are located within the Banco de Mexico, the Central Bank–which in turn is in the Financial Sector, whose head is the Secretary of the Treasury. FICART, on the other hand, is part of BANRURAL, whose Chairman of the Board is the Secretary of Agriculture and Water Resources. Lending, however, is through the banks, which are now state-owned. There are no special trust funds for vegetable production or marketing. FIRA rediscounts loans to vegetable producers. They also have special programs to support agro-industrial development and food exports. Some lending to vegetable processors and exporters is carried out under these programs. FIDEC lending has supported the internal marketing of vegetables.

The large number of institutions involved in food marketing pose strong obstacles to effective coordination (IICA). There is frequent overlapping of functions, leading to institutional jealousies. In fact, with so many government agencies involved in the food marketing system there are differences in the way that the system is conceptualized, resulting in confused and contradictory policies and actions. At times this has given the vegetable industry a great deal of flexibility, ably playing one institution against the other to promote its interests. The overall effect, however, has probably been more negative than positive. The lack of a defined policy and responsibilities has led to the inability of the industry to focus on the changing domestic and international markets and opportunities.

## FOOD POLICY AND THE VEGETABLE INDUSTRY IN MEXICO

Mexico's formal food policies have centered around two major concerns: achieving self-sufficiency in production in basic food products (corn, beans, wheat, and rice); and assuring basic consumption. Vegetables are not considered as basic food crops, although they are used extensively in traditional Mexican cooking. As a result, although there is concern about consumer level vegetable prices and availability, there is not a specific vegetable policy.

## Self-Sufficiency

Agriculture production over time has not grown fast enough to keep up either with Mexico's growing population or with the income elastic led increase in demand. In order to satisfy growing food needs, Mexico in the early 1970s returned to the world market, purchasing both food products and foodstuffs. Imports grew throughout the decade. Following a severe drought in 1979, they reached over 10 million metric tons in 1980. More than the drain on foreign exchange earnings, it was the concern about the growing dependence on imports, especially from the United States, needed to feed its population that motivated the Lopez Portillo Administration to undertake an all-out effort to increase food production.[1] Its rather unrealistic goal was to achieve self-sufficiency in basic food products by 1982.[2]

Export vegetable production, according to some members of the Lopez Portillo Administration, took land out of basic food production: Mexico was feeding the foreign market while its people went hungry. The country's interdependence on the United States grew both as a supplier of food and as a end market for vegetable exports. The fall in oil prices and the drastic downturn in the Mexican economy cut short the implementation of the government's food program. Its short life[3] accounts for its having little influence on vegetable production. In some instances, nevertheless, land resources were temporally reallocated into basic food crops in response to attractive government subsidy programs.

The de la Madrid Administration, while affirming the concern for self-sufficiency, redefined the objective of government policy as that of food sovereignty. This concept is purposely ambiguous:

> Food sovereignty...finds its place in the revolutionary tradition of preserving and safeguarding for the nation decisions regarding every significant aspect of the welfare, freedom and security of Mexicans. Food self-determination, a fundamental aspect within the concept of national sovereignty, must be pursued in consumption standards. It includes the free and sovereign election of the components of this pattern. It implies, similarly, an independent capacity to guarantee the satisfaction of the minimum actual requirements of the whole population with our own resources. It also supposes technological self-determination (de la Madrid).

This gave the Administration greater flexibility in dealing with its critics. Through 1987 it was able to claim success as imports fell, exports grew, and the agricultural trade generated a net monetary surplus. Agriculture exports were promoted by the government as part of the overall export policy. This represented a radical change from the previous Administration. Nevertheless, agricultural policy still stressed solving food trade deficits through increased domestic production rather than by enhanced export promotion.

To stimulate food production the Mexican government has traditionally relied on two basic instruments; prices and subsidies. Falling real farm gate prices for basic agricultural commodities have continually been identified as a major reason for the slowdown in the growth of production. There have been short-run attempts at raising real farm prices, but these have been abandoned in the face of rising inflation. The long term trend has been, and continues to be, downward. Pricing policies at the producer level go hand in hand with price controls at the consumer level. At the farm level price policy has worked to depress relative sector prices. With consumer prices fixed, any increase over the guarantee price would mean a reduction in the size of the marketing margin and negatively impacting on profits. This turns guarantee prices into ceiling rather than floor prices.

Price policy focuses on basic food items. Vegetables are not included within the price support mechanisms. This probably is a blessing in disguise. Without controls at the consumer levels, vegetable prices have been free to fluctuate according to conditions in both the domestic and export markets. Although vegetable prices have demonstrated a high degree of variability, vegetable prices have grown faster than all agricultural prices in general, and significantly higher than cereal and oilseed prices.

The favorite alternative for stimulating production without having a short-term direct effect on inflation is through subsidies.[4] Through state-owned enterprises, such as PRONASE (seeds) and FERTIMEX (fertilizers), the government has sought to assure availability of basic production inputs at low relative prices. Financial institutions such as FIRA (bank loans), ANAGSA (insurance) have offered subsidized production and capital loans and insurance. Prices for irrigation–water and electricity–are lower than for industrial uses and are probably below their actual costs. Additionally, price controls exist on a number of inputs.

Vegetable producers have been able to take advantage of the numerous subsidies available to Mexican agriculture. A relatively large portion of production is on irrigated land. Although there are frequently shortages of subsidized credit, technically it is available for vegetable production. Additionally, the government seed company does produce and distribute vegetable seeds.

Vegetable producers, by not coming under the price support scheme, while at the same time being able to take advantage of subsidies, have the best of both worlds. The questions which have to be addressed are: the extent to which subsides used for vegetable production promote reallocation of resources away from basic food crops in detriment to stated government policy; and whether or not the benefits are evenly distributed among producers.

## Assuring Consumption

In order to guarantee basic food consumption the Mexican government has principally stressed food availability and prices. The orientation of policy in this area and the choice of policy instruments relate to the basic view regarding the functioning of the market and the way in which it works.

Policymakers have seen the process of food distribution as a struggle between small groups of powerful intermediaries and large numbers of weak producers, consumers, and small-scale retailers. As a result of this vision, consumption-level government food policy has centered on either direct distribution to consumers or to retailers, rather than in efforts to modernize the marketing system. The government is also directly involved in the industrial production of food products. Although the government does not process vegetables, its retail stores at one time sold canned vegetables under its own private Alianza label.

Price control represents an additional food policy instrument. Its coverage has been extremely wide, running from such diverse items as animal crackers and soda pop all the way to tortillas and powdered milk. Fresh vegetables are not subject to price controls. A number of processed vegetables, however, do come under price controls (Table 5.1).

Price policy has focused on achieving congruent and realist relative prices. For those products under price controls, policy has undergone modifications which have permitted greater flexibility in setting price levels. At the beginning of the Administration 110 product groups were subject to rigid price control, and another 31 product groups were subject to registration. As of 1986, only 23 remained under rigid controls. However, this group included all of the products in the basic consumption package (NAFINSA). Up through 1987 as controlled prices grew faster than inflation, consumer food purchasing power has declined and consumption patterns changed.

## Macroeconomic Policy

In December of 1987, faced with the prospect of hyperinflation, the Mexican government put into place on economic stabilization program, known as the Economic Solidarity Pact. This program emphasized a reduction in spending, cutbacks on subsidies, the accelerated opening of the economy and the sale of government owned companies. It also put into place a price freeze on all goods and services subject to price controls, as well as maintained a fixed parity.

Table 5.1. Fruits and Vegetables Subject to Price Controls

| TYPE | PRODUCT |
|---|---|
| Registered | Canned Figs in Syrup |
| Controlled | Baby Food |
| | Canned Serrano Chile[a] |
| | Canned Jalapeño Chile[a] |
| | Canned Cut Green Chiles[a] |
| | Tomato Paste[a] |
| Conditional | Canned Garbanzos |
| | Canned Mangos |
| | Canned Pears |
| | Canned Guayaba |
| | Canned Apple |
| | Canned Peaches |
| | Canned Sliced Pineapple |
| | Canned Peas |
| | Canned Corn |
| | Canned Serrano Chile[b] |
| | Canned Jalapeño Chile[b] |
| | Canned Cut Green Chiles[b] |
| | Tomato Paste[b] |

SOURCE: Secretaria de Comercio y Fomento Industrial

[a] Less than 1 kg.

[b] More than 1 kg.

When the Pact was signed it was understood that it would have a cost for the economy. It was expected, nevertheless, that agriculture would be among the least affected. However, as the Pact has been operationalized, this has not been the case.

Among the first measures to improve public sector finances was the upward adjustment in a number of government produced goods and services. This included an 85% increase in fertilizer and energy costs. This caused vegetable production costs to rise, in many cases well above the general inflationary level. In January, interest rates reached 150% which put further pressure on net farmer income. The implementation of the price freeze in

March limited the extent to which past increases in production costs to the farmers could be recouped through higher prices. In fact, no guarantee price was announced for the dry edible bean crop. While fresh vegetables were not under price controls, prices for many processed vegetables were frozen.

Minimum wages were frozen through the rest of the year. This softened the production cost raises for commercial and especially export vegetable producers. Nevertheless, the total effect of the upward adjustment of input prices with a fixed exchange rate has weakened the export competitiveness of Mexican vegetables.

The implementation of the Economic Solidarity Pact had a significant impact on the food industry. The process of opening up the economy has accelerated. In 1982, 43.2% of all food products were subject to import controls. The average tariff level was 20.63%. By December of 1987 only 9.4% of all food products were subject to import controls, and the average tariff level had fallen dramatically to 9.22%. While the number of items subject to import controls have remained the same since the Economic Solidarity Pact, the average tariff level as of March fell to 7.0%. Vegetable producers have recently complained about dumping on the Mexican market.

From a macroeconomic perspective, there is no doubt about the need for the Pact. Nevertheless, agricultural development policy took second place to macroeconomic concerns. The vegetable production system has begun to respond accordingly. The question is whether or not these changes in food policy are short term measures to support the Pact, or if they will become part of a longer term program that again involves increased subsidies and controls of agriculture?

## MARKETING POLICY AND THE VEGETABLE INDUSTRY

### Domestic Marketing

Government policy in support of farmer marketing efforts has generally taken second place to efforts designed to promote production. The focus of farmer organizations even when organized for marketing has stressed production level efficiencies. The one type producer organization contemplated under Mexican law whose sole purpose is marketing members' output, for example, legally only includes farmers already associated into production level groups, i.e., "unions" and ejidos. Formal farmer marketing policy, therefore, has not really had a marketing orientation.

Government involvement in the domestic fruit and vegetable marketing system has been limited. For the most part it has concentrated on physical infrastructure, i.e., wholesale market places and, most recently, with the SNIM on the development of support institutions. The Echeverria Administration, however, set up special programs thorough which the government became directly involved in marketing these products. The major one for vegetables was the Fideicomiso de Productos Perecederos. This was closed down during the Lopez Portillo Administration.

As part of the overall food policy programs, in 1985 the de la Madrid Administration established the National Program for the Supply of Fruits and Vegetables (Program Nacional de Abastos de Productos Hortofruticolas). It identifies as the major problems for marketing fruit and vegetables:

1. the difficulty for farmers to directly market their production through organized groups;
2. a low share received by farmers of the final consumer price;
3. a large concentration of marketing profits in a small number of middlemen:
4. nonproductive intermediation;
5. speculation and extremely high consumer level prices;
6. spoilage; and
7. market disarticulation (SARH).

Additionally, the nation's financial system is criticized for not considering marketing as a priority item, which has resulted in low-level formal financing for marketing of fruits and vegetables. To improve fruit and vegetable marketing systems, the main efforts under this program focused around promoting farmer marketing organizations and programming production. There was also the concern for enhancing transportation and other market infrastructure, as well as promoting quality norms.

Changes in the Secretary of Agriculture as well as the deterioration of the economic situation limited the operational ability of this program. Nevertheless, it is doubtful that it could have ever fully achieved its objectives. The main strategies were based on the ability to successfully program planting and control volumes of produce arriving at the markets. However, there were no built-in sanctions to guarantee compliance with established planting and marketing guidelines.

## Export Marketing

For the overall economy, Mexico's move towards a more open economy during the de la Madrid Administration has focused on both promoting exports and facilitating imports. Export policy with regard to food products, nevertheless, has not been clearly defined. Food policy has placed assurance of domestic availability above export market expansion.[5] The suspension of cattle exports in June 1988 is an example of the willingness to put consumer welfare above exporter benefits.[6]

Macroeconomic policy decisions have had an important effect on the vegetable export industry. The radical shift in the exchange rate policy has made producing in Mexico highly competitive. From being overvalued throughout most of the Lopez Portillo Administration–especially since 1978–the peso has been undervalued since 1983. Real wages have also fallen. The decline in the real wage rate combined with the undervalued peso has meant that labor costs are very low in Mexico. It is felt that agricultural and manufactured food exports are more sensitive to labor costs than to variations in the exchange rate. The labor intensive nature of Mexico's vegetable industry has brought down the cost of producing, making Mexican products highly competitive and profitable in the international market.

The contraction of the domestic market has been an important factor in accelerating agricultural vegetable exports. The domestic consumption of fresh and processed vegetables is concentrated in the middle to high income groups (Figure 5.1). A fall in real income in these strata–especially in the middle income levels–along with an increase in under- and unemployment in the rest of the population caused a shift back to basic food staples. At the same time there was a growing dependence on food subsidies to satisfy basic consumption needs. The export market for many producers became the only viable option for staying in business.

Export promotion has, for the most part, centered around efforts to simplify and decentralize administrative procedures (SARH). In bilateral contacts with U.S. officials, Mexican Secretary of Agriculture officials have continually argued for greater access to the American market.

The government's major impact in the vegetable export market is its support of the National Union of Vegetable Producers (UNPH). Most commercial fruit and vegetable producers tend to be associated with the UNPH through local grower organizations. It is responsible for assuring the orderly marketing of fruits and vegetables in both the domestic and foreign markets. It has undertaken marketing studies, supported agronomic research, paid for trips by Mexican public sector officials to international negotiating meetings, and even engaged in lobbying in Washington.

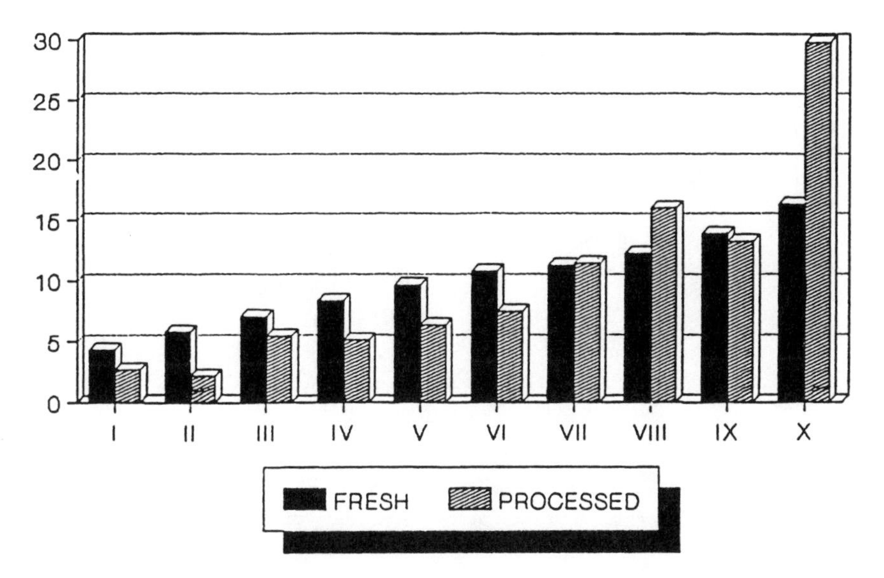


Figure 5.1. Distribution of Consumer Expenditures on Fresh and Processed Vegetables by Decile (Percent of Total Market)

SOURCE: INEGI.

The UNPH's real strength, however, comes from authority that the government has granted it to authorize and control exports. Controlled exports account for over three-fourths of the total value of fresh fruit and vegetable exports (Figure 5.2). Growers must register their intent to plant controlled export fruits and vegetables. After comparing intentions with export market perspectives, the UNPH determines the amount to be planted. Only those farmers, either individually or through their associations, who adhere to the UNPH guidelines are eligible to receive export permits. It is the ability to manage export permits that gives the UNPH the power to enforce its planting program.[7] Producers who violate UNPH guidelines can be sanctioned with the suspension of their export permits.

The UNPH further regulates the amount of produce going onto the export market through quality control management. When supplies are tight, standards are relaxed. Likewise, when an oversupply situation threatens to lower prices, quality control becomes stringent.

At the major border crossing points the UNPH maintains offices to inspect exports. The Mexican Customs Agency is also required to assure that UPNH permits are in order before allowing vegetables to be exported. At the smaller

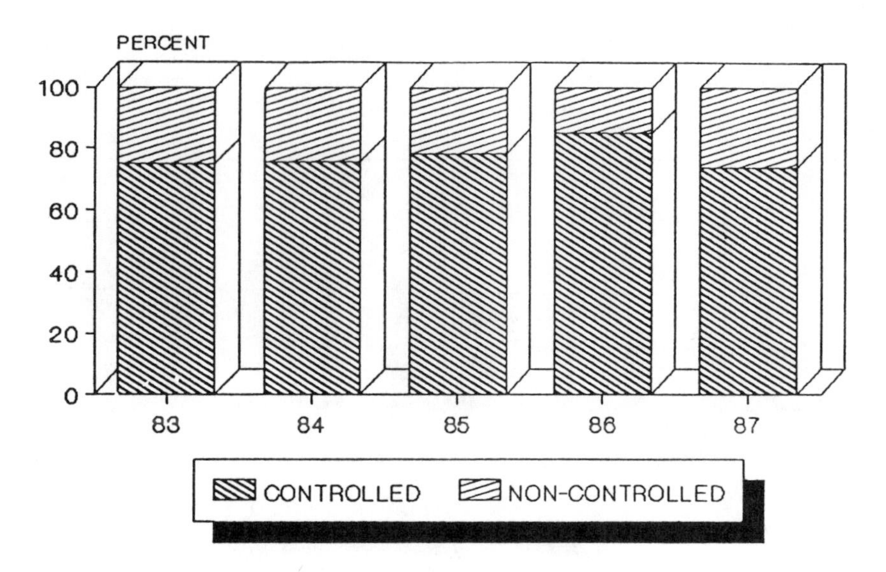


Figure 5.2. Participation in Fresh Fruit and Vegetable Export Value: by Type of System

SOURCE: UNPH, SARH.

crossing points enforcement is lax. Recently, as a result, the UNPH has petitioned U.S. authorities to prohibit permit produce imports that do not have the proper UNPH documentation.

## VEGETABLE PRODUCTION

Agricultural production is characterized by a large number of small units, in both the ejidal and non-ejidal (private) sector. Data from the last available census show that over half of the private farms are under 5 hectares in size. On the average there are only 4.5 hectares of available crop land per ejidatario (Secretary of Agrarian Reform). Although it varies from crop to crop, large non-ejidal farmers account for a relatively large proportion of the commercial output. They produced 57.4% and 49.5% of the fruit and vegetable output, respectively. High capital investment and operating costs limit small farmer participation in commercial vegetable production. The small non-ejido farms account for only 3% of the fruit and vegetable production in the country.

Agricultural production has grown slowly over the past years. This is mainly due to the fall in consumer demand and the contraction in both public and private investment. Vegetable crops have shown the highest growth rate for any crop group during this period, due in large measure to the growth in the export market (Figure 5.3).

Although fresh fruits and vegetables are available throughout the year, production does follow a seasonal pattern (Table 5.2). For certain markets vegetable production is highly concentrated in a small number of locations. There are two growing seasons. The first planting season takes place in the fall, with harvest in the spring. Since this is the dry season, most crops depend on some form of irrigation. About 58% of the vegetable crop is harvested during this cycle, with an important portion of the production being exported. The second planting cycle takes place in the late spring or early summer, with the harvest coming in the fall. Most of the production is for the domestic market. This is due to both the output mix favoring local demand (i.e., chiles) and the competition from U.S. producers for the American market.

In addition to being concentrated on larger farms, fruit and vegetable production is also concentrated in a small number of states in specific regions of the country. Vegetable production, for example, is centered in the Bajio

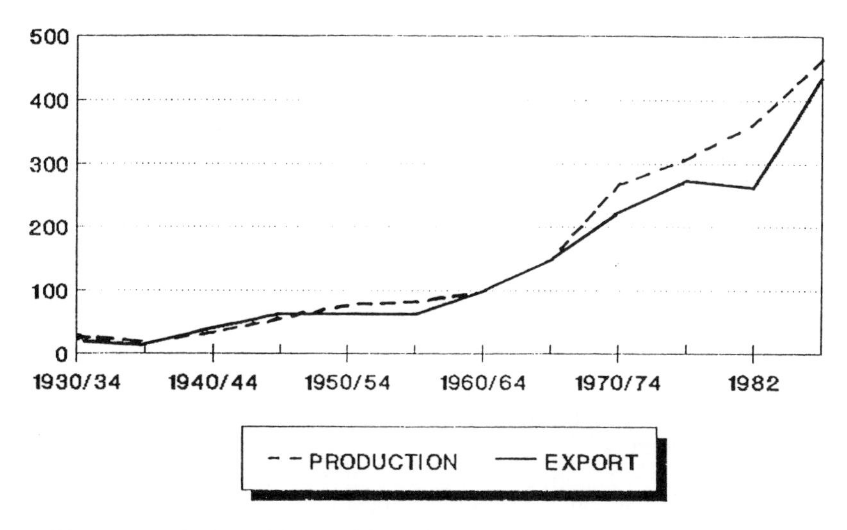


Figure 5.3. Index of Vegetable Production and Exports: 1930/34-1985 (1960/64=100)

SOURCE: SARH *Conumos Aparente*, UNPH Various Annual Reports.

Table 5.2. Percent of Vegetable Production by Growing Season

| Product | Fall/Winter Plantings | Spring/Summer Plantings |
|---|---|---|
| Alcelga | 33.40 | 66.60 |
| Beet | 69.70 | 30.30 |
| Beet | 22.61 | 77.39 |
| Broccoli | 35.81 | 64.19 |
| Brussels Sprouts | 96.51 | 3.49 |
| Cabbage | 48.98 | 51.02 |
| Carrot | 46.45 | 53.55 |
| Cauliflower | 73.73 | 26.27 |
| Celery | 66.84 | 33.16 |
| Coriander | 40.45 | 59.55 |
| Cucumber | 87.25 | 12.75 |
| Dry Chile | 9.89 | 90.11 |
| EBO | 82.49 | 17.51 |
| Eggplant | 99.40 | 0.60 |
| Garlic | 88.03 | 11.97 |
| Green Chile | 41.34 | 58.66 |
| Green Tomato | 41.83 | 58.17 |
| NBO | 90.00 | 10.00 |
| Okra | 59.62 | 40.38 |
| Onion | 58.80 | 41.20 |
| Parsley | 44.12 | 55.88 |
| Peas | 38.16 | 61.84 |
| Radish | 43.09 | 56.91 |
| Spinach | 75.65 | 24.35 |
| Squash | 48.26 | 51.74 |
| String Beans | 56.40 | 43.60 |
| Tomato | 63.06 | 36.94 |
| Total | 58.08 | 41.92 |

SOURCE: Secretaria de Agricultura y Recursos Hidraulicos

and Northwest regions. Most of the vegetable production, as well as annually planted fruit, is farmed on irrigated land (Table 5.3). This limits drought risks. This is very important in Mexico and has given greater stability to the export industry. At the same time, given the high production costs, the risks involved in planting on rain-fed land, except in certain regions of the country, are too great.

Table 5.3. Percent of Total Vegetable Production on Irrigated and Rainfed Land

| Product | Irrigated Land | Rainfed Land |
|---|---|---|
| Acelga | 14.86 | 85.14 |
| Beet | 100.00 | 0.00 |
| Broccoli | 100.00 | 0.00 |
| Brussels Sprouts | 100.00 | 0.00 |
| Cabbage | 95.18 | 4.82 |
| Calabash | 93.04 | 6.96 |
| Carrot | 78.30 | 21.70 |
| Cauliflower | 97.86 | 2.14 |
| Celery | 86.73 | 13.27 |
| Chayote | 5.95 | 94.05 |
| Coriander | 100.00 | 0.00 |
| Cucumber | 98.46 | 1.54 |
| Dry Chile | 85.87 | 14.13 |
| EBO | 34.12 | 65.88 |
| Eggplant | 100.00 | 0.00 |
| Garlic | 97.06 | 2.94 |
| Green Chile | 75.71 | 24.29 |
| Green Tomato | 71.27 | 28.73 |
| Lettuce | 98.01 | 1.99 |
| Okra | 100.00 | 0.00 |
| Onion | 77.32 | 22.68 |
| Potato | 35.54 | 64.46 |
| Peas | 53.56 | 46.44 |
| Radish | 98.22 | 1.78 |
| Red Tomato | 84.47 | 15.53 |
| Spinach | 42.67 | 57.33 |
| String Beans | 98.97 | 1.03 |
| Squash | 10.00 | 90.00 |
| Sweet Potato | 57.30 | 42.70 |
| Wild Radish | 100.00 | 0.00 |
| Total | 67.18 | 32.82 |

SOURCE: Secretaria de Agricultura Recursos Hidrualicos.

## VEGETABLE EXPORTING

Production of fresh vegetables for export is centered in Northwest Mexico (Figure 5.4), with most of the output destined for the winter U.S. market. Purchasing contracts are often used for the winter U.S. market. About half of the total value is shipped between January and April (Figure 5.5). Toma-

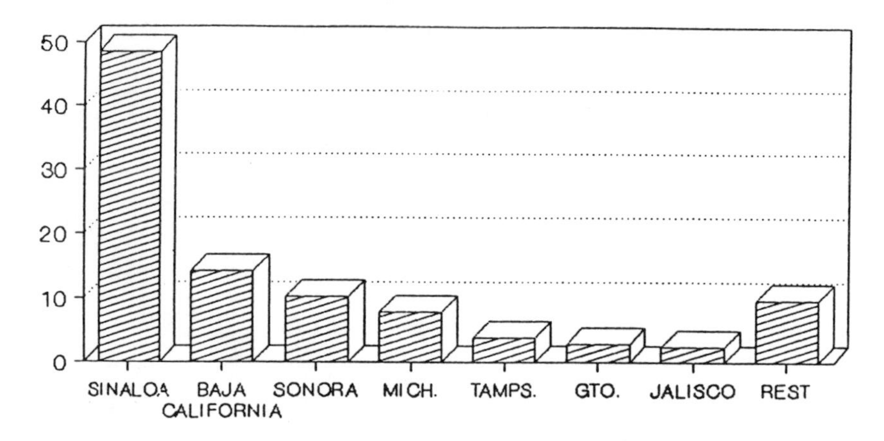


Figure 5.4. Location of Fresh Fruit and Vegetable Export Industry (Percent of Total Volume)

SOURCE: UNPH Annual Report Based on 1986-1987 Market Year.

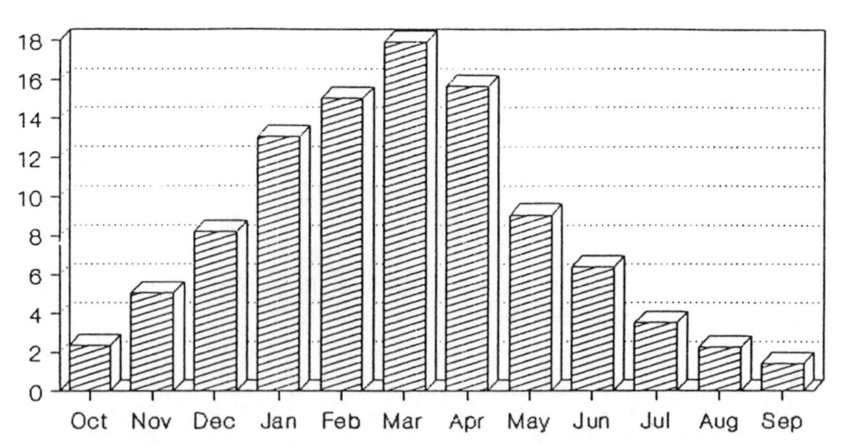


Figure 5.5. Monthly Distribution of Fruit and Vegetable Exports (Percent)

SOURCE: UNPH Annual Report Based on 1986-1987 Market Year.

toes are by far the most important product. Exports are almost exclusively shipped by land. Most of the produce moves through border crossing points in the Northwest, with Nogales being the most important (Figure 5.6).

Exports have long played an important role in the Mexican vegetable industry, fluctuating between 16% and 28% of total production (Figure 5.7).

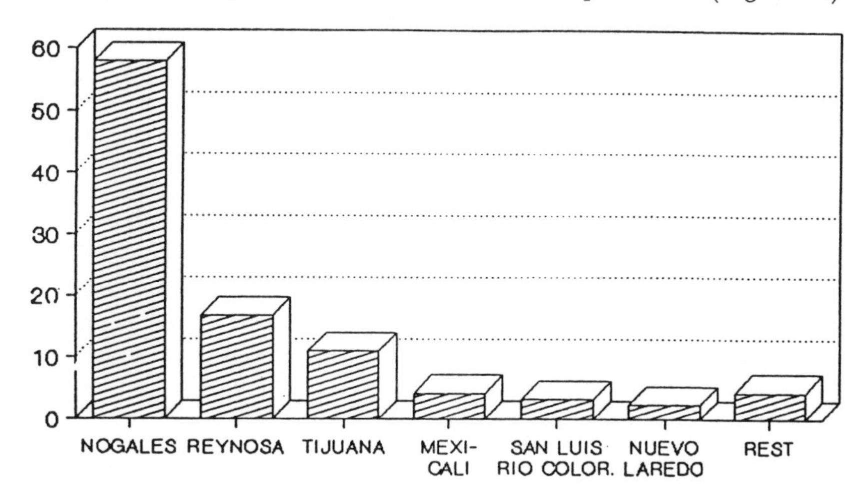


Figure 5.6. Port of Export for Fruits and Vegetables (Percent of Total)
SOURCE: UNPH Annual Report Based on 1986-1987 Market Year.

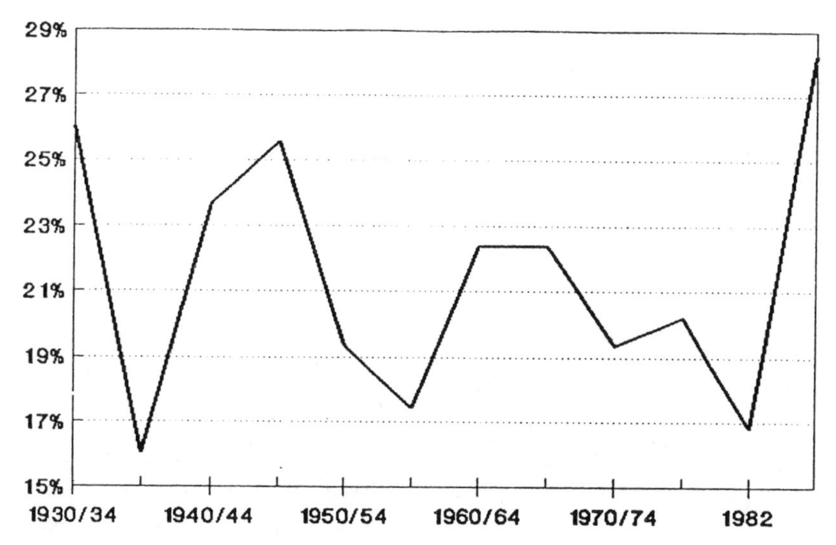


Figure 5.7. Vegetable Exports as a Percent of Production From 1930/35-1985

SOURCE: SARH *Consumos Aparentes* UNPH Various Annual Reports.

Substantive growth in vegetable exports, however, began in the 1960s as a result of the simultaneous growth of both the U.S. and Mexican economies combined with the breakdown of the Cuban tomato export industry. Exports began to level off in the mid-1970s and on into the early 1980s. Land tenure problems during the latter part of the Echeverria Administration brought a slowdown in the rate of investment. By the end of the decade, spurred on by oil money, the rapidly growing domestic market was absorbing a larger share of domestic output. The overvalued exchange rate was also cutting away at Mexico's competitiveness.[8] Since 1982, as a result of the changes in the economic situation, the Mexican vegetable industry has been export led.

The successful growth of the fresh winter vegetable export industry has been traced to a number of factors:

1. "Mexico [having] invested heavily··· in irrigation facilities, particularly on the west coast;
2. several [irrigation] districts have better climate for winter production of certain crops than other areas in the United States;
3. labor supplies are ample;
4. much U.S. capital and technology have gone into the development of farm operations;
5. medium-term development credit for growing and packinghouse investments was available through official sources;
6. strong Mexican growers' associations play an active role;
7. local markets take up to 40 percent of the lower-quality production" (Goldberg); and
8. the forward integration of Mexican producer–distributors into the U.S. market.

The processed vegetable export industry has developed separately from the fresh vegetable export industry. It is centered in a different part of the country, with a larger component of direct foreign investment. With the development of the frozen food industry in the United States, the possibility of establishing plants in Mexico became attractive due to: the counter-growing season which would reduce inventory costs, low labor costs, and long-term political stability. The early plants were processing strawberries and asparagus. From 1967 to 1977 there was slow growth in the number of plants and a movement towards processing broccoli and cauliflower. Between 1977 and

1982 there was hardly any growth as the dollar profits shrank. Only one new plant was reported to have been built during this period. From 1982, however, the industry has experienced dynamic growth, coming as a result of the changes in economic policy. It is estimated that between 11 and 16 new plants have been built over the last 6 years. An important aspect of the recent growth has been the incorporation of Mexican capital into the industry. Wholly owned Mexican operations now outnumber foreign and joint venture operations.

Within the Mexican government there is some question as to the extent of the support that should be given to manufactured food exports. The concern centers around the number of foreign food companies operating in and exporting from Mexico. The benefits from government promotion, it is argued, would go primarily to strengthening multinational corporations.

Mexico's fresh and frozen vegetable exports are concentrated in a few products and essentially in one market (Figure 5.8). The strong commercial ties with the United States[9] are due to being the largest single market in the world and the closest to Mexico. Mexico's border with the United States

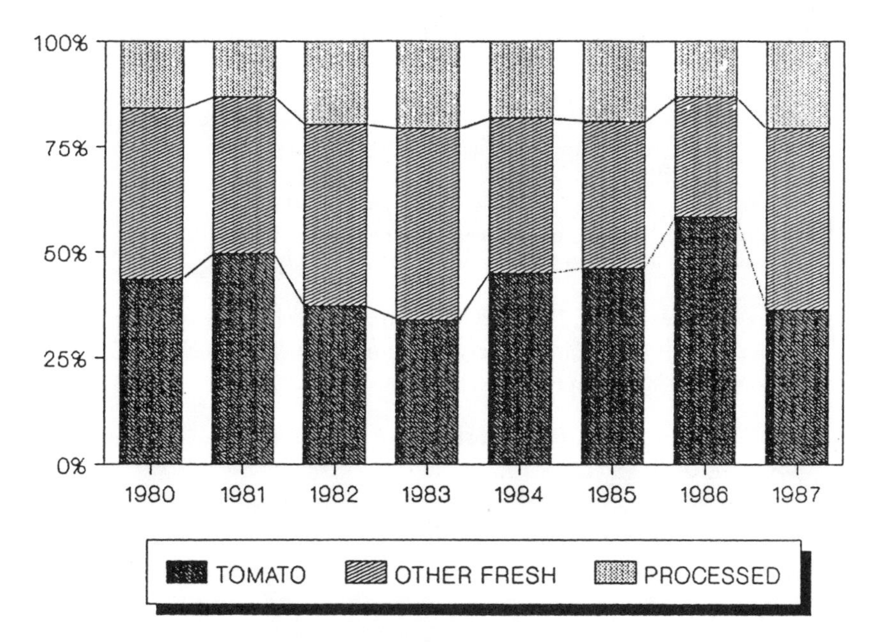


Figure 5.8. Share of Total Vegetable Export Value
SOURCE: UNPH Annual Reports.

translates into access with a minimum of infrastructure investment. This is especially important to the fresh fruit and vegetable export industry. Sea transportation to Europe and Asia is not sufficiently agile to handle Mexico's needs. Air transportation remains too expensive for most export products.

Additionally, it should be remembered that production of some exports had its origins in supplying specifically the U.S. market (e.g., vegetables, feeder cattle, etc.).

Financial and technical support for various export goods continues to come from the United States. Financing frequently comes from buyers, although there is some bank financing. Technical support takes the form of research and availability of plant varieties and other specialized inputs. In some cases the buyer will provide the Mexican grower with seed stock. Exporters see these arrangements as strengthening buyer bargaining power.

In spite of the volume having increased, the value of fruits and vegetables sold in the U.S. market has not increased. The UNPH has identified eight areas where efforts must be made to improve Mexico's export positions:

1. Marketing Practices: The Mexican producer is not in control of his production; that is, he does have a real presence in the U.S. market. This allows for some distributors and brokers to take advantage of growers.

2. Production: Much still needs to be done in order to improve production level organization. Likewise, the UNPH complains about the lack of an export mentality among producers.

3. Financing: There is an excessive dependence on distributors for financing.

4. Quality: There is insufficient quality control. Some exporters will sell different quality products under the same label. The shelf life of Mexican produce is considered too short.

5. Volume: The volume for export is too large,[10] and Nogales is overcrowded.

6. Tax Policy: The Mexican government taxes inputs at too high a level.

7. U.S. Policy: There are systematic attacks to discredit Mexican produce in the U.S. market.

8. Protectionism: To protect its producers the U.S. maintains unnecessarily high tariff levels on Mexican produce. Additionally, a number of

non-tariff barriers to trade are said to exist thereby limiting access to the U.S. market.

## CONCLUSIONS

Vegetable marketing policy has been formulated within the larger context of national food marketing objectives. At times this has resulted in contradictory sets of instruments and market signals. This has been accentuated by the fact that marketing policy was often based on the assumption that the market could not be trusted as the ultimate instrument of resource allocation. Rather than attempt to correct market imperfections, the choice was for greater state intervention. The government expended its strength and energy in maintaining its own apparatus rather than promoting change, development, and modernization in the food marketing system.

To manage this system a complex network of government institutions evolved. Lines of authority were not clear; clientele groups varied; and there was often infighting. A wide range of regulations and controls have limited the aggressive development of the domestic market, while working to limit access by new entrants.

Over the last 6 years significant changes have taken place in the Mexican food marketing system in general and in the vegetable marketing system in particular. Many of the changes, however, have undoubtedly come about as a result of changes in macroeconomic policy and the need to bring order to public sector finances. Food policy in the final analysis is subject to larger macrolevel, and vegetable marketing is an afterthought.

The export market has grown considerably over the last 5 years. In large measure it is due to a combination of favorable government macroeconomic policies and a contraction of the domestic market. There are, nevertheless, a number of shortcomings in this effort and constraints on future market development. The expansion of the export industry took place, with few exceptions, without the active involvement of Mexican exporters. They have reacted to a favorable situation by increasing the volume onto the market. Export sales continue to be highly concentrated into one market.

Entry by Mexican growers and manufacturers into the export market is difficult. Their knowledge is limited as to both the available opportunities as well as how to go about selling into the foreign market. An important aspect is the need to grow varieties or produce the quality that the market demands. The lack of knowledge is exacerbated by the lack of trained personnel marketing infrastructure and investment in research. This situation works to limit new product development. And when it has taken place, the foreign buyer has frequently taken the initiative. For frozen vegetables, Mexican producers followed the lead of foreign corporations. The export market has grown, probably more the result of the changing economic situation than a reaction to a specific set of vegetable export policies.

Improvement in vegetable marketing systems can have a favorable impact on both producer and consumer welfare. Conflicting sets of policies and competing institutions, however, have limited market efficiencies and development.

## NOTES

[1] The Carter Administration's decision to suspend additional sales to the Soviet Union at about this same time gave credence to the Food Power arguments and underscored Mexico's dependence and vulnerability *vis à vis* the United States.

[2] It must be remembered that it was not until March of 1980 that the Lopez Portillo Administration brought together a clearly defined set of food policy objectives through the creation of the Sistema Alimentario Mexican (SAM). The choice of 1982, the end of the presidential period, as the year for achieving self-sufficiency in basic products was political. Eighteen months is not nearly long enough to bring about technological, structural, and institutional changes in agriculture.

[3] Announced in March of 1980, it impacted only on three and one-half growing seasons before the economic crisis of 1982.

[4] There are obviously very real negative and inflationary effects through their impact on the deficit and the resulting nonmarket resource allocation.

[5] This is a legitimate policy goal of the government. In the United States, for example, in the early 1970s faced with a potential shortage of soybeans, exports were suspended. Again, in 1988, facing the possibility of a severe drought, the U.S. government was reported to be considering limiting exports. The Canadian government was also evaluating its domestic requirements to determine its export policy.

[6] It is questionable whether or not suspending cattle exports adequately deals with the key factors contributing to the shortage of meat in the Mexico City market. This debate, however, is beyond the scope of this report.

[7] The UNPH's charter also includes the promoting of orderly fruit and vegetable marketing in the domestic market. Its lack of success, among other reasons, is due to the fact that it has no instrument equivalent to the export permits by which it can exert control over growers and other domestic marketing agents.

[8] In late 1981 leaders in the vegetable industry were seriously questioning the future of the export business. They were considering a major effort redirecting the focus of their activities towards the domestic market.

[9] Mexico's market is the United States. In 1987, sales to the United States accounted for 83.5% of all agricultural and manufactured food exports. Of the 52 most import/export goods, the United States is the major buyer for all except honey (Federal Republic of Germany), meat (Japan), and garbanzos (Spain).

[10] The UNPH has tended to emphasize limiting export volume in order to support prices. It has been argued that this has allowed Florida to get a larger share of the market to the detriment of Mexican interests.

## REFERENCES

Churchman, C. West. *The Systems Approach.* New York: Dell Publishing Co., Inc., 1968.

de la Madrid, Miguel. *El Plan Nacional de Deserrollo:1983-1988.* Mexico, D.F., 1983.

Goldberg, Ray. *Agribusiness Management for Developing Countries: Latin America.* Cambridge, Mass.: Ballinger Publishing Company, 1974.

Harrison, Kelly, James D. Shaffer, and Michael T. Weber. *Fomenting Improvements in Food Marketing in Costa Rica.* East Lansing: Michigan State University, Latin America Studies Center, 1975.

Harrison, Kelly, et al. *Improving Food Marketing Systems in Developing Countries: Experiences from Latin America.* East Lansing: Latin American Studies Center, 1974.

IICA. *Analisis Institucional de la Comercializacion Agropecuaria en Mexico.* Mexico, D.F., 1987.

Moyer, Reed. *Marketing in Economic Development, Occasional Paper No.*

*1.* East Lansing: Michigan State University, Institute for International Business Studies, 1965.

NAFINSA. *El Mercado de Valores.* "El Cambio Estructural en el Comercio Interior de Mexico, 1983-1986," p. 805.

Powelson, John P. *Institutions of Economic Growth: A Theory of Conflict Management in Developing Countries.* Princeton: Princeton University Press, 1972.

Riggs, Fred W. *Administration in Developing Countries: The Theory of the Prismatic Society.* Boston:Houghton-Mufflin Co., 1964.

Sanderson, Steven E. *The Transformation of Mexican Agriculture: International Structure and the Politics of Rural Change.* Princeton: Princeton University Press, 1986.

SARH. "Programa Nacional de Abasto de Productos Hortofrut colas." Mexico, 1985.

Schmid, A. Allan. "Analytical Institutional Economics: Challenging Problems in the Economics of Resources for a New Environment." *American Journal of Agricultural Economics*, Vol. 54, No. 5 (December), 1972.

Secretary of Agrarian Reform. The Structure and Quality of Ejido Land. Unpublished data.

Shwedel, S. Kenneth. *Marketing Problems of Small Farm Agriculture: A Case Study of the Costa Rican Potato Market.* East Lansing: Michigan State University, unpublished Ph.D., 1977.

UNPH, *Informe Anual.* Ixtapa, Mexico, 1984.

UNPH, *Informe Anual.* Mozztlan, Mexico, 1985.

UNPH, *Informe Anual.* Ixtapa, Mexico, 1987.

# POLICIES AND INSTITUTIONS: DISCUSSION

Enrique E. Figueroa
*Cornell University*

Although Pierson and Allen's (PA) paper is very polished, easy to follow, and to the point, I nonetheless feel the paper was not written for economists. I expected more economics in the paper. For example, what is the return on investment on the various produce displays? Are there quantitative measures of consumer psychographics? If not, what is the least cost process for obtaining and utilizing these psychographic elements? Given the preceding, let me touch on a few points.

Allen and Pierson identified retail produce demand as elastic while most of us in the field recognize that firm level demand is inelastic. Where in the marketing chain does the responsiveness to price increase? I think this is an important issue, but one that was not addressed by the presentation. The presentation accurately described how consumers have changed–particularly in their perceptions about produce. It is healthier, more nutritious, etc. However, the authors failed to mention that the consumer also scrutinizes produce more than before. Retailers need to be cautious in not forgetting the potential negative perceptions of consumers.

An important point concerning retail produce departments is the level of profit margins. Why and how do produce departments maintain relatively high margins? Is it inherent in the produce business? Should the strategy be to maintain high margins or should one believe that demand is elastic and lower the price? Allen and Pierson provide no direction on this issue.

As a descriptive paper, the PA paper was done quite well. The overview of how the consumer has changed is thorough, the section on heightening the consumer's value perception is informative, and the listing of retailer strategies which respond to the changing consumer is comprehensive. However, I would argue that extending the supply season for a commodity does not necessarily imply a higher quality product. In fact, I would argue the opposite outcome. Also, the increase of ethnic consumers–Hispanics and Asians–has altered the produce mix as well as the demand for products.

The PA model of market linkages–grower/distributor, distributor/retailer, and retailer/consumer–are of critical importance in understanding the performance of the markets. Firms interested in entering the produce business need to have an appreciation of how price, quality, reliability, etc., are transmitted through the markets. I recognize that the intent of the paper was not to model nor to describe these market linkages, but to point out the importance of these factors. Lastly, a comment about the use of scanning data. Within the last 5 years, many retailers have begun to compile scanning data. Of what value are these data? How accessible are the data to researchers? Should researchers pursue the use of these data? I would have liked at least cursory treatment of the subject.

Dr. Polopolus's delineation of public policies affecting the country's vegetable industry is succinct but thorough. The eight types of public policy affecting the industry are appropriate and encompassing, however, I would suggest adding a ninth–Land Grant University education policy. How are resources allocated at the Land Grant level to the industry? How does the industry affect the policy process of the Land Grant institutions? Of specific interest is the disproportionate allocation of educational and research funds to the production arena, disproportionate relative to resources allocated to programs concerning the product after it leaves the "farm gate."

I would also suggest that more attention be directed to the markets for processed vegetables. Although the paper primarily addresses fresh markets, both markets are closely linked. In addition, regulatory policy affecting the processing sector will no doubt affect the supply of fresh products. In regard to regulation, the number of PACA claims filed in the last 3 years has increased dramatically. In fact, legislation has been passed to grant statutory authority for increasing the PACA fee. The implication is that the number of market participants has increased and that some of the new participants are not as reputable as existing ones. From a policy perspective, is the PACA still a viable entity to regulate the produce industry? Should some of its responsibilities be amended?

State vs. federal jurisdictional responsibilities are becoming a difficult issue–particularly regarding the monitoring of pesticide residues on fresh product. California, for example, passed Proposition 65. Among other things, it requires that the state establish safe standards for pesticides. The produce industry in California is lobbying to have federal standards continue to apply. Also, if a particular state decides to ban the in-state use of a particular chemical compound (alar, for example), does this mean that any product with residues of the banned product **cannot** enter the state?

Trade associations are playing a greater role in policy formulation. This can be attributed to both the increase in the number of associations as well as to the size of their budgets. Although not technically trade associations, market order administrative committees also are increasing their visibility in the policy arena. Dr. Polopolus mentions the role of market orders, but not with respect to their role as trade associations.

Lastly, I want to mention the issue concerning the reliability of the data used for formulating or analyzing policy. Government and to a lesser extent trade associations now contract for independent studies. In certain situations, trade association staff conduct studies. What is the reliability of these studies? Accurate and timely data are very important to policy analysis. Policymakers need to insist on the best data available.

Mr. Shwedel makes some interesting and important points in his paper. Mexico now obtains 3.4% of nonoil foreign earnings from fruit and vegetable exports. He attributes this situation to the government's policy of diversifying its export base. The impact of a devalued currency has also been a major contributor to the growth of vegetable exports. In addition, the growth in the country's population and the underemployment rate of 35% have provided a large pool of labor for the production of labor intensive crops–fruits and vegetables. One point that is not made in the paper is the disproportionate accumulation of foreign earnings to the export oriented enterprises. That is, the costs of production are in pesos while the selling price of the product is in dollars. Many vegetable producers will not put the products in the domestic Mexican market; therefore, all favorable currency movements are captured by the exploiting firms.

Mr. Shwedel indicates that the pesticide residue issue is viewed by Mexican producers as a significant potential threat to their ability to continue exporting fresh vegetables. In addition, the presence of U.S. market order regulations can also pose a threat to the continued growth of vegetable exports to the U.S. market. Both of these threats are political in nature and both can be ameliorated if more U.S. firms establish production and/or marketing enterprises in Mexico.

# POLICIES AND INSTITUTIONS: DISCUSSION

Charles R. Brader
*U.S. Department of Agriculture*

The preceding papers on policies and institutions in the Western Hemisphere vegetable marketing system gave well-informed insights. However, it is particularly interesting to note their different perspectives regarding policy. Shwedel repeatedly cites shortcomings of massive government intervention into a national economy. Polopolus points out that the "invisible hand of unfettered competition normally does an adequate job of providing for efficient resource use and fairness in market transactions." However (in the U.S. context), he goes on to support the idea that government intervention in private markets is necessary to achieve socially efficient resource allocation. Pierson and Allen address attitudes and behaviors in the market system. But except for safety issues, they seem unconcerned with government intervention, taking for granted good, freely accessible market information and unfettered competition.

While I am not an expert in the macroeconomic policies of the many countries in our hemisphere or the Mexican government in particular, I would add to Dr. Shwedel's views regarding the use of stringent controls to achieve economic stabilization. The dimension I would like to add is a comment on the experience of application in this country.

Many of us have witnessed wage and price controls in World War II, during the "Korean Conflict" and then in the 1970s under the Cost of Living Council and the Council on Wage and Price Stability. In these experiences, only the World War II controls worked well. At that time, the full spectrum of the economy was controlled–wages, prices, rents, and rationing. And remarkable stability was attained. But the uniting forces of major war and patriotism were necessary ingredients. Our other experiences have been much less effective, with resource allocations quickly skewed, inequities abundant, and black markets and profiteering evident. With this record, we have no taste for broad economic controls, and I am aware of no experience in history in which this has been a popular approach.

Discussions of "intervention" in the U.S. agricultural economy have been on a different plane. Dr. Polopolus has identified the basic spectrum of U.S. Government programs designed to augment our marketing system. I suggest that the use of "augmentation" may be preferable to "intervention," particularly when contrasted to broad-base economic stabilization. It is also much more appropriate in describing voluntary programs, such as market news, grading and marketing orders.

Since I represent the Agricultural Marketing Service, which is responsible for many of the activities described in Dr. Polopolus's paper, I'd like to add some specific comments by category.

I agree fundamentally with his views on *market information*. But I would like to make a distinction between Market News and the information provided by the National Agricultural Statistical Service (NASS). The latter deals with monthly, seasonal and annual data on acreage, yield, production price and income. Market News concentrates on the short term, providing daily and, in some circumstances, more frequent information on commodity prices and volumes.

I believe that Dr. Polopolus's reference to the cutbacks in Federal expenditures for vegetable market information refers principally to NASS data. Significant reductions have occurred in this type of information because of reductions in both Federal and State budgets, particularly in the early 1980s.

In Market News, there was also a significant fund reduction several years ago resulting in the closing of five terminal market offices and narrowing of the base of certain kinds of information. However, these reductions have been largely offset by other initiatives. We have gone to user fees for printed reports, generating about $500,000 annually for fruit and vegetable reports. Automation has been increased, with the utilization of "FAX" equipment the latest example. We have also added reports for subtropical products, flowers, herbs, Chilean imports and truck rates, and hope to make progress in developing an Agency-wide electronic data base for market news information.

I am not optimistic regarding the recovery of some of the abandoned NASS series on vegetables. Instead, I believe that we shall have to accept some limitations and look to sources such as scanning data to further develop our analytical perspectives. Even a return to the level of commodity coverage of many years ago by NASS would still be inadequate because of the explosion in the number of produce items now being consumed in our country.

In the arena of *grading*, I would make a distinction between grade standards and the certification activity we call inspection. There are some 150 standards for fresh fruits and vegetables and another 150 plus for processed fruits and vegetables. It is usual that these standards form the basis of inspection activity. However, the third-party aspect of the service is often used by the specification buyers who do not exclusively use Federal grade standards as their specifications. This is the case even when inspectors are utilized for quality control in plants or for quality certification in contract disputes.

Turning to *marketing orders*, it is true that vegetable marketing orders concentrate in the use of grade and size regulations to deal with disorderly marketing and avoid the use of volume management authorities. These orders are clearly oriented toward activities intended to stimulate demand. It is interesting to note that Federal marketing orders in the United States do not regulate quantity through the variation of quality controls (such efforts proved unproductive for Maine potatoes and Florida tomatoes in the 1960s and early 1970s).

An interesting digression here may be a reference to the activities of vegetable grower organizations in Mexico directed at the U.S. market. These organizations limit exports of a number of vegetables by varying minimum quality standards. Perhaps they have been more successful, since they have continued this practice for a number of years.

A final comment regarding marketing orders is to address the statement that generic advertising is not popular among Federal vegetable programs. Perhaps this is an overstatement. In fact, the programs for onions and Florida tomatoes contain substantial promotional budgets. And as for potatoes, the national programs of the Potato Board and several state programs may obviate the need in the perspective of growers.

Moving to comments on the Federal Government's *fair trading* activities, I would like to state that the Perishable Agricultural Commodities Act (PACA) has been well described as to purpose and mechanics. However, the PACA is not essentially grower oriented. It affects all traders in fresh and frozen fruits and vegetables, from growers to consumers; and all in the marketing chain, except those at each end–growers and consumers–are licensed. There are currently about 16,000 licensees who pay a basic $300 annual fee; Congress just increased the fee cap to $400, recognizing a sharp increase in costs of administering this program in recent years. In 1984, the statute was amended to give trust protection to sellers of the affected commodities. And while this new dimension has received overwhelming industry support, it has required a staffing increase of nearly 50% since its inception.

At this point I would like to interject a reference to one more government program, the *Commodity Procurement Program*, providing assistance to vegetable growers. Under Section 32 of Public Law 320, 30% of import duty funds are made available, primarily to assist perishable nonbasic agricultural commodities. This forms the basis of our surplus removal activities for vegetables. Together with appropriated funds for domestic feeding programs, we typically purchase some $150 million worth of fruits and vegetables for distributions to schools and other eligible institutions. In most years we buy sizable quantities of potato and tomato products, as well as peas, beans, sweet corn and sweet potatoes. Both the mix of commodities and the quantities acquired are influenced by the need for surplus removal by domestic producers.

I would like to comment on one additional category, that of *Food Safety and Health.* Both Polopolus, and Pierson and Allen, correctly identify this as an important issue of our time. The dimension which I would like to add is the issue of "who pays"? Specifically, I'd like to address the issue of "chemical residues."

Recently I had the opportunity to travel to Switzerland, where I observed that a large proportion of fresh produce is labeled as "organic" in major supermarkets. The firm's management explains that they are filling a consumer want and go to considerable expense, including soil testing, to provide the desired assurance. In this country, private agencies are providing supermarkets, particularly in California, with product testing designed to assure "chemical free" produce.

This issue is a long way from being resolved. However, I would point out that the high level of assurance desired by some is extremely expensive. For example, I observed in Nogales early this year that we had up to 70 user-fee-funded inspectors certifying grade on imported produce, while only one taxpayer-funded FDA person was sampling for health and safety purposes. Furthermore, examination for residues, as an example, requires time-consuming tests on expensive, sophisticated equipment. We now have some 5,000 licensed Federal-State inspectors for produce. The cost of a similar sized cadre checking produce for safety with sophisticated equipment would be incredibly expensive.

It is not clear that any further investment in testing of produce for residues or other safety and health purposes related to fruits and vegetables is justified. However, I am convinced that we will encounter debate on this issue for some time to come.

# SECTION III: TRADE LINKAGES IN THE WESTERN HEMISPHERE

# 6

# FROM COMPETITION TO COORDINATION IN VEGETABLE TRADE: THE CASE OF MEXICO AND CALIFORNIA

Roberta L. Cook
*University of California at Davis*

## INTRODUCTION

The U.S. fruit and vegetable industry has been experiencing an increase in import competition in the 1980s. Many regions of the world, particularly Mexico, Chile, and the Caribbean Basin Initiative (CBI) countries, are expanding fruit and vegetable exports to the United States. Although imports have doubled since 1980, because of their small base and the growth in the overall market, they still represented only 17% of total U.S. consumption of fresh fruits and vegetables in 1986. However, the import share of the U.S. market continues to rise and imports have recently achieved significant market shares for some commodities.

The objectives of this paper are to discuss:

1. the reasons behind and the policy implications of the rapid growth in fruit and vegetable imports; and

2. the case of the emerging relationship between California and Mexico in the production and marketing of vegetables.

## THE GROWTH IN VEGETABLE IMPORTS AND THE LACK OF A POLICY CONSENSUS ON IMPORTS

Standard assumptions regarding the effect of imports on U.S. agricultural producers must be modified when discussing the vegetable industry. It is generally assumed that U.S. agricultural producers do not operate in other countries, indeed, that most operate in only one region of one state. Hence, it is presumed that they will advocate protectionist policies when faced with significant imports.

In contrast, California vegetable growers-shippers are frequently multiregional and increasingly source internationally as well via joint ventures with producers in other countries. This enables them to extend shipping seasons and sell products produced in several locations via one marketing organization. The rapid growth in multilocation firms has contributed to a high degree of integration of the Mexico-California-Arizona vegetable industries. Since most vegetable crops are not perennials, the location of production can shift readily, based on relative production and marketing costs and growing season. Trends in the production and marketing arrangements of California vegetable growers-shippers are important, because California alone accounts for almost half of total U.S. production.

Another major factor contributing to the policy debate on fresh vegetable imports is the position of food retailers. Since storage is possible for most foods, seasonality of production does not affect monthly supply. In contrast, for perishable foods if imports are not permitted during periods of low U.S. supply, then retailers experience a loss in sales. In the past, retailers dealt with low winter supplies of produce by committing a limited amount of floor space to the produce department. However, in the 1980s, retailers have responded to the growth in consumer interest in produce by significantly expanding the space allocated to produce departments. Selling space devoted to produce now averages 15% of supermarket floor space, up from 3 to 4% in the smaller stores of the 1970s (Pierson and Allen). The average number of items handled in a produce department has gone from 65 in 1975 to over 250 in 1988 (Pierson and Allen). In fact, many chains have repositioned their entire marketing strategy around the produce department. Consequently, it is vital that this space is full all year, making the retail demand for year-round produce a compelling force in favor of imports.

Given the overwhelming demand for produce imports, and the integration of many California and Arizona producers with foreign production operations, the possibility of achieving significant protectionist measures is greatly lessened. To achieve protectionist policies, producers in the affected industries must present a united front. Given the disparity of interests prevailing at the shipping point level in the vegetable industry, between those that are operating internationally and those that are not, this consensus is difficult to achieve. Witness the failure of the California legislature to pass a country-of-origin labeling bill, due to dissension within agri-industry and opposition from retailers. Country-of-origin labeling legislation has also been defeated at the national level.

The number of California firms operating overseas, especially in Mexico, continues to grow on a monthly basis. The change in relative labor costs and the need to extend shipping seasons to meet buyer demand are not the only factors underlying this shift in the location of production. Supply-driven factors like urban encroachment and high water costs in southern California coastal production regions and the increasingly constraining regulatory environment in California have also played a critical role in this transition (Cook and Amon).

Other forces behind the growth in import competition in frozen and fresh vegetables include:

1. the accelerating rate of technological development and its international dissemination;
2. the electronic communication revolution which allows for ready identification and analysis of economic opportunities; and
3. the global deregulation of financial flows that facilitates timely foreign investment in identified opportunities (Moulton and Runsten).

Hence, the attempt of debt-ridden countries to expand vegetable exports as a means of generating foreign exchange is only one of many forces driving the growth in U.S. fruit and vegetable imports. Because many of these forces are beyond the scope of national public policy, firms must respond with adaptive strategies, rather than simply relying on policy interventions.

Another issue influencing the U.S. response to fruit and vegetable imports is the timing of imports. For example, imports from Chile of asparagus, grapes and other fruits, and kiwis and asparagus from New Zealand are contraseasonal. Consequently, not only are domestic producers presumably not harmed by these imports, but they may benefit as well. The argument is that contraseasonal imports cause consumers to become accustomed to consuming commodities such as asparagus, grapes and soft fruits during the off-season, thereby increasing the overall demand throughout the entire year.

However, the effect of contraseasonal imports on annual demand appears to vary by commodity. For example, while per capita consumption of grapes has increased during the 1980s, peach per capita consumption has actually declined slightly. Certainly many other variables beyond seasonal availability enter into consumer purchase decisions, including perceptions of quality, relative prices, nutritional and health concerns and perceptions of the price/value relationship offered by any given product.

Furthermore, some of these commodities are storeable and hence may have overlapping shipping seasons and compete with California product. Also affected are early and late season varieties and regions that ship while foreign shipping seasons get started or wind down.

In addition, since many produce items may have a high degree of substitutability, the expanded number of nontraditional items now available during the winter may adversely affect consumption of the traditional fresh winter fruits and vegetables. Furthermore, while fresh produce consumption has indeed expanded, by 21% between 1980 and 1986, much of this growth has simply been a shift from canned fruits and vegetables to fresh. Hence, wider availability of fresh fruits and vegetables during the winter months may have a further adverse effect on the demand for canned fruits and vegetables produced domestically.

## NEW MEXICAN PRODUCTION REGIONS

The case study approach can be useful in examining emerging international relationships in the vegetable industry. The most dynamic evolving relationship is embodied in the California-Mexico connection. Traditionally, Mexico has produced primarily winter vegetables and has competed most directly with Florida. For example, in the case of tomatoes, California does not ship during the January to April period when Mexico and Florida jointly supply the winter market (see Figure 6.1). However, during the 1980s new

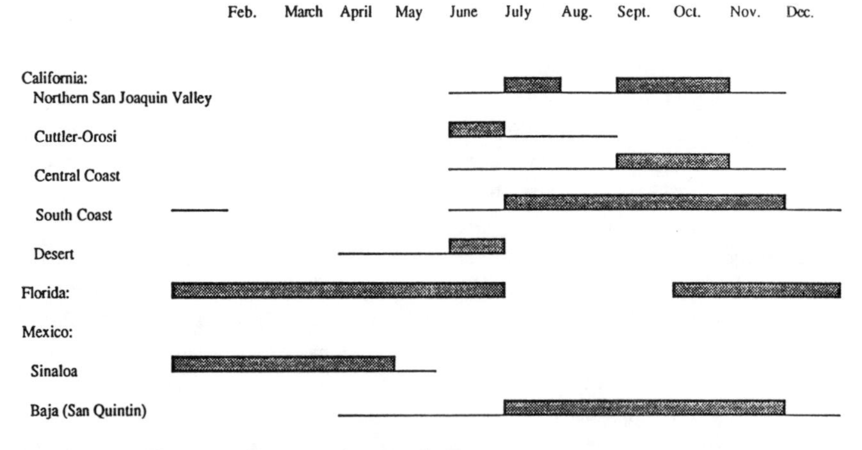


Figure 6.1. Shipping Seasons for Fresh Tomatoes

SOURCE: USDA, Marketing California Tomatoes, 1985, July 1986, Union Nacional de Organismos de Productores de Hortalizas y Frutas, Boletin Anual Temporada, 1985 -1986.

vegetable production regions have begun to emerge in Northwestern Mexico, and their shipping seasons overlap with Southern California. This changes the competitive relationships between the two countries. On the other hand, much of the production developing in these new Mexican regions has been set up and financed by California and Arizona growers. In essence, a coordinated relationship is developing to meet the demand of U.S. buyers for a year-round supply of produce.

Several commodities are instructive of the new relationship evolving between Mexico and the United States. They are fresh broccoli, frozen broccoli and cauliflower, and fresh market tomatoes. The new production regions that will be emphasized are the Baja peninsula of Mexico and the Mexicali-San Luis valleys which are located directly below the Imperial Valley of California and the Yuma production area of Arizona.

## Agriculture in the Coastal Region of Baja

The coastal production region of Baja includes Ensenada and San Quintin and covers 60,000 hectares of farmland, about 18% of which is in vegetable production. Tomato production is concentrated in the San Quintin area, about 150 miles south of the U.S.-Mexican border.

Irrigation in this area is from groundwater sources whose quality has been declining. The aquifer interfaces with seawater and a lack of replenishing rain has caused salinity levels to increase markedly. Of the 700 wells located in the San Quintin Valley, 50% exhibit salinity levels of 2,000 to 3,000 parts per million (SARH, 1987). Due to the scarcity and salinity of water in the San Quintin area, local authorities restrict the drilling of wells. Furthermore, because suitable water is often not available at the production sites, it has to be pumped several miles, increasing the cost of farming in this area (Cook and Amon).

Despite the severe water and land constraints, tomato production in Baja increased dramatically in the 1980s. The production increase is due to improved yields and the adoption of drip irrigation, since acreage remained stable as shown in Table 6.1. Despite the fixed land base, tomato shipments from Baja grew from 26,170,000 pounds in 1980 to 250,570,000 in 1986. This was equivalent to 36% of California shipments in 1986, up from 3% in 1980 (see Table 6.2). The decline in tomato shipments from Baja in 1987 was due to weather problems and 1988 shipments appear to be returning to 1986 levels. While Baja tomato exports have apparently stabilized, some additional expansion in the production of other vegetables may still occur if the crop mix changes, shifting land out of field crop production.

Two major sources of investment have fueled the growth of vegetable production in San Quintin in the 1980s–from the United States and from

Table 6.1. Fresh Market Tomato Area Harvested, Yield and Production in Baja California, 1970-1986

| | Area | | | Yield | | | Production | | |
|---|---|---|---|---|---|---|---|---|---|
| Year | Mexicali | Coast | Total | Mexicali | Coast | Total | Mexicali | Coast | Total |
| | hectares | | | tons per hectare | | | tons | | |
| 1970 | 0 | 756 | 756 | 0 | 12 | 12 | 0 | 9,313 | 9,313 |
| 1980 | 138 | 3,890 | 4,028 | 27 | 30 | 29 | 3,736 | 116,700 | 120,436 |
| 1981 | 177 | 3,622 | 3,799 | 21 | 27 | 26 | 3,713 | 96,462 | 100,175 |
| 1982 | 63 | 3,651 | 3,714 | 20 | 32 | 32 | 1,248 | 116,884 | 118,132 |
| 1983 | 28 | 3,027 | 3,055 | 20 | 34 | 34 | 560 | 104,226 | 104,786 |
| 1984 | 42 | 4,169 | 4,211 | 24 | 31 | 31 | 1,000 | 129,643 | 130,643 |
| 1985 | 66 | 4,269 | 4,335 | 20 | 36 | 36 | 1,328 | 156,145 | 157,473 |
| 1986 | 33 | 4,162 | 4,195 | 43 | 37 | 37 | 1,424 | 156,426 | 157,850 |

SOURCE: Secretaria de Agricultura y Recursos Hidraulicos, Dirección de Economia Agrícola. Oficina Regional de Mexicali.
NOTE(S): To convert hectares to acres, multiply them by 2.47.

Table 6.2. Total Shipments of Fresh Tomatoes from California and Baja, 1980-1987

| | 1980 | 1981 | 1982 | 1983 | 1984 | 1985 | 1986 | 1987 |
|---|---|---|---|---|---|---|---|---|
| | 10,000 pound units | | | | | | | |
| California | 76,606 | 78,499 | 74,821 | 67,300 | 60,794 | 66,867 | 70,261 | 80,957 |
| Baja | 2,617 | 2,431 | 7,097 | 13,584 | 17,026 | 18,985 | 25,057 | 19,834 |

SOURCE: U.S. Department of Agriculture, Agricultural Marketing Service, *Marketing California Tomatoes*, various issues.

mainland-based (e.g., Sinaloan) Mexican growers (Cook and Amon). Sinaloan growers are large volume operators and their state-of-the-art production practices have enabled them to achieve San Diego yields in tomatoes, averaging 2,500 cartons per acre.

The entrance of the Sinaloan growers to Baja production has been motivated by two key forces. First, the need to extend shipping seasons into the summer and fall in order to meet the demand of U.S. buyers for a year-round supply of vegetables. Secondly, mainland growers are attracted to Baja because they can transfer their workers there until production begins again in Sinaloa, thus enabling them to maintain a more stable labor supply. Research done by Thompson, Amon and Martin indicates that significant costs are incurred if growers have to completely reassemble their work forces in the fall.

U.S. investment in Mexico has been attracted by lower labor, water and land costs. Regional shifts are occurring within California as well, as urbanization pressures in coastal areas and high water costs ($500/acre foot in San Diego County) contribute to an expansion in vegetable acreage in the central valley of California. Table 6.3 shows the regional shifts in fresh market tomato acreage in California.

Table 6.3. California Fresh Market Tomato Harvested Acreage by Production Region, 1980-1986

| Production Area | 1980 | 1981 | 1982 | 1983 | 1984 | 1985 | 1986 |
|---|---|---|---|---|---|---|---|
| | | | | acres | | | |
| Northern San Joaquin Valley | 9,300 | 8,260 | 10,300 | 11,420 | 11,600 | 12,100 | 11,650 |
| Cuttler-Orosi | 5,160 | 5,010 | 3,700 | 4,520 | 5,800 | 7,500 | 7,450 |
| Central Coast | 5,000 | 5,060 | 4,400 | 3,400 | 3,200 | 3,200 | 3,400 |
| South Coast | 7,840 | 8,960 | 7,500 | 7,120 | 4,340 | 3,450 | 3,030 |
| Imperial Valley | 1,200 | 1,250 | 1,360 | 1,450 | 1,500 | 1,300 | 1,000 |
| Other | 2,000 | 1,560 | 1,440 | 1,390 | 1,460 | 1,050 | 2,070 |
| State Total | 30,500 | 30,100 | 28,700 | 29,300 | 27,900 | 28,600 | 28,600 |

SOURCE: California Crop and Livestock Reporting Service, *California Vegetable Crops*, various issues, 1980-1985; California Agricultural Statistics Service, *California Vegetable Crops 1985-1986*, July 1987.
NOTE(S): One acre equals 0.40 hectare.

Clearly, San Diego has experienced a significant decline in acreage in the 1980s and the development of the vine-ripe tomato deal in Baja has particular significance for San Diego because the shipping seasons are almost completely overlapping. Since shipments from Baja are heaviest from September through November (Figure 6.1), the development of the tomato industry has severely encroached on the fall market window formerly relied on by San Diego county. Yet, because many of the San Diego growers are now operating in Baja, in essence there has just been a shift in the location of production.

The rapid growth in Baja vine-ripened tomato exports is partly the result of a significant cost advantage relative to Southern California. As shown in Table 6.4, the estimated production and packaging cost of San Quintin tomatoes c.i.f. Chula Vista is $3.89 per carton (grower interviews) vs. $5.10 per carton for San Diego, according to Schrader (1987).

The majority of this cost differential is in labor costs. Most production

Table 6.4. Tomato Production and Marketing Costs in San Quintin, Mexico 1987

| Vine-Ripened Tomatoes | Cost/Carton |
|---|---|
| | U.S.dollars |
| Pre-harvest[a] | $1.20 |
| Picking | .30 |
| Packing | .70 |
| Carton | .85 |
| Transportation to Border | .35 |
| UNPH Tax | .01 |
| Duties | .48 |
| Total Cost | $3.89 |

SOURCE: Grower Interviews, Cook and Amon.

[a]Yield of 2,500 cartons/acre.

inputs such as seed, pesticides, and herbicides are imported from the United States, hence, costs for these inputs are at U.S. levels, plus a 5 to 10% "surcharge" for input handling costs at the border. However, for a labor-intensive crop like vine-ripened tomatoes, Mexico's labor cost advantage ($3 per day vs. $40 in San Diego) becomes significant. Land rent and water costs are also substantially lower.

Yet water and land constraints in San Quintin are threatening the viability of the vegetable industry and causing producers to seek new land farther south on the Baja Peninsula. Vegetable production is beginning to develop in the Vizcaino area (300 miles south of the U.S.-Mexican border), in northeastern Baja near the gulf of California, and production is expanding in Santo Domingo (600 miles from the border)–a traditional fresh tomato production area. Of these regions, Vizcaino seems to have the most potential for development. However, transportation costs to the border are significantly higher than from San Quintin, and there may be more bureaucratic obstacles to the entry of U.S. growers imposed by the governmental authorities in the state of Southern Baja.

The interdependency of the Baja and California vine-ripe tomato markets is demonstrated by the recent decision to incorporate Mexican tomatoes into the California state marketing order for tomatoes. Any tomatoes handled in California (regardless of origin) are subject to a handler assessment. In this manner, out-of-state beneficiaries of California tomato research who desire to market in California must contribute to the development of improved technology. By reducing the free rider issue of Baja grown tomatoes, dissension over the expansion of this industry has been ameliorated.

### Vegetable Production in the Mexicali-San Luis Valleys

While the Mexicali and San Luis valleys overlap the state lines of Baja, California and Sonora, they can essentially be considered as one production region. The climate and soil conditions are similar to desert growing areas across the border and are suitable for most vegetables during the winter season, except tomatoes. The valleys together have 325,000 hectares of agricultural land, of which 207,000 hectares are irrigated (SARH, 1987). In 1987, horticultural production took place on only 5% of the available irrigated land. Besides Colorado River water there are some 700 deep wells and salinity has not become a serious constraint.

Consequently, the potential for a significant expansion in vegetable production exists by shifting land out of field crops. Research done at CIANO (Center for Agricultural Research in the Northwest) in Sonora indicates that the net return per cubic foot of water is three times higher for most vegetables and fruit crops than for field crops. Hence, there are incentives to change the crop mix. Nevertheless, vegetable production in this area depends on the derived demand from U.S. shippers and distributors. To date the principal vegetable crops produced in this region are green onions (2201 has), asparagus (2867 has), radishes (504 has), and melons and watermelons (2387 has) (SARH, 1988).

## U.S. IMPORTS OF FROZEN VEGETABLES FROM MEXICO

A major vegetable freezing industry has developed in the Bajio area of Central Mexico. This industry was established and financed in the early sixties by U.S. processing firms (Heinz, Del Monte, Campbells, etc.). The firms adapted technology to the region and trained growers to produce to specifications on a contract basis. Today there is a large pool of growers in Central Mexico experienced in broccoli and cauliflower production and several Mexican firms have become significant suppliers of the U.S. market. Many of these also have access to sufficient capital to consider alternative marketing strategies, such as production for the fresh market (Moulton and Runsten).

Since broccoli is a dual usage crop, the phenomenal growth in Mexican frozen broccoli exports to the United States as shown in Table 6.5 (from 27,747,000 lbs. in 1983 to 164,416,000 lbs. in 1987) has adversely affected

Table 6.5. Frozen Broccoli and Cauliflower: Shares of the U.S. Market

| Year | California Pack | Market Share | Other U.S. | Market Share | Imports from Mexico | Market Share | Imports from Guatemala | Market Share | Other Imports | Total |
|---|---|---|---|---|---|---|---|---|---|---|
| | 1,000 lb. | percent | 1,000 lb. | percent | 1,000 lb. | percent | 1,000 lb. | percent | 1,000 lb. | 1,000 lb |
| 1978 | 265,088 | 90.8 | 11,431 | 3.9 | 13,930 | 4.8 | 1,475 | 0.5 | 57 | 291,981 |
| 1979 | 298,618 | 95.1 | -0- | 0 | 12,213 | 4.2 | 2,149 | 0.7 | 88 | 314,069 |
| 1980 | 290,657 | 92.4 | -0- | 0 | 19,110 | 6.1 | 4,607 | 1.5 | 181 | 314,555 |
| 1981 | 288,700 | 86.3 | 18,055 | 5.4 | 22,542 | 6.7 | 5,161 | 1.5 | 120 | 334,578 |
| 1982 | 303,850 | 82.7 | 31,666 | 8.6 | 26,759 | 7.3 | 4,675 | 1.3 | 436 | 367,386 |
| 1983 | 260,359 | 81.6 | 24,999 | 7.8 | 27,747 | 8.7 | 3,238 | 1.0 | 2,566 | 318,909 |
| 1984 | 327,535 | 76.0 | 38,229 | 8.9 | 55,318 | 12.8 | 10,023 | 2.3 | 63 | 431,168 |
| 1985 | 309,836 | 71.4 | 46,970 | 10.8 | 63,376 | 14.6 | 12,666 | 2.9 | 1,105 | 433,953 |
| 1986 | 275,159 | 62.3 | 49,360 | 11.2 | 96,837 | 21.9 | 18,124 | 4.1 | 2,189 | 441,669 |
| 1987 | 261,903 | 51.6 | 50,557 | 10.0 | 164,416 | 32.4 | 27,844 | 5.5 | 2,559 | 507,279 |

**Cauliflower**

| Year | California Pack | Market Share | Other U.S. | Market Share | Imports from Mexico | Market Share | Imports from Guatemala | Market Share | Other Imports | Total |
|---|---|---|---|---|---|---|---|---|---|---|
| | 1,000 lb. | percent | 1,000 lb. | percent | 1,000 lb. | percent | 1,000 lb. | percent | 1,000 lb. | 1,000 lb |
| 1978 | 96,771 | 68.1 | 30,742 | 21.7 | 11,808 | 8.3 | 1,914 | 1.4 | 448 | 141,68 |
| 1979 | 76,957 | 69.2 | 24,173 | 21.8 | 5,887 | 5.3 | 3,969 | 3.6 | 153 | 111,13 |
| 1980 | 66,369 | 70.2 | 18,397 | 19.5 | 6,060 | 6.4 | 3,642 | 3.9 | 19 | 94,48 |
| 1981 | 85,370 | 71.9 | 19,791 | 16.7 | 10,412 | 8.8 | 3,090 | 2.6 | 72 | 118,73 |
| 1982 | 85,339 | 64.5 | 26,305 | 19.9 | 13,306 | 10.1 | 7,083 | 5.4 | 181 | 132,21 |
| 1983 | 71,779 | 59.0 | 28,762 | 23.6 | 17,571 | 14.4 | 3,238 | 2.7 | 276 | 121,62 |
| 1984 | 72,062 | 54.2 | 30,044 | 22.6 | 27,559 | 20.7 | 3,069 | 2.3 | 206 | 132,94 |
| 1985 | 67,074 | 51.0 | 27,543 | 21.0 | 32,869 | 25.0 | 2,835 | 2.2 | 1,119 | 131,44 |
| 1986 | 64,631 | 50.9 | 24,489 | 19.8 | 24,347 | 27.1 | 2,159 | 1.7 | 1,337 | 126,96 |
| 1987 | 51,244 | 37.6 | 26,514 | 19.5 | 55,878 | 41.0 | 1,614 | 1.2 | 1,023 | 136,27 |

SOURCE: American Frozen Food Institute, *Frozen Food Pack Statistics*, various years; U.S. Department of Commerce, Bureau of the Census, *U.S. Imports for Consumption.* Schedule E.

NOTE(S): Before U.S. Exports, which are mainly to Canada, ignores carryover stocks.

the U.S. fresh broccoli market as well. Specifically, Mexico has captured a 32.4% share of the U.S. market for frozen broccoli, thereby limiting the extent to which producers can divert production to the processing market when low prices prevail in the fresh market. A similar situation exists for cauliflower, with Mexico's share of the U.S. market increasing from 14.4% in 1983 to 41.0% in 1987, larger than the California share.

Frozen asparagus imports from Mexico have also experienced major growth. While imports are still minor relative to total U.S. consumption, they have increased fourfold from 1,044,302 lbs. in 1980 to 4,575,493 in 1987 (Pradhan and Moulton).

Despite a decline in U.S. imports of frozen broccoli and asparagus from Mexico in 1988 relative to 1987 (for the first eight months), Mexico's competitive position appears strong (American Institute of Food Distribution).

Moulton and Runsten indicate that the robust nature of competition from Mexico is derived from low labor costs, good capitalization, current technology and good access to the U.S. market. As indicated in Table 6.6, total broccoli production costs in Mexico are less than preharvest costs in the U.S.

While fuel, fertilizer and other energy sources are subsidized, their elim-

Table 6.6. Estimating Costs to Produce Broccoli in Mexico and California, 1986

| | Mexico | California |
|---|---|---|
| | U.S. dollars per acre | |
| Pre-harvest | $268.77 | $799.09 |
| Overhead | 91.00 | 161.00 |
| Harvest & Transport | 64.62 | 450.00 |
| Fixed Costs | 54.00 | 95.50 |
| Total Costs | $478.39 | $1,505.59 |
| Cost per pound | 6.5 cents | 15.1 cents |

SOURCE: For Mexico, Kirby Moulton and David Runsten, *The Mexican Frozen Vegetable Industry*, University of California, Cooperative Extension, Berkeley, December 1986; for California, various Cooperative Extension sample cost studies and interviews with growers.

NOTE(S): Mexican costs are for Guanajuato, calculated in June 1986; California costs are 1986 University of California sample costs with wages and land rents adjusted downward to to reflect actual practice.

American costs are based on an average payable yield 7,316 pounds/acre (8.2 metric tons/hectare) from a 1983 survey; yields may be higher now, although the same varieties are being grown.

Californian costs are based on the California 1986 average broccoli yield of 10,000 pounds/acre (11.2 metric tons/hectare).

ination would be unlikely to reduce Mexico's cost advantage resulting from lower labor costs. And Moulton and Runsten conclude that exchange rate fluctuations are unlikely to significantly affect Mexico's competitive position, given the continuing expansion in exports in the face of a decline in the undervaluation of the peso. Certainly the development of efficient export marketing channels by the multinational firms greatly facilitates the movement of Mexican product into the U.S. market.

The growth in frozen broccoli and cauliflower imports from Mexico has had an adverse effect on independent processors operating only in California, reducing profits and employment. Yet the fragmented structure of the broccoli industry and the lack of industrywide organization via a marketing order or commission has inhibited the ability of the California industry to develop effective competitive responses.

## THE IMPORTANCE OF INDUSTRY STRUCTURE AND ORGANIZATION

Industry structure and organization appear to have an important effect on the competitive position of California agri-industries. It is instructive to compare and contrast the frozen vegetable industry with the frozen strawberry industry.

When the Bracero program ended in the 1960s, California feared a loss of the strawberry industry to Mexico due to the highly labor-intensive nature of strawberry production. In reality, California has continued to gain market share relative to both Mexico and other regions of the United States (Runsten). California has a state strawberry marketing order and has consistently invested in the varietal development and other research areas necessary to retain a technological advantage (the 1988-89 research budget of the Strawberry Advisory Board is $642,000). Figure 6.2 shows the gap in strawberry yields which has developed since the 1950s between California and Mexico and the Pacific Northwest.

California also has a generic promotion and advertising program for strawberries with a 1988-89 budget of $2.5 million. Neither Mexico nor any other state has an organized industrywide research and promotional program of any significance.

Another relevant factor is the structure of the California strawberry industry. The California industry is composed of many medium size firms and grower cooperatives and is not dominated by a single firm capable of transferring technology to Mexico on a significant scale.

In contrast, the frozen vegetable industry is comprised of several large

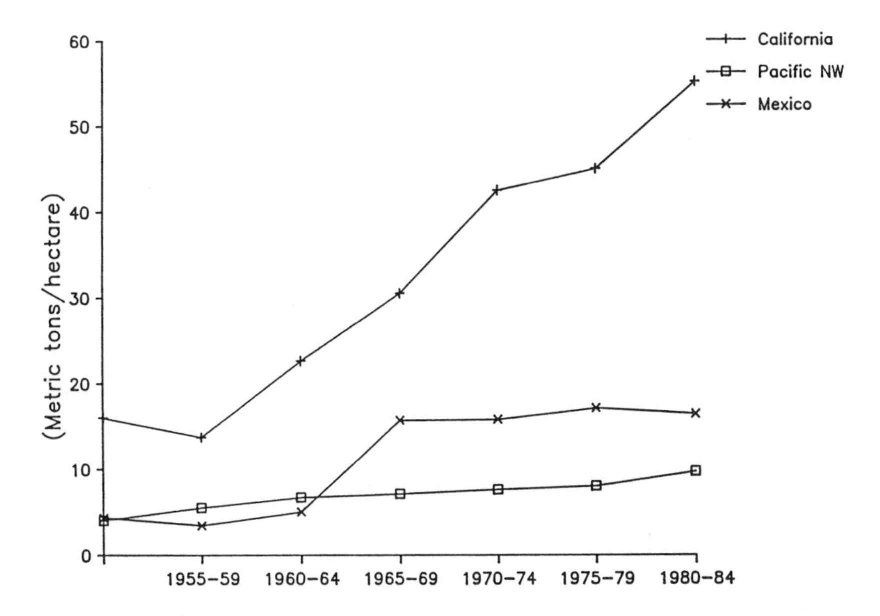


Figure 6.2. Strawberry Yields. California, Mexico and Pacific Northwest

SOURCE: USDA, Agricultural Statistics, various issues, and Fruit Situation & Outlook Report, Sept. 1986.

multinational firms with sufficient resources to affect the overall market. Secondly, the frozen vegetable industry does not benefit from an organized program supporting research and/or promotion such as through a marketing order.

## MEXICAN FRESH BROCCOLI AND STRAWBERRY EXPORTS TO THE UNITED STATES

While fresh broccoli imports from Mexico are still only 3% of the U.S. market, nevertheless, this represents a tripling of its market share between 1986 and 1987. As shown in Table 6.7, imports have expanded from zero in 1980 to 7,996,320 lbs. in 1986 and 24,749,000 lbs. in 1987. Part of this growth has come from the Bajio area of Central Mexico as Mexican vegetable processors have expanded into fresh. Fresh asparagus imports from Mexico have also increased markedly, up from 7,202,766 lbs. in 1980 to 24,001,332 in 1987 (Pradhan and Moulton).

Table 6.7. Fresh Broccoli Imports to the United States, 1980-1987

| | 1980 | 1981 | 1983 | 1984 | 1985 | 1986 | 1987 |
|---|---|---|---|---|---|---|---|
| | | | thousand pounds | | | | |
| Mexico | 0 | 730 | 0 | 3,458 | 4,012 | 7,996 | 24,749 |
| Other Countries (Canada, Guatemala El Salvador, Israel Malaysia, Monserrat) | 212 | 2 | 272 | 154 | 450 | 536 | 260 |
| Total | 212 | 732 | 272 | 3,612 | 4,462 | 8,344 | 25,009 |

SOURCE: U.S. Department of Commerce, *U.S. Imports for Consumption and General Imports*, Ft. 246, various issues.
NOTE(S): Import figures for 1982 are not available.

Furthermore, other new fresh market export industries are emerging in Mexico, such as strawberries from Baja California. Strawberry production in Baja was initiated as recently as 1985 and expanded to 1,200 acres and 4 million trays in 1987. Shipments are expected to continue to grow at a rapid rate and investments in forced air cooling systems are being made. In addition, the largest and, arguably, the most technologically advanced fresh strawberry producer group (Driscoll) has financed a pilot strawberry production project in Northwestern Mexico in order to begin the shipping season during the winter months.

If other California firms were to adopt this strategy, the transfer of state-of-the-art strawberry production and handling technology to Mexico might occur on a significant scale. Once the technology is transferred and Mexican growers involved in the joint ventures have acquired sufficient capital, they can pursue independent expansion policies. This is in effect what happened with frozen vegetables; U.S. firms may have underestimated the independent production capability of Mexican firms and their ability to compete in the U.S. market.

In the long run, the current international diversification strategies of California firms may contribute to an accelerated exit of firms from California, given their own investment in the development of new production regions which could eventually become competitors.

## MAQUILADORAS FOR VEGETABLES

Another example of the emerging relationship between California and Mexico in the vegetable industry is the recent decision of the California Department of Food and Agriculture (CDFA) to approve the establishment of a "maquiladora" in Mexico to package carrots grown in the Imperial Valley and destined for the U.S. market. The maquiladora concept has been heavily used by U.S. manufacturing firms. Maquiladoras import inputs into Mexico duty-free, assemble the products there to take advantage of low labor costs, and then pay duty only on the value added in Mexico when "exporting" to the U.S. market.

The applications of the maquiladora concept to agriculture are new and have interesting implications. For vegetable crops which are not highly labor-intensive at the production and harvesting levels, Mexico may not have a significant cost advantage. For these crops the greatest potential for cost savings may be in the packaging stage. Hence, it could be considered advantageous by California and Arizona growers to produce in the less risky U.S. environment and merely package in Mexico (for crops that aren't highly perishable). Indeed, the marketing and infrastructure advantages of producing in California may make this a common scenario for those operating close to the border.

## MARKETING STRATEGIES FOR CALIFORNIA AND MEXICAN VEGETABLE GROWERS

Traditionally, California has pursued a marketing strategy of operating as a high volume, least cost producer. Clearly, California can no longer be described as the least cost producer for a wide variety of vegetable crops. Yet it takes time for industry perceptions to change and adapt to a new marketing environment. An alternative strategy pursued by a growing number of California growers-shippers is that of targeting the product attribute market for differentiated products. Examples of firms pursuing this strategy are Sunworld of Irvine and Fresh Western Growers of Salinas.

The entrance of new players into the fresh vegetable industry is also affecting the marketing environment in California. Due to the decline in consumption of canned fruits and vegetables, many processors (e.g., Dole, Campbell's, Pillsbury-Green Giant, Kraft, and Del Monte) have entered the fresh market during the 1980s and have brought with them their branded marketing mentalities. Successful branding of produce is difficult because of the following requirements:

1. year-round availability of product;
2. a consistent, high quality supply;
3. a differentiated product; and
4. proper handling throughout the cold chain.

Without these conditions a consumer brand (as opposed to a grade label) is not economically viable, since the development of a "consumer franchise" for a product requires costly consumer advertising. This kind of investment would not be profitable for a product available only seasonally, for example. The growth of contraseasonal imports is reducing this constraint, but because of the perishability of fresh produce, the industry is still grappling with the other requirements. Yet clearly, as the large firms invest in consumer brands and tackle the obstacles, they will depend on foreign imports to fill the gaps when U.S. supplies are low. This is a powerful force in favor of imports.

Because of the difficulty of clearly differentiating produce, given the variable intra- and interseasonal quality, brands may have a higher success rate if they are associated with value-added products such as precut and microwaveable products. Hence, consumer interest in convenience-oriented products and industry interest in branded marketing may offer an advantage to the larger firms with past brand marketing experience and large resource pools. As a result, the introduction of brands is expected to affect industry structure at the shipping point level. Smaller firms with insufficient capital to invest in consumer brands or without sophisticated quality control programs in their foreign operations may be at a disadvantage in a branded environment.

Yet the success of brands in produce remains to be seen. It has not been demonstrated that the majority of retailers will support brands and pay a price premium. Survey data from the Food Marketing Institute/Produce Marketing Association show a lack of consensus on the part of retailers on the benefits of brands. Retailers do respond favorably to branded products as an informational merchandising technique, where the physical brand label or package includes recipes, ripening or nutritional information.

Although the ability of shippers to develop successful consumer franchises remains to be seen, branding will bring both an advertising and informational/merchandising jolt to produce. This may be an important competitive factor for exporting countries attempting to penetrate the U.S. market and raises an interesting question with regard to marketing strategies. Will countries such as Mexico continue to pursue a least cost, high volume strategy or will they attempt to forward integrate into the U.S. market and develop branded, value-added products?

Mexico's ability to move into the high growth category of value-added, convenience-oriented products may be limited by the costly market research and sophisticated packaging and postharvest technology required. If Mexico is to pursue these strategies it may be merely as part of the supplier network for large U.S. firms who set the specifications and transfer the technology.

## CONCLUSIONS

The internationalization of the fruit and vegetable industry and changing consumer demand is ushering in a new marketing era. While imports are expanding rapidly, much of this production has been set up and financed by sectors of California agriculture itself. The propensity of many California firms to shift operations out of state and out of country makes it difficult for the state's agricultural industry to speak with one voice.

Compelling demand and supply side factors favor a continuation of the transfer of production capacity to other areas. On the other hand, California's natural advantages of diverse climates and long growing seasons, combined with highly developed production, postharvest and distribution technology, ensure California's agricultural importance in the fruit and vegetable industry. Although the location of the production may change, California firms are bound to continue to play a major role in the financing and marketing of production from new regions. Yet, in order to maintain a leadership role, California must continually invest in the research and development necessary for a competitive advantage, and must look to innovative marketing strategies emphasizing high quality, differentiated products.

## REFERENCES

American Frozen Food Institute. *Frozen Food Pack Statistics*, various years.

American Institute of Food Distribution. "The Food Institute Report," November 5, 1988.

California Agricultural Statistics Service. *California Vegetable Crops 1985-1986*, July 1987.

California Crop and Livestock Reporting Service. *California Vegetable Crops*, various issues.

Cook, Roberta, and Ricardo Amon. "Competition in the Fresh Vegetable

Industry" in *Report of a 1986-87 Study Group on Marketing California Specialty Crops: Worldwide Competition and Constraints.* University of California Agricultural Issues Center, Davis.

Moulton, Kirby, and David Runsten. *Frozen Vegetable Industry of Mexico.* University of California Cooperative Extension, Berkeley, December 1986.

Pierson, Thomas R., and John W. Allen. *The Produce Industry in Transition: Focus on Marketing.* Paper presented at a workshop on Markets for Vegetables in the Western Hemisphere: Trends, Policies, and Linkages, Rutgers University, September 6-7, 1988.

Pradhan, V.S., and Kirby Moulton. *Statistical Tables of Asparagus Imports into the United States.* University of California Cooperative Extension, Berkeley, April 1988.

Runsten, David. "Competition in Strawberries" in *Report of a 1986-87 Study Group on Marketing California Specialty Crops: Worldwide Competition and Constraints.* University of California Agricultural Issues Center, Davis.

Runsten, David, and Kirby Moulton. "Competition in Frozen Vegetables" in *Report of a 1986-87 Study Group on Marketing California Specialty Crops: Worldwide Competition and Constraints.* University of California Agricultural Issues Center, Davis.

Schrader, Wayne. *San Diego County Agricultural Directory of Services and Guidelines to Production Costs and Practices 1987-1988.* University of California Cooperative Extension, San Diego County, 1987.

Secretaria de Agricultura y Recursos Hidraulicos (SARH). *Direccion de Economia Agricola.* Oficina Regional de Ensenada, February 1987.

Secretaria de Agricultura y Recursos Hidraulicos (SARH). *Direccion de Economia Agricola.* Oficina Regional de Mexicali, March 1987.

Secretaria de Agricultura y Recursos Hidraulicos (SARH). Centro de Invdestigaciones Forestales y Agropecuarias de Baja California, September 1988.

Thompson, Gary, Ricardo Amon, and Philip L. Martin. "Agricultural Development and Emigration: Rhetoric and Reality." *International Migration Review*, Volume XX, Number 3, Fall 1986.

U.S. Department of Agriculture. *Agricultural Statistics*, various issues.

U.S. Department of Agriculture. *Fruit and Situation Outlook Report*, September 1986.

U.S. Department of Agriculture, Agricultural Marketing Service. *Marketing California Tomatoes*, various issues.

U.S. Department of Agriculture, Economic Research Service. *Foreign Agricultural Trade of the United States, Calendar Year 1985 Supplement*, July 1986, and *Preliminary U.S. Trade Figures Calendar Year 1986*, March 1987.

U.S. Department of Commerce, Bureau of Census. *U.S. Imports for Consumption and General Imports*, Ft 246, various issues.

U.S. Department of Commerce, Bureau of Census. *U.S. Imports for Consumption*, Schedule E.

# 7

# AN EMPIRICAL ANALYSIS OF WORLD VEGETABLE TRADE

Amy Larsen Sparks
*U.S. Department of Agriculture*

## INTRODUCTION

International trade in fresh vegetables has become increasingly important to both developed and developing nations. United Nations data indicate that trade in fresh vegetables, SITC 054, increased about fourfold between the years 1962-1982. The total quantities of imports and exports of fresh vegetables among the major participating regions of Latin America, the United States, Canada, the European Economic Community (EEC), the Middle East, the Far East, Africa, and the non-EEC Western European nations in 1963 were 3.69 million and 3.59 million metric tons, respectively. By 1982 those totals had increased to 14.82 and 13.33 million metric tons. These data clearly demonstrate tremendous growth in the last two decades. Trading partners have changed, as well as the degree of regional competition. The potential for market growth and, hence, changing market shares, is of paramount importance to those regions attempting to expand their export markets.

There are two major blocs of trade in fresh vegetables, within and among the Americas, or the Western Hemisphere, and within and among Eurasia. The majority of trade in fresh vegetables occurs within these two blocs; however, there are economic forces at work changing these patterns. The fastest growing import markets, besides Western Europe, are the Far East, Africa, and the Middle East. While they are still relatively small markets, they do represent windows of opportunity for vegetable exporters. These markets are also becoming more accessible due to technological changes and improvements in infrastructure. However, trade between the American regions and the EEC is seriously hampered by the Common Agricultural Policy (CAP).

Vegetable trade depends directly on the importing region's demand for the particular product: data indicate that supply levels have little impact on the quantities or patterns of vegetable trade. Demand may differ according to the source of supply. An empirical measurement of these demands is essential to evaluate pricing policies and to form long-run trade projections. Towards this end, a simultaneous system for world vegetable trade, a general form of which is laid out in this article, was estimated. For the purposes of empirical implementation, the SITC code of 054, fresh vegetables, was used. This is a high level of aggregation but it is justified because the purpose of the study was to examine world vegetable trade and the Western Hemisphere's participation in it, and not the characteristics of the trade of particular types of vegetables.

This article discusses international trade in fresh vegetables from the Western Hemishpere's perspective, where the Western Hemisphere includes the regions of Latin America, the United States, and Canada. The size of the import and export markets of these regions will be discussed, and how they relate to each other as well as the other major regions involved in vegetable trade, as revealed by the data and parameter estimates. Simulations, in which product prices were varied and the impacts on product demands measured, are also discussed.

## WORLD VEGETABLE TRADE PATTERNS

### Levels, Percentages, and Growth of Production

Table 7.1 presents levels of production by region, regional percentages of total world production of fresh vegetables for 1962 and 1982, and the 1982 levels divided by the 1962 levels. This final column will be interpreted as a growth rate for production levels. Thus world production of fresh vegetables grew at a rate of 1.39 from 1962 to 1982; that is, the 1982 level was 1.39 times the 1962 level. Latin America, the United States, and Canada all showed growth in production levels above those of the world rate.

### Levels, Percentages, and Growth of Trade

Tables 7.2, 7.3, and 7.4 use 1962 as a base and present the ratios of 1982 quantities of imports and exports for inter- and intraregional trade to 1962 quantities by region and for the world as a whole, where the world consists of the eight regions selected for this study. The absolute levels of intraregional trade were much higher than those of interregional trade, 550 million versus 3.7 million in 1962 and 750 million versus 14.8 million in 1982 for imports. However, the levels of growth were higher for interregional than intraregional trade, 4.01 versus 1.36.

Table 7.1. Levels, Percentages and Growth of Production of Fresh Vegetables, 1962 to 1982.

| Region | 1962 | % of World | 1982 | % of World | 1982/1962 |
|---|---|---|---|---|---|
| | metric tons | | metric tons | | |
| Latin America | 45,318,517 | 8.31 | 69,589,880 | 9.20 | 1.54 |
| U.S. | 31,809,228 | 5.83 | 46,547,992 | 6.15 | 1.46 |
| Canada | 3,429,409 | 0.63 | 5,861,669 | 0.77 | 1.71 |
| W. Europe | 105,171,715 | 19.28 | 98,171,002 | 12.98 | 0.93 |
| Middle East | 10,526,320 | 1.93 | 46,266,742 | 6.12 | 4.40 |
| Far East | 290,000,000 | 53.16 | 390,000,000 | 51.56 | 1.34 |
| Africa | 59,232,133 | 10.86 | 100,000,000 | 13.22 | 1.69 |
| World | 545,487,322 | 100.00 | 756,437,285 | 100.00 | 1.39 |

NOTE(S): The EEC and non-EEC Western European regions are not presented separately because, although the countries in Europe considered in this analysis did not change, for some their status as EEC members did. Thus, the composition of the two regions changed from 1962 to 1982. If the two regions were presented separately it would be unclear as to what had caused growth or lack of growth, expansion in members or a change in the level of participation in trade. The important issue in this table is the absolute level of change in European interregional trade.

Table 7.2. Levels of Growth of Interregional Import Quantities, 1962 to 1982

| Region | 1962 | 1982 | 1982/1962 |
|---|---|---|---|
| | metric tons | metric tons | |
| Latin America | 204,453 | 225,246 | 1.1017 |
| U.S. | 315,787 | 1,141,592 | 3.6151 |
| Canada | 464,714 | 679,947 | 1.4632 |
| W. Europe | 2,463,681 | 11,540,888 | 4.6844 |
| Middle East | 54,086 | 198,499 | 3.6701 |
| Far East | 73,205 | 536,520 | 7.3290 |
| Africa | 120,444 | 504,027 | 4.1847 |
| World | 3,693,370 | 14,826,719 | 4.0144 |

NOTE(S): See note on Table 7.1.

Table 7.3. Levels of Growth of Interregional Export Quantities, 1962 to 1982

| Region | 1962 | 1982 | 1982/1962 |
|---|---|---|---|
| | metric tons | metric tons | |
| Latin America | 241,001 | 997,392 | 4.1392 |
| U.S. | 680,314 | 1,458,805 | 2.1443 |
| Canada | 252,491 | 684,132 | 2.7095 |
| W. Europe | 1,534,126 | 2,481,683 | 1.6177 |
| Middle East | 180,860 | 707,811 | 3.9136 |
| Far East | 109,873 | 7,729,112 | 70.3459 |
| Africa | 666,741 | 375,745 | 0.5636 |
| World | 3,595,509 | 14,434,680 | 4.0146 |

NOTE(S): See note on Table 7.1. Also, 1962 was an abnormally low year for Far Eastern exports, therefore the 1963 level of 109,873 was used.

Table 7.4. Levels and Growth of Intraregional Import Quantities, 1962 to 1982

| Region | 1962 | 1982 | 1982/1962 |
|---|---|---|---|
| | metric tons | metric tons | |
| Latin America | 45,248,604 | 68,817,734 | 1.52 |
| U.S. | 31,452,394 | 46,489,441 | 1.48 |
| Canada | 3,651,676 | 6,045,948 | 1.66 |
| W. Europe | 106,341,421 | 107,494,045 | 1.01 |
| Middle East | 10,368,301 | 45,757,430 | 4.41 |
| Far East | 290,000,000 | 380,000,000 | 1.31 |
| Africa | 58,395,811 | 100,000,000 | 1.71 |
| World | 550,000,000 | 750,000,000 | 1.36 |

NOTE(S): See note on Table 7.1.

Comparing Table 7.1, levels of production, with Tables 7.2, 7.3, and 7.4, levels of inter- and intraregional trade, it is clear that the vast majority of fresh vegetables remain in the region in which they are produced. These are not the vegetables of interest in this paper. This study analyzes fresh vegetables traded between regions. While these make up a small percentage of total fresh vegetable production, their share is growing rapidly.

From Table 7.2 it is clear that none of the Western Hemisphere regions experienced growth in their fresh vegetable imports equalling that of the world average. The United States is closest, with its imports growing at a rate of 3.6. Latin America and Canada, however, essentially maintained the status quo in the levels of their imports. The fastest growing import markets outside of the Western Hemisphere were the Far East, Western Europe, Africa, and the Middle East, all of which had rates of growth higher than those for the Western Hemisphere. In absolute quantities, Western Europe was by far the largest market.

On the export side, Latin America showed strong growth, more than quadrupling its exports from 1962 to 1982 (see Table 7.3). Canada showed a growth rate of 2.7 and the U.S. of 2.1. Western Hemisphere export growth was stronger than its import growth. On a world scale, however, fresh vegetable exports were dominated by those from the Far East, which showed a growth rate of 70. Africa's exports declined to 50% of their 1962 level.

The fact that the combined European regions were among the fastest growing for vegetable imports and comprised the largest markets for vegetables has major implications. The CAP is a very effective mechanism for limiting imports into the EEC from those nations or regions with which it does not have preferential trading arrangements. The Western Hemisphere does not have these agreements. It is very possible that the CAP has hindered the growth of Latin American, U.S., and Canadian exports and kept them below the world level.

## A WORLD TRADE MODEL

A world trade model based on the one outlined by Armington which distinguishes between products by place of production was constructed (Armington). This is a two-stage allocation model where total demand for a good such as vegetables is first determined; this market demand is then independently allocated among competing sources of supply, or products. A constrained estimation procedure is used to guarantee that estimated world exports equal world imports. Weak separability and homotheticity are both assumed by this theoretical approach.

The structure of the international trade environment was built into the trade model. Demand and export supply equations were specified for only the major trading regions listed earlier. Tariff barriers and preferential treatments were incorporated into the model, as were exchange rates, transportation and handling costs, regional incomes and demographic patterns.

An important issue in a model which distinguishes products by place of production is the degree of substitutability which exists between products. With eight differentiated products, all competing in eight different markets, there would be an inordinate number of parameters to be estimated if no limits were placed on their substitutability. To alleviate that problem, the Constant Ratio of Elasticities of Substitution (CRES) technical relationship was imposed on the trade system. This constrains the elasticities of substitution between any pair of competing products in a market to vary by a constant proportion, but the substitutability between every product in that market is not necessarily identical. The CRES technical relationship determines the functional nature of the product demands from competing supply regions.[1]

All of the functional relationships of the world trade system in fresh vegetables were estimated in double log form. The parameters of the product demands, however, have very specific and important relationships to the CRES technical relationship. This section will present the model, the four types of functional relationships and the identities, in its general form. In this way, it is clear which are the dependent and the independent variables in the different relationships and it is clear how tariff barriers are accounted for in the model.

## Functional Relationships

Let i and j subscripts denote regions of demand and supply, respectively.

(1) $X_i\cdot = f(P_i\cdot, GDP_i, Pop_i\cdot)$ Market Demands

(2) $X_{ij} = f(P_{ij}, P_i\cdot, X_i\cdot)$ Product Demands

(3) $[X \cdot j - X_{jj}] = f(F\cdot_j, X\cdot_j)$ Export Supplies

(4) $C_{ij} = f(F_{ij}, \mathit{Year})$ CIF Import Prices

where Year is a proxy for transportation and handling costs.

## Identities

(5) $P_{ij} = [(1 + T_{ij})C_{ij}]$ Market Price

where

$T_{ij}$ = costs of tariffs and preferential treatments between importing region i and exporting region j, expressed in percentage terms.

(6) $Pi\cdot = [\sum_j P_{ij}X_{ij}/X_i\cdot]$ Average Market Price

(7) $F\cdot_j = [\sum_i F_{ij}X_{ij}/X\cdot_j] = F_{jj}$ Average FOB Export Price
where

$F_{jj}$ = the domestic price of product j. A product produced and consumed domestically does not incur costs associated with shipping and barriers to entry. It is therefore assumed to be equal to the average of all FOB export prices for that producing region.

(8) $X_i\cdot = \sum_j X_{ij}$ Demand Restriction

(9) $X\cdot_j = \sum_i X_{ij}$ Supply Restriction

(10) $X_{jj} = X\cdot_j - X_{ij}$ Domestic Demand
where $i = j$.

The system is simultaneous and was estimated with nonlinear two-stage least squares. The parameters, while biased, are consistent. A simultaneous estimation technique was used as it is likely, when estimating demand and supply equations in international trade research, that the use of ordinary least squares would yield biased and inconsistent results (Goldstein and Khan).

Statistics regarding the fit and performance of the model indicate that, in general, the model does a good job in capturing the economic forces involved in international fresh vegetable trade. The Durbin Watson statistics are usually close to two, indicating little serial correlation and a well specified model. Due to the highly restrictive, nonlinear nature of the model, R-square statistics are not valid for statistical tests. For this reason, root mean square percent errors and Theil Inequality Coefficients were also used to evaluate the performance of the fresh vegetable trade model. They indicate that, in general, the model predicts the observed data points well and captures turning points in the data.

## PARAMETER RESULTS AND THEIR IMPLICATIONS

Tables 7.5 to 7.7 present the parameter results for each region for three of the functional relationships. In this section the more crucial results with respect to Western Hemisphere participation in world vegetable trade will be discussed for market demands, product demands, and export supplies.

Looking at the market demands, all three Western Hemisphere regions have inelastic price responses, with Canada's likely being statistically insignificant. There are two statistically valid income parameters, those for Latin America and Canada. Latin America's is inelastic while that for Canada is elastic and negative. This could indicate that in Canada fresh vegetables are an inferior good. However, it probably indicates that the model was not performing as well as it could in this particular instance. If reduced forms could be calculated, it is likely that this parameter would be positive. Population results are insignificant for both Latin America and the United States while significant and highly elastic for Canada.

Table 7.5. Market Demand Parameters and t-Statistics

| | | $\delta(i0)$ | $\delta(i1)$ | $\delta(i2)$ | $\delta(i3)$ |
|---|---|---|---|---|---|
| i = 1 | Latin America | 17.019 (9.68) | -0.455 (-1.58) | 0.430 (2.15) | -0.234 (-.65) |
| i = 2 | U.S. | 15.144 (1.76) | -0.431 (-1.04) | 0.642 (.85) | -0.528 (-.20) |
| i = 3 | Canada | 3.179 (1.15) | 0.117 (.71) | -1.115 (-2.08) | 5.552 (3.27) |
| i = 4 | E.E.C. | 14.205 (5.16) | -0.722 (-1.64) | 0.153 (.78) | 0.272 (.86) |
| i = 5 | Middle East | 48.222 (.55) | -1.781 (-.66) | 3.119 (.55) | -9.48 (-.41) |
| i = 6 | Far East | 14.506 (5.28) | 0.204 (1.89) | -0.023 (-.21) | 0.800 (1.68) |
| i = 7 | Africa | 12.475 (22.15) | 0.011 (.43) | -0.033 (-.39) | 1.009 (6.87) |
| i = 8 | Non-E.E.C. W. Europe | 11.417 (4.55) | -0.113 (-1.06) | 0.045 (.51) | 1.027 (2.45) |

NOTE(S): $LogX(i.) = log\delta(i0) + \delta(i1)logP(i.) + \delta(i2)$ $logGDP(i) + \delta(i3)logPOP(i.)$. Degrees of freedom for each of these equations is 17.

The product demand parameters lend insight into the forces operating between regions to drive their trade. The largest import market in the world, the EEC, has very distinct characteristics in its demands for Western Hemisphere products. Its price parameter for U.S. vegetables is highly elastic; as

Table 7.6. Product Demand Parameters and t-Statistics

| Regions | | ——Partner Regions—— | | | | | | | |
|---|---|---|---|---|---|---|---|---|---|
| | | Latin America | U.S. | Canada | EEC | Middle East | Far East | Africa | Non-EEC W. Europe |
| Latin America | A | . | . | 1.810 | 0.481 | 0.067 | -2.242 | -0.989 | -1.173 |
| | | (.) | (.) | (.90) | (.47) | (.03) | (-1.27) | (-.65) | (-1.37) |
| | B | . | . | 1.029 | 2.577 | 7.127 | 0.848 | 1.431 | 2.691 |
| | | (.) | (.) | (.28) | (1.68) | (1.20) | (.38) | (.75) | (4.28) |
| U.S. | A | -0.620 | . | . | -0.086 | -1.654 | -1.285 | -0.481 | -2.158 |
| | | (-1.98) | (.) | (.) | (-.55) | (-2.06) | (-2.90) | (-.81) | (-1.44) |
| | B | 4.131 | . | . | -0.098 | 9.571 | 3.271 | 2.279 | -0.991 |
| | | (8.01) | (.) | (.) | (-.16) | (4.83) | (2.63) | (2.37) | (-.62) |
| Canada | A | -0.537 | -0.523 | . | . | -0.761 | -0.508 | 1.058 | -0.573 |
| | | (-3.69) | (-5.58) | (.) | (.) | (-.51) | (-.56) | (.67) | (-1.10) |
| | B | 0.416 | 1.162 | . | . | 7.746 | 2.079 | -3.239 | -1.627 |
| | | (1.17) | (9.72) | (.) | (.) | (3.35) | (2.40) | (-1.14) | (-1.35) |
| E.E.C. | A | -0.280 | -4.079 | 3.823 | . | . | -3.921 | -0.400 | 1.851 |
| | | (-.36) | (-2.28) | (1.83) | (.) | (.) | (-14.98) | (-.49) | (2.53) |
| | B | -3.240 | 0.393 | .811 | . | . | -0.838 | -0.005 | -0.140 |
| | | (-1.57) | (.16) | (.13) | (.) | (.) | (-.63) | (-.01) | (-.11) |
| Middle East | A | 1.517 | -1.841 | -0.849 | -2.131 | . | . | -2.476 | -2.156 |
| | | (.74) | (-1.84) | (-.69) | (-6.41) | (.) | (.) | (-1.90) | (-3.38) |
| | B | 0.858 | 1.077 | 1.786 | 1.808 | . | . | 0.860 | 0.739 |
| | | (.45) | (2.75) | (3.84) | (8.95) | (.) | (.) | (2.43) | (4.49) |
| Far East | A | -0.798 | 0.955 | -3.634 | -1.265 | -2.888 | . | . | -0.005 |
| | | (-.53) | (.70) | (-1.24) | (-2.29) | (-3.18) | (.) | (.) | (1.24) |
| | B | 2.135 | 4.716 | 11.952 | 3.285 | -2.136 | . | . | 4.742 |
| | | (.37) | (3.77) | (2.42) | (3.77) | (-.58) | (.) | (.) | (1.29) |
| Africa | A | -1.264 | -2.567 | -1.928 | -1.550 | 0.472 | -1.277 | . | . |
| | | (-.78) | (-3.71) | (-2.57) | (-1.06) | (.92) | (-1.11) | (.) | (.) |
| | B | 15.830 | 3.683 | 4.961 | 2.391 | 7.234 | 3.142 | . | . |
| | | (7.43) | (2.53) | (2.18) | (3.61) | (8.20) | (1.70) | (.) | (.) |
| Non-EEC W. Europe | A | . | -5.348 | 3.706 | 2.704 | -3.484 | -0.070 | -4.773 | . |
| | | (.) | (-1.57) | (5.23) | (3.08) | (-7.55) | (-.16) | (-4.12) | (.) |
| | B | . | 1.529 | 0.353 | -0.106 | 3.729 | -7.623 | 6.293 | . |
| | | (.) | (.31) | (.14) | (-.16) | (1.68) | (-1.61) | (1.31) | (.) |

NOTE(S): A = Relative price parameter; B = Market size parameter. Statistical model is $logX(ij) = log\phi(0ij) + \phi(1ij)logP(ij) - \phi(1ij)logP(i\cdot) + \phi(2ij)logX(i\cdot)$. Degrees of freedom for each of these equtions is 18.

the price of U.S. vegetables drops, EEC demand for this product rises by four times the amount of the decrease. This is empirical evidence that the CAP of the EEC has hurt U.S. exports. The CAP raises the price in the EEC of U.S. vegetables above the world price, causing, according to these results, a strong drop in demand. Recall that the growth in U.S. exports of fresh vegetables was below the world average. If trade negotiations could lower the tariff levels imposed by the CAP, it is possible that U.S. exports would increase dramatically.

Other significant results with respect to the EEC include a negative,

Table 7.7. Export Supply Parameters and t-Statistics

| | | $\rho(0j)$ | $\rho(1j)$ | $\rho(2j)$ |
|---|---|---|---|---|
| i = 1 | Latin America | -30.476<br>(-3.05) | 0.427<br>(3.11) | 2.478<br>(4.50) |
| i = 2 | U.S. | 31.663<br>(1.03) | 1.504<br>(1.63) | -0.901<br>(-.53) |
| i = 3 | Canada | 0.185<br>(.04) | 0.192<br>(2.18) | 0.835<br>(2.93) |
| i = 4 | EEC | 5.407<br>(.62) | 0.156<br>(2.11) | 0.472<br>(.97) |
| i = 5 | Middle East | 3.159<br>(1.15) | 0.015<br>(.12) | 0.567<br>(3.71) |
| i = 6 | Far East | -590.36<br>(-1.69) | -5.420<br>(-1.18) | 30.474<br>(1.74) |
| i = 7 | Africa | 52.710<br>(5.20) | 0.243<br>(1.52) | -2.136<br>(-3.93) |
| i = 8 | Non-EEC W. Europe | 11.417<br>(.43) | -0.123<br>(8.88) | 0.045<br>(1.28) |

NOTE(S): Statistical model is: $log[X(.j) - X(j\ j)] = logp(0_j) + p(1_j)log(Y._j) + p(2_j)logX(i_j)$
Degrees of freedom for each of these equations is 18.

elastic market size parameter for Latin American vegetables. As the EEC market for fresh vegetables grows, evidence indicates that its demand for Latin American vegetables will decline. The EEC price parameter for Canadian vegetables is positive and highly elastic, indicating that this product is demanded for its quality.

The Middle East, Far East, and Africa are three of the fastest growing markets for fresh vegetables. Their market size parameters indicate, with a few exceptions, that as these markets grow, their demands for Latin American, U.S., and Canadian fresh vegetables will grow. The price parameters, particularly for Africa, are also elastic. As the prices of Western Hemisphere vegetables to Africa, and to some extent the Middle East and Far East, fall, demand for these products will grow. Technological changes and improvements in infrastructure are operating to lower prices. Thus, two forces are in motion to increase Middle Eastern, Far Eastern, and African demands for Western Hemisphere vegetables, increases in market size and declines in prices.

Results of particular importance regarding Western Hemisphere relations among themselves include the United States having an inelastic price relationship with Latin American vegetables but a positive and very elastic market size parameter. As the U.S. market for fresh vegetables grows, its demand for Latin American vegetables will grow. Canada has inelastic price responses to both Latin American and U.S. vegetables and an inelastic market size response to Latin America. However, its market size response to U.S. vegetables is elastic; as the Canadian market grows, its demand for U.S. vegetables will grow.

Significant results for the Western Hemisphere as regards the export supply relationship include an elastic average export price response for the U.S. As the average export price of U.S. vegetables increases, this region's exports of fresh vegetables will increase. This possibly indicates that the U.S. exports a high quality product; as the price rises to match its value perceived domestically, the amount supplied for export rises. Latin America shows a very elastic response with respect to total production; as production in that region rises, the amount it supplies for export will rise.

## SIMULATIONS ON PRODUCT PRICES

Simulations were carried out on the world vegetable system in which the estimated parameters were used to simulate the effects of product price changes on levels of product demands. The simulations were done on an equation by equation basis. Impacts on the entire system with a change in an explanatory variable in one of the equations were not measured. The reason for this approach is that the system is very large and highly nonlinear. It was not possible, with current procedures and options within SAS, to simulate this system in a simultaneous system.

Because the simulations were carried out strictly on an equation-by-equation basis, where actually all the variables are determined simultaneously, the impacts measured are only partial effects. To capture the total effects, the simulations would have to be carried out taking account of the effects on the whole system. This is because a change in an independent variable in one equation would affect all dependent variables in the trade system.

Selected product demands were simulated with the product prices varied from 80 to 120% of their 1982 levels. Changes in tariff or nontariff barriers could cause product prices to vary by this amount, as well as exchange rate fluctuations and/or technological changes and improvements in infrastructure, lowering shipping costs. This set of scenarios yields useful information to policymakers attempting to understand the impacts of current monetary and trade policies of their own governments and those of their trading partners. It could also help them formulate new policies in these realms designed to maximize the gains to their countries from participation in fresh vegetable trade.

The selection of trade flows for the simulation was based on characteristics of Western Hemisphere vegetable trade. Latin America essentially does not use tariffs as a barrier to fresh vegetable entry, and hence its demands for different products were not simulated, as the main interest in this section is the impact of changes in tariff levels. U.S. demand for Canadian vegetables was not simulated as this demand parameter was not estimated due to redundancy in the econometric system. EEC demands for all three Western Hemisphere vegetables with price changes were simulated. Middle Eastern and African demands for U.S. vegetables were simulated, not to measure the effects of tariff changes, but to measure the effects of price decreases due to declines in shipping costs. These regions' demands for Latin American and Canadian vegetables were not simulated as the quantities moving between these regions were so small that the parameter estimates are probably meaningless. Results of the simulations are presented in Table 7.8.

U.S. demand for Latin American vegetables increases 14% with a price decrease of 20%, whereas its demand for EEC vegetables increases very moderately with price decreases. If the U.S. lowers its tariffs on Latin American vegetables, or if Latin American currencies drop in value relative to the U.S. dollar, demand for Latin American vegetables in the U.S. market will increase moderately. However, U.S. demand for EEC vegetables will only increase

Table 7.8. Product Demand Simulations: Product Prices Varied

| % 1982 Product Price | Demanding Region | U.S. | | Canada | | EEC | | | Middle East | | Africa |
|---|---|---|---|---|---|---|---|---|---|---|---|
| | Supplying Region | Latin America | EEC | U.S. | Latin America | U.S. | Latin America | Canada | EEC | U.S. | U.S. |
| 80 | | 1.148 | 1.019 | 1.124 | 1.127 | 2.485 | 1.064 | 0.426 | 1.609 | 1.508 | 1.773 |
| 90 | | 1.068 | 1.009 | 1.057 | 1.058 | 1.537 | 1.030 | 0.668 | 1.252 | 1.214 | 1.311 |
| 100 | | 1.000 | 1.000 | 1.000 | 1.000 | 1.000 | 1.000 | 1.000 | 1.000 | 1.000 | 1.000 |
| 110 | | 0.943 | 0.992 | 0.951 | 0.950 | 0.678 | 0.974 | 1.440 | 0.816 | 0.839 | 0.783 |
| 120 | | 0.893 | 0.984 | 0.909 | 0.907 | 0.475 | 0.950 | 2.008 | 0.678 | 0.715 | 0.626 |

slightly with a lowering of tariff barriers. This simulation result, together with the statistically insignificant parameter estimates on the U.S. demand for EEC vegetables, suggests that market forces do not govern U.S. imports of EEC vegetables. Evidence seems to indicate that trade agreements, and not prices, regulate U.S. imports of EEC vegetables.

Canada's demand for Latin American and U.S. vegetables varies almost identically, in terms of percentage change, with price changes. With a 20% drop in price, Canada's demand for both Latin American and U.S. vegetables increases 12%.

EEC demands for Western Hemisphere vegetables show wide variation vis-à-vis the product involved. Its demand for Latin American vegetables shows only a 6% increase with a 20% decrease in price, whereas that for Canada drops almost 60%. These results indicate that Canadian vegetables are demanded by the EEC for their quality, or that the model is not performing well and this result of a positive price relationship is an inaccurate representation of the situation under scrutiny. EEC demand for U.S. vegetables increases dramatically with a price drop, increasing by 250% with a 20% change in price. If trade negotiations could lower the CAP tariffs on U.S. vegetables, EEC demand for this product would increase significantly. This would help the United States participate more fully in international vegetable trade, as the EEC is the largest import market in the world.

Middle Eastern and African demands for U.S. vegetables will increase significantly with price decreases; more than 50% with a 20% decrease in the price. Lowering of transportation and handling costs and improvements in infrastructure are operating to lower the costs of shipping between these regions and the Western Hemisphere.

## SUMMARY

World trade in fresh vegetables quadrupled between 1962 and 1982. The Western Hemisphere regions of Latin America, the United States, and Canada participated in this growth, although on neither the import nor the export side did that growth quadruple. Hence these regions lag somewhat behind world growth in this trade.

The American regions trade primarily among themselves; however, there are economic forces operating to change that pattern. Empirical evidence indicates that the CAP of the EEC hinders U.S. exports to that market, which is the largest vegetable market in the world. If trade negotiations can lower the CAP tariff on U.S. vegetables, its exports to the EEC will increase.

The Third World markets of the Middle East, Far East, and Africa, while small in absolute quantities, show strong growth in terms of imports. Empirical results indicate that as these markets grow and as prices to them of American vegetables decline, Western Hemisphere exports to those regions will increase.

## NOTES

1. The derivation is beyond the scope of this article. The interested reader is referred to work contained in Sparks.

## REFERENCES

Armington, P.S. "A Theory of Demand for Products Distinguished by Place of Production." *IMF Staff Papers*. 16(1969):159-177.

Goldstein, Morris, and Mohsin S. Khan. "The Supply and Demand for Exports: A Simultaneous Approach." *The Review of Economics and Statistics*, 60(1970):275-285.

Sparks, Amy Larsen. "A Simultaneous Econometric Model of World Vegetable Trade: Implications for Market Development." Unpublished Ph.D. dissertation, University of Florida, 1987.

United Nations Standard International Trade Classification, (SITC), revised. Statistical Papers Series M, No. 34, New York, 1961.

# 8

# A CONCEPTUAL ANALYSIS OF VEGETABLE TRADE

Rigoberto A. Lopez and Emilio Pagoulatos
*University of Connecticut*

## INTRODUCTION

The volume of international trade in vegetables has been growing more rapidly than the volume of world vegetable production since the early 1960s. Fresh vegetable trade, in particular, has increased fourfold since 1962 while production has increased 40% over the same time period (Sparks). The trend towards internationalization of the vegetable sector has paralleled the increased integration of the grain and oilseed sectors in the world economy (MacKintosh).

In spite of ample evidence of the substantial increase in world trade of vegetables and the role of vegetables as a potential source of income for small farmers as well as of well-balanced nutrition (Kelly and Andrew), little empirical work has been done on vegetable trade. The objective of this paper is to lay down some of the key issues important for future empirical work in this area, with special reference to the vegetable industry in the Western Hemisphere.

## WORLD VEGETABLE TRADE

Vegetables can be supplied in fresh or processed form. Tables 8.1 and 8.2 present the world trade flows for fresh (SITC=054) and processed (SITC=055) vegetables, respectively. In 1984, the most recent year for which world trade matrix data were readily available, the value of world trade in fresh vegetables was nearly three times (2.76) as large as that in processed vegetables. The European Economic Community (EEC) was the largest importer and exporter of fresh vegetables, with most of its trade taking place among the Community's partners. The United States, Japan, countries classified as

Table 8.1. World Trade Matrix for Fresh Vegetables, U.S. $million, 1984

| Exporting Region | Importing Region | | | | | | | | | |
|---|---|---|---|---|---|---|---|---|---|---|
| | CAN | USA | MX | CC | SA | EC12 | MFE | JP | ROW | Total Exports |
| Canada (CAN) | 0 | 102.4 | .1 | 24.2 | 22.0 | 34.5 | 5.9 | 8.1 | 26.4 | 223.4 |
| USA | 254.4 | 0 | 15.7 | 34.5 | 64.2 | 95.7 | 46.4 | 84.8 | 20.1 | 615.8 |
| Mexico (MX) | 21.8 | 442.9 | 0 | 5.8 | 19.0 | 40.5 | NA | 9.7 | .6 | 515.4 |
| C. America/ Carib.(CC) | 25.1 | 496.2 | NA | 33.9 | .3 | 42.7 | .1 | NA | .7 | 599.0 |
| S. America(SA) | 1.1 | 12.2 | NA | 4.1 | 44.7 | 38.7 | 2.9 | 2.0 | .7 | 106.3 |
| European Com.(EC12) | 10.3 | 65.1 | 1.3 | 32.9 | 18.6 | 3,021.3 | 87.9 | 19.7 | 396.5 | 3,653.2 |
| Middle/Far East(MFE) | 3.2 | 16.4 | NA | 1.6 | .6 | 854.5 | 198.7 | 345.6 | 20.9 | 1,441.5 |
| Japan(JP) | .1 | 4.3 | NA | n | .1 | .5 | 15.5 | 0 | .5 | 21.0 |
| Others(ROW) | 2.0 | 15.0 | 1.3 | .1 | .7 | 365.5 | 48.5 | 168.3 | 74.8 | 680.8 |
| Total Imports | 318.0 | 1,154.7 | 18.4 | 137.1 | 170.2 | 4,493.8 | 405.8 | 638.3 | 545.0 | 7,881.2 |

SOURCE: Computed from United Nations, *1984 Commodity Trade Statistics Yearbook*, and *1984 Supplement to the World Trade Annual*, Vols. I-IV.
NOTE(S): Totals may not add up exactly due to rounding errors. An "n" indicates that the reported figure was less than $50,000 (.05 million). An "NA" indicates lack of reporting or zero trade.

"Rest of the World" (ROW), Middle/Far Eastern Countries, and Canada were the other major world importers. Along with the EEC, other major exporters included Middle/Far Eastern countries, ROW, the United States, Central America and Caribbean countries, and Mexico.

The pattern of trade in processed vegetables was similar to that of fresh vegetables, with the EEC being the dominant importer and exporter. Other important importing regions included the United States, ROW, Middle/Far Eastern countries, Japan, and Canada. The Middle/Far Eastern countries, ROW, the United States, and Japan were the world's largest exporters of processed vegetables, besides the EEC.

Table 8.2. World Trade Matrix for Processed Vegetables, U.S. $million, 1984

| Exporting Region | Importing Region | | | | | | | | | |
|---|---|---|---|---|---|---|---|---|---|---|
| | CAN | USA | MX | CC | SA | EC12 | MFE | JP | ROW | Total Exports |
| Canada (CAN) | 0 | 4.3 | NA | 0.7 | .1 | 13.6 | 1.5 | 1.0 | 5.8 | 26.9 |
| USA | 26.6 | 0 | .7 | 9.7 | 3.4 | 25.0 | 9.5 | 18.5 | 15.8 | 112.3 |
| Mexico(MX) | 1.7 | 32.7 | 0 | .1 | .1 | 6.2 | .1 | .1 | 4.9 | 45.9 |
| C.America/ Carib.(CC) | 0.5 | 9.9 | NA | 1.1 | .1 | .3 | NA | .1 | n | 12.1 |
| S.America(SA) | 3.6 | 7.9 | NA | n | .8 | 10.4 | NA | 2.7 | 2.0 | 27.4 |
| European Com.(EC12) | 36.7 | 252.3 | NA | 25.2 | 1.2 | 1,105.3 | 116.4 | 11.9 | 224.2 | 1,772.4 |
| Middle/Far East(MFE) | 17.1 | 194.6 | NA | .1 | .4 | 97.0 | 57.6 | 107.8 | 40.5 | 515.1 |
| Japan(JP) | 2.3 | 15.6 | NA | .1 | 0.9 | 1.0 | 80.7 | 0 | 1.2 | 101.8 |
| Others(ROW) | 14.3 | 69.6 | NA | .5 | .1 | 106.1 | 2.9 | 5.6 | 30.9 | 233.5 |
| Total Imports | 102.7 | 586.9 | .7 | 37.6 | 7.3 | 1,367.9 | 267.8 | 147.6 | 329.0 | 2,847.6 |

SOURCE: Computed from United Nations, *1984 Commodity Trade Statistics Yearbook*, and *1984 Supplement to the World Trade Annual,* Vols. I-IV.
NOTE(S): Totals may not add up exactly due to rounding errors. An "n" indicates that the reported figure was less than $50,000 (.05 million). An "NA" indicates lack of reporting or zero trade.

Table 8.3 presents an overview of the world trade shifts among major trading regions in fresh vegetables from 1962 to 1982. The most striking changes involve the emergence of Asia as the world's major net exporter of fresh vegetables and the increasingly dominant role of the EEC as the world's largest net importer. The United States and the Middle East continue as important net exporters of fresh vegetables, while Canada and other (non-EEC) Europe became net exporters in 1982 from being net importers in 1962. Finally, Latin America and Africa changed to net importers in 1982 from a net exporting position in 1962.

Table 8.3 also contains data on broad indicators of *export propensity* (exports relative to domestic production) and *import penetration* (imports rel-

Table 8.3. World Trade in Fresh Vegetables

| Country Blocks: | 1962 | | | 1982 | | |
|---|---|---|---|---|---|---|
| | Net Trade (1,000 MT) | Exports as % of Output | Imports as % of App. Cons. | Net Trade (1,000 MT) | Exports as % of Output | Imports as % of App. Cons. |
| Latin America | 36.5 | .530 | .450 | -31.7 | .280 | .320 |
| U.S.A. | 364.5 | 2.14 | 1.00 | 317.2 | 3.13 | 2.47 |
| Canada | -212.2 | 7.36 | 12.76 | 4.2 | 11.67 | 11.61 |
| Europe | -929.5 | 1.46 | 2.32 | -9,059.2 | 2.53 | 10.76 |
| EEC | -53.5 | NA | NA | -9,374.4 | NA | NA |
| Other Europe | -876.1 | NA | NA | 315.2 | NA | NA |
| Middle East | 126.7 | 1.72 | .520 | 207.2 | .880 | .430 |
| Asia | -33.2 | .014 | .025 | 7,192.6 | 1.98 | .140 |
| Africa | 546.3 | 1.13 | .205 | -128.3 | .375 | .503 |

SOURCE: A.H. Sparks, *A Simultaneous Econometric Model of World Vegetable Trade: Implications for Market Development.* Ph.D. Dissertation, Univ. of Florida, 1987.
NOTE(S): Net Trade = Exports (X) - Imports (M) in 1,000 MT. Exports as a % of Output = Exports (X)/Output (0) x 100. Imports as a % of apparent consumption = Imports (M)/Apparent Consumption (0-X+M) x 100.

ative to domestic production). Although the behavior of these indices is difficult to interpret for such large country and commodity aggregates, it is still possible to draw some general patterns. One observes an increase in the export propensity index for the United States, Canada, Europe, and Asia, while the index declined for Latin America, the Middle East, and Africa over the 1962-82 period. In the case of import penetration, one observes a general increase for the United States, Europe, Asia, and Africa, and a decline for the remaining regional groups. Generally speaking, the available evidence strongly suggests that the period between 1962 and 1982 was one of both greater export propensity and import penetration of vegetable markets worldwide.

The picture that emerges after 1982, particularly in the Western Hemisphere, is dominated by two events. First is the sharp increase of the U.S. dollar in international markets between 1980 and 1985, leading to a massive U.S. trade deficit and a correspondingly large inflow of capital. The second major event is the growth of the international, and particularly Latin American, debt crisis. The latter event led to a period of severe adjustment for Latin America associated with attempts to increase exports and cut back on imports. Overall, vegetable trade in the Western Hemisphere appears to have been profoundly influenced by these two events during the 1980s (General Accounting Office).

Several facts emerge from the limited available evidence on trade patterns in the area. First, Canada continued as a major net importer of vegetables in the Western Hemisphere, while Mexico increased its presence as a major exporter of vegetables. The United States, in turn, saw a reversal in its vegetable trade balance from a surplus in the early 1980s to a $500 million deficit in 1986. Furthermore, it appears that fresh and frozen vegetable trade has grown more rapidly than processed vegetable trade during the 1980s (General Accounting Office).

The performance of other Western Hemisphere countries in the vegetable trade market has been rather mixed during the period of 1962 to 1982. For example, Venezuela and Chile have been successfully exporting potatoes, tomatoes, and dry beans. In Central America and the Caribbean, notable exporters have been Guatemala (broccoli, cauliflower, and snow peas), the Dominican Republic, and Jamaica (cucumbers and sweet peppers). Other countries in the area have been less successful in diversifying their agricultural export sector beyond their sugar and banana monocultures.

Unquestionably, a permanent solution to Latin America's current debt crisis and the resumption of sustained economic growth will require a further strengthening of the external sector's capacity as a source of foreign exchange earnings. The agricultural economy, the fruit and vegetable sector in particular, contains the promise of enhanced exports from these countries. However, a number of constraints to expanding trade of vegetable crops in the Western Hemisphere may prove critical to this challenge. The following section identifies some of these constraints by examining the nature and characteristics of vegetable trade in order to assess the potential for expanded trade in these products.

## CONSTRAINTS AND OPPORTUNITIES

A number of factors affect the volume and pattern of world vegetable trade. These factors generally focus on differences in supply and demand conditions among countries. They also include the role of public policies that may enhance or reduce trade as well a natural impediments to trade such as the cost of freight and insurance, especially for perishable products.

### Supply Factors

Differences in supply are captured in the various bases of comparative cost advantages in the production of particular commodities. Several models of trade exist that attribute such comparative cost differences to differences in technology and in endowments of factors of production (land, labor, capital).

In general, the wide range of vegetable species and cultivars available, the wide variation in climatic conditions, and land and water availability even within the largest or smallest country in the Western Hemisphere suggest that the availability of natural resources is *not* an important constraint to the production and trade of vegetables (Kelly and Andrew).

The seasonality in production and the availability of skilled labor and capital, however, appear to be important factors in vegetable trade. While seasonal availability can be interpreted as a constraining factor, it can also provide opportunities associated with "export windows" to countries with seasonal deficits. Coordination of supply sources with different production seasons may provide great benefits to supply, retail, and buying institutions year-round (Steele). Vegetable crops have specific research needs associated with different varieties, resistance to pests and diseases, etc., that require trained staff for research and technical support. Furthermore, expansion of vegetable exports by countries in the Western Hemisphere is predicated on either the presence of a local entrepreneurial class or on the ready availability of foreign investment. As a case in point, U.S. investment has been critical to the expansion of Mexico's vegetable production and exports (Cook and Amon). This may prove to be a constraint in enhancing exports in the postdebt crisis environment in the area.

A final supply factor of importance to the future competitiveness of the Western Hemisphere vegetable sector is technological change and innovation. Technological change improves productivity and international competitiveness by either reducing production costs of existing products or by introducing new or modified products. Improved vegetable technology often results in varieties that withstand transport better and are more uniform in quality and appearance (Sarris). Plant genetics and biotechnology may provide opportunities for new product development crucial in targeting vegetable crops to specific market niches (Carter and Nuckton). Once scientists are able to control desirable characteristics of vegetables, the opportunity for marketing branded products is vast.

## Demand Factors

The role of demand in determining international trade is emphasized in models that concentrate on the importance of consumer preferences and differentiated products. A steady increase in the demand for vegetables in the Western Hemisphere is an important prerequisite for an increase in trade in the area. Such an opportunity is offered by recent demographic shifts toward an older population in the United States, changing life-styles such as eating away from home, and increased diet, nutrition, and health concerns, especially in the United States and Canada. Chronic degenerative diseases–like cardiovascular diseases, cancer, and diabetes–are responsible for 80% of the deaths in the United States. To reduce the risk of these diseases, the National Academy of Sciences' Committee on Diet, Nutrition, and Cancer recommended, in 1982, the reduction of fat intake and an increase in the consumption of fruits, vegetables, and whole-grained cereals.

Recent sociodemographic changes have increased the relative importance of vegetable consumption expenditures (Blaylock and Smallwood). Increased income and life-style changes, fostering an increasing demand for variety, quality, and convenience, favor domestic and foreign vegetable trade, particularly when sales are tailored to specific needs and preferences of individual markets (Carter and Nuckton).

Product quality and other physical characteristics (such as taste and appearance) and product differentiation are important demand factors in vegetable trade. This trade is composed of many products that are distinguishable not only in kind (e.g., tomatoes vs. carrots) and stage of processing (e.g., fresh vs. processed) but also in terms of quality, season of production, and country of origin. One can safely say that vegetables are differentiated commodities in the eyes of consumers, and that quality changes, marketing strategies, and interproduct substitution play an important role in world markets.

One implication of product quality and differentiation is to provide opportunities for the development of export niches for vegetable crops. Quality and safety concerns associated with chemicals and pesticide residues or food irradiation, however, represent a constraint to vegetable trade in the future (Gahr). A similar obstacle to trade may be associated with the quality standards and grades that are an integral part of many vegetable marketing orders in the United States.

Another implication of product differentiation is that it results in the simultaneous export and import of similar products, a phenomenon known as two-way trade or intraindustry trade. In other words, local producers may export to satisfy segments of foreign demand and at the same time face import competition in some parts of the domestic market.

In addition to quality, consumers will likely become more concerned with possible health risks of pesticide and chemical residues in foods, particularly fruits and vegetables. Pesticide residue has been shown to be one of the leading health concerns of U.S. consumers (van Ranvenswaay). A 1985 report of the National Academy of Sciences singled out vegetables as the leading carrier of nitrogen residues which reduce the oxygen-carrying capacity of the blood (Doyle). The movement towards pesticide-free vegetables is gaining momentum (Figueroa).

## Government Policies

The role of governments in providing protection from imports or incentives to local production or exports represents an artificial barrier to vegetable trade. Nominal tariffs for fresh and processed vegetables are rather low in major industrial country markets as evidenced by the barriers listed in Table 8.4. Tariffs for frozen and processed vegetables tend to be higher than those for fresh vegetables. The actual tariff paid by imports from developing countries may be lower than those in Table 8.4 because of the preferential treatment afforded to these countries by the Generalized System of Preferences, the Lome and Yaounde Conventions, and the Caribbean Basin Initiative.

As tariffs have declined in importance in recent years, attention has increasingly focused on various nontariff measures that countries utilize to change their trade patterns. These measures have become both more vis-

Table 8.4. Nominal Tariffs Affecting Vegetable Exports in Major Industrial Country Markets, Percent

| Commodity Group | Canada (M.F.N.) | U.S.A. (M.F.N.) | Japan | EEC |
|---|---|---|---|---|
| Fresh Vegetables: | | | | |
| Asparagus | 5.5 cts/lb. (no<15%)(*15.0) | 25.0 | | |
| Cucumbers | 2.25 cts/lb. (no<15%)(*15.0) | 3.0 cts/lb (*11.2) | | |
| Onions | 2.5 cts/lb. (no<12.5%)(*12.5) | 1.75 cts/lb (11.4) | 10.0 | 12.0 |
| Peppers | 2 cts/lb. (no<10%)(*10.0) | 25.0 cts/lb (*5.7) | | |
| Potatoes | 35.0 cts/100 lb. (*2.9) | 35.0 cts/100 lb (*3.9) | 5.0 | 7.0 |
| Tomatoes | 2.5 cts/lb (no<15%)(*15.0) | 2.1 cts/lb. (*9.1) | | |
| Frozen Vegetables: | | | 10.0 | 18.0 |
| Asparagus | 22.5 | 25.0 | | |
| Broccoli | 20.0 | 17.5 | | |
| Brussels sprouts | 20.0 | 25.0 | | |
| Cauliflower | 20.0 | 17.5 | | |
| Mushrooms | 15.0 | 3.2 cts/lb. + 10% | | |
| Potatoes | 10.0 | 10.0 | | |
| Dried Vegetables: | | | | 16.0 |
| Beans | 1.5 cts/lb. | 0.75 ct/lb. | 10.0 | |
| Peas | Free | 0.4 ct/lb. | 10.0 | |
| Canned Vegetables: | | | | |
| Asparagus | 22.5 | 17.5 | 16.0 | 22.0 |
| Peas | | | 20.0 | 24.0 |
| Corn | 12.5 | 12.5 | 17.5 | 8.0 + VC |
| Tomatoes | 13.6 | 14.7 | | |
| Mushrooms | 20.0 | 3.2 cts/lb. + 10% | | |

SOURCE: Agriculture Canada, *Tariffs on Selected Agricultural Products*, June, 1980.
NOTE(S): An asterisk (*) denotes ad valorem equivalent computed as specific tariff as a percent of 1985 import unit value. VC = variable component.

ible, as a result of lower tariffs on vegetable trade, and more widespread, as governments have found them to be a convenient replacement to tariffs (Baldwin). A summary of the major nontariff barriers affecting vegetable exports in developed country markets is presented in Table 8.5. In addition to the more traditional quantitative restrictions (import quotas), international trade of vegetables is constrained by a bewildering array of other government measures that range from import licensing and compliance with health, sanitary, and technical standards to various minimum price and variable levy

Table 8.5. Nontariff Measures Affecting Vegetable Exports in Major Industrial Country Markets

| Country | Potat.,Tomat. Onions | Veg. Frozen | Veg. Prsvd. | Veg.Prsvd. in Brine | Veg.Prsvd. NES | Veg. Dried | Beans, Peas |
|---|---|---|---|---|---|---|---|
| Australia | H | | | | | H | H |
| Austria | *Q/*D | | | | *V | | |
| Canada | | | | | | | |
| EEC | *D/*P | | | | | | |
| | *V/*F | *D | *D/*V | *D | *D | *D | |
| Benelux | *Q/*D | | | *D/F | *F | | |
| Denmark | *Q | *Q | | | | *Q | |
| France | *Q/*D | *Q/*D | | | | *Q/*D | *D/H |
| Germany | *Q | | | | *Q | *Q | |
| Italy | *D | | | | *D | | |
| U.K. | *Q | *Q | | | *Q | *Q | |
| Finland | *D | | *D | | | | *D |
| Japan | *Q/H | H | H | H | H | H | *Q/H |
| New Zealand | *D | | | D | *D | *D | *D |
| Norway | D/P | | | *D | *Q/D | *D | |
| Sweden | D | D | D | D | D | D | D |
| Switzerland | *Q/*D | *D | | *D | *Q/*D | *D | *Q/D |
| | *H | | | | | | *F |
| United States | H | | | | *V | | |

SOURCE: UNCTAD, *Liberalization of Barriers to Trade in Primary and Processed Commodities*, UNCTAD Secretariat, TD/B/C.1/239, January 1983.

NOTE(S): Asterisk(*) before a symbol indicates that the measure affects only part of total imports of a product. Measures shown for individual EEC members are additional to those applied at the level of the EEC. Nontariff measures are defined as:

Q=Quotas, including "voluntary" export restraint.
D=Discretionary import licensing.
H=Health, sanitary, and technical standards.
P=Minimum price systems.
V=Variable levy or charge.
F=Fixed fiscal changes based on CIF import value.

schemes. Moreover, products in their processed forms seem to be relatively more subject to these nontariff measures than the raw forms. The information presented in Table 8.5 also indicates that Canada and the United States are less frequent users of nontariff barriers in vegetable trade as compared to other developed countries.

A number of tariff and nontariff barriers also exist in several Latin American countries that present obstacles to the expansion of vegetable trade within the region. The most common among these barriers are import quotas, restrictive import licensing, and the use of foreign exchange restrictions and multiple exchange rates (U.S. Department of Agriculture).

The developing countries, including Latin America, represent an important source of future demand growth and the most likely markets for food. Their demand, however, will continue to be constrained by their heavy indebtedness. For example, while developing countries reduced food imports by 5% between 1981 and 1985, Chile's imports fell 65%, Argentina's 59%, Brazil's 46%, Mexico's 18%, and Venezuela's 12% (Sanderson and Mehra).

### Product Transfer Factors

A final challenge to enhancing vegetable exports in the Western Hemisphere is associated with the high transfer costs for these products. The cost of international freight and insurance for bulky or perishable items, such as fresh vegetables, may equal or exceed the value of the products shipped (Carter and Nuckton). In addition to the cost of delivering products to the market destination, one needs to consider the cost of handling and storage of vegetable crops that are critical to product quality and acceptability by final consumers. For these reasons, innovation in postharvest technology and development of an efficient export infrastructure can significantly affect the pattern of trade in the area.

## PESTICIDE RESTRICTIONS

This section presents a simple, two-country model to analyze the likely effects of pesticide regulation on vegetable trade. The assumptions of the model are as follows:

1. There are two countries that trade on a single time period.

2. Pesticide use reduces the private production costs, and thus, causes a positive shift of a supply curve. Pesticides benefit the farmer by reducing crop losses due to reduction of pests or substituting for labor

and energy in the case of herbicides. Other societal costs such as environmental damage, health consequences, or subsequent insects or weed resistance are not included.

3. Consumers are unaware of pesticide residue content, and thus, their demand is independent of pesticide content in the commodity in question. Although consumers are concerned about pesticide residues (van Ravenswaay), they generally lack information about which products contain chemical residues or what are the real risks involved. This market failure is often used to justify government intervention.

4. Competitive supply and demand conditions and, for the sake of simplicity, zero transfer costs.

5. There is no other form of government intervention except pesticide residue restrictions.

Figure 8.1 illustrates the effects of pesticide use on vegetable trade between two countries or regions. ES represents the export supply of country I (supply minus demand), and ED represents the import demand of country II (demand minus supply). Trade equilibrium under unrestricted use of pesticide occurs at $(P^p, X^p)$ price-volume point. Next, assume that pesticides are bilaterally banned, thus raising the private cost of production in both countries. The pesticide restriction will shift (ES leftward and ED rightward) as supply in both countries declines (and demand curves are unaffected). The new trade equilibrium occurs at $(P^{np}, X^{np})$, at a higher equilibrium price. Whether the quantity of vegetable trade increases, decreases, or stays the same depends on the relative effects of pesticide restrictions on supplies in both countries. Thus, the realignments of comparative (absolute) advantages under restricted pesticide uses, depend on how various countries or regions adapt to alternative technologies or methods of production, including low-input, labor-intensive, or integrated-pest-management agriculture.

## CONCLUDING REMARKS

This paper briefly examines the pattern of world vegetable trade and provides an assessment of the potential for enhanced exports in the Western Hemisphere. Such potential may be critical for many Latin American countries as they attempt to ease out the current debt crisis through trade expansion. The various constraints and opportunities for greater Western Hemisphere vegetable trade on both supply and demand sides of the market

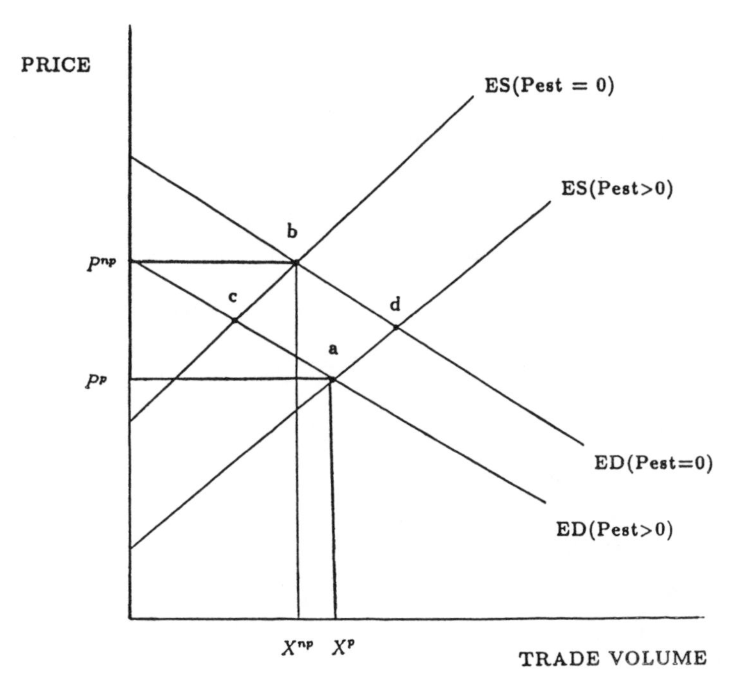


Figure 8.1. Effects of Pesticide Restrictions on Agricultural Trade

are examined, and particular attention is placed on government barriers to such trade. Whether the potential for expanding vegetable trade will be realized in the area will depend on how producers, traders, and governments will respond to the challenges involved.

## REFERENCES

Baldwin, R.E. *Non-Tariff Distortions of International Trade.* Washington, D.C.: The Brookings Institution, 1970.

Blaylock, J.R., and D.M. Smallwood. *U.S. Demand for Food: Household Expenditures, Demographics, and Projections*, Technical bulletin 1713, Washington, D.C.: ERS, USDA, February 1986.

Carter, H.O., and C.F. Nuckton. *Marketing California's Specialty Crops: Worldwide Competition and Constraints.* Davis, Calif.: University of California Agricultural Issues Center, 1987.

Cook, R., and R. Amon. "Competition in the Fresh Vegetable Industry." In *Competition at Home and Abroad.* Report of a 1986-87 study group on Marketing California Specialty Crops: Worldwide Competition and Constraints, Davis, Calif.: University of California Agricultural Issues Center, 1987.

Figueroa, E. Marketing: Agricultural New Frontier. Cornell University, Department of Agricultural Economics, Staff Paper 88-13, 1988.

Gahr, W. "Food Safety and Quality: A Research Agenda for Competing in the World Marketplace." In *Consumer Demands in the Marketplace: Public Policies Related to Food Safety, Quality, and Human Health,* K.L. Clancy, ed. Washington, D.C.: National Center for Food and Agricultural Policy, Resources for the Future, 1988.

General Accounting Office, *Agricultural Trade: Trends in Imports of Fruits, Vegetables, and Other Agricultural Products.* Washington, D.C.: U.S. GAO, RCED-87-177FS, September 29, 1987.

Kelly, J.F., and C.O. Andrew. "A Conceptual Model of International Trade for Vegetables." *The Journal of the Australian Institute of Agricultural Science,* (1979):44-49.

MacKintosh M. "Fruit and Vegetables as an International Commodity." *Food Policy.* 2(1977):277-292.

Sanderson, F.H., and R. Mehra. "Brighter Prospects for Agricultural Trade." In *U.S. Agriculture in a Global Setting: An Agenda for the Future,* M.A. Tutwiler, ed. Washington, D.C.: National Center for Food and Agricultural Policy, Resources for the Future, 1988.

Sarris, A.H. *World Trade in Fruits and Vegetables: Projections for an Enlarged European Community.* For Agric. Econ. Rep. No. 202, Washington, D.C.: ERS, USDA, August 1984.

Sarris, A.H. Empirical Models of International Trade in Agricultural Commodities. In *Imperfect Markets in Agricultural Trade.* A. McCalla and T.E. Josling, eds. Montclair, N.J.: Allanheld, Osmon & Co. Publishers, 1981.

Sparks, A. A Simultaneous Econometric Model of World Vegetable Trade: Implications for Market Development. Ph.D. dissertation, University of Florida, 1987.

Steele, D.V., "Nontraditional Winter Crops Called Caribbean Key to Winning Markets." *The Packer*, January 21, 1987.

USDA, *Trade Policies and Market Opportunities for U.S. Farm Exports.* FAS, USDA, December, 1987.

van Ravenswaay, E. "How Much Food Safety Do Consumers Want? An Analysis of Current Studies and Strategies for Future Research." In *Consumer Demands in the Marketplace: Public Policies Related to Food Safety, Quality, and Human Health*, K.L. Clancy, ed. Washington, D.C.: National Center for Food and Agricultural Policy, Resources for the Future, 1988.

# 9

# TRADE OF HORTICULTURAL PRODUCTS: A CARIBBEAN BASIN PERSPECTIVE

Rodolfo Quiros Guardia
*Interamerican Institute for Cooperation on Agriculture*
*Costa Rica*

## INTRODUCTION

The purpose of this paper is to discuss the policy and research issues that, if addressed, would improve and strengthen the trade ties in the fresh vegetable market between Caribbean Basin (CBI) countries and importing countries of the Northern Hemisphere, such as the United States and EC.

Historically, the exportation of fresh fruit and vegetables by the CBI developed to fill the demand for fresh produce in an off-season market in the United States and EC. But the growth in consumer demand and income was not the only reason for the increase in exports. The off-season market actually developed because there was a concurrent revolution in the information and transportation systems that allowed the CBI countries to fill this growing demand.

When discussing the ways to increase the level of vegetable trade for CBI countries, it is important to keep the relative size of the market in perspective. The amount of fresh fruit and vegetables imported by the United States and EC is very small compared to their domestic production, and this is especially true of vegetables. Hence, growth in the vegetable export market is not big enough to potentially increase the GNP of CBI countries by a significant percentage.

## SPECIFIC POLICY AND RESEARCH ISSUES

The six major issues that require the attention of researchers and policymakers to overcome obstacles in the growth of fresh produce trade include macroeconomic policies, institutional support for an export drive, comparative and competitive advantages, the debt crisis and the development of an infrastructure, market windows and other demand issues, and tariff and nontariff barriers to trade.

## Macroeconomic Policies

Mexico and most CBI and South American countries have utilized the development model based on import substitution of finished, semi-economic finished, and consumer durables over the past 20 years to form their economic development policy decisions. Based on this ideological and policy history, there are a number of built-in biases against the evolution and growth of "non-traditional" export markets, such as the fresh product market. These biases can be found in the institutions through which the physical products are sold and the monetary, credit and capital, markets, particularly those in American countries undergoing structural adjustments.

A few key macroeconomic policies are responsible for restricting trade linkages. First, the structure of external tariffs in most CBI countries is highly protective, and therefore they are in effect antiexport policies which prevent the development of new export markets on both the product and input sides. Second, malaligned exchange rate policies between importing and exporting countries create one of the most detrimental obstacles to the undertaking of new export product enterprises. Third, stringent credit and monetary policies make it difficult for producers to get financing of operating costs and almost impossible to get investment funds. Fourth, fiscal policies such as taxation of export products can prevent trade, although it is often possible for exporters to evade these types of policies. Finally, protectionist policies in importing countries have historically been a hindrance to the establishment of trade linkages between CBI and importing countries, but this will be discussed in more detail later in the text.

## Institutional Support for an Export Drive

The second major issue which negatively affects CBI trade links is problems that plague the institutions which support and drive export trade. These problems include rigidities in the legal and operational institutions that govern or administer trade. For example, a country could design a series of macroeconomic policies to encourage and enhance export trade but it can take several years before these new processes are fully internalized and properly implemented by bureaucratic agencies. Full compliance means that government employees must be re-educated and business people given time to react or adjust to new rules, and these require a significant investment in time and energy. Therefore it is essential that policies are kept in place for a reasonable length of time to ensure continuity and market stability for producers. The trade-off for adjustment time and stability is that it is impossible for policymakers to react quickly to changing market conditions which can create difficulties in achieving steady, sustained growth in exports.

### Comparative and Competitive Advantages

The third major policy and research issue that must be addressed is the evaluation of the existence of a comparative advantage in the production of an export good. Simply looking at the quality and quantity of resources within a country does not yield enough information to make this evaluation. Other factors must be considered such as technology, support services, and continuing research.

Technology plays a role in establishing a comparative advantage both through a country having access to the technology and through the actual performance of that technology when it is transferred or imported to a producing country. For example, a seed variety developed in the U.S. may have certain yield and resistance characteristics which do not fully manifest when the variety is grown in another country under slightly different growing conditions. Efficiency in support services for export production is also necessary to actually realize a potential comparative advantage. These services include timely, accurate market information and transportation and financial services. Finally, to develop or maintain a comparative advantage requires continuing research which entails implementing policies to support and encourage this research. In sum, export projects fail when investors look at comparative advantage only in a textbook or traditional sense without considering the realistic competitive advantages that do or do not exist in the marketplace.

### The Debt Crisis and the Development of an Infrastructure

The debt crisis faced by some CBI countries affects their ability to develop and maintain export trade by preventing them from creating a sufficient infrastructure to allow for market penetration and presence.

When undertaking international trade of perishable products, it is essential that the postharvest marketing chain is efficient in getting the goods to final consumers in a timely manner. An efficient marketing chain requires that good road systems, ports, and facilities exist to prevent producers from incurring large hidden costs and even failures in establishing or maintaining export trade of a product. The debt crisis has made it impossible for some CBI and other exporting countries to maintain or improve their infrastructure with public sector funds, and unfortunately the private sector has not had the financial capital available either. Since many of these exporting countries are not creditworthy, donor countries or international lending agencies are reluctant to supply the needed funds. A more viable alternative may be joint ventures between importer and exporter countries as a way to gain capital, and also technical assistance, transfer of technology, and access to markets for exporter countries. As with any market venture, there are risks involved that must be evaluated thoroughly before undertaking a project.

## Market Windows and Other Demand Issues

A fifth set of issues in developing trade links involves a thorough analysis of the characteristics of the demand for an export product. Market windows must be found; however, it should be noted that windows are not stable but can and do change over time, as in the case of the EC when Spain and Greece joined the common market. A country undertaking export trade must also be aware of the different segments in the market to find the greatest opportunity for establishing trade links. The markets for fresh vegetables in the Northern Hemisphere, the United States and EC for example, are not homogeneous but in fact have significant economic and ethnic differences. Other demand issues to consider are the ease of entry and exit into the market, pricing practices, distribution of risks and marketing margins, and the usual financial arrangements within the distribution system.

## Tariff and Nontariff Barriers to Trade

The final major issue to be addressed is the existence of both tariff and nontariff trade barriers in importing countries. Although much of this topic is addressed elsewhere in this volume, several remarks are in order. First, it is obvious that the successful marketing of fresh horticultural products is not only a function of technical and economic efficiency. The roles of both tariff and nontariff barriers are important determinants of the direction and volume of horticultural trade. Important barriers include the use of quantitative restrictions such as seasonal quotas, seasonal tariffs, and "antidumping" measures. Other factors include the cartelization of the transport industry, the credibility of export inspection systems, ambiguity in the application of chemical residues rules, and disparities in the quality standards for exports and domestic markets.

## CONCLUSIONS

There are three main conclusions that can be drawn with respect to developing policy and research agenda to strengthen the trade ties between CBI and the countries in the Northern Hemisphere. First, the fresh vegetable market may provide an opportunity for diversity in the exports of CBI countries, but they cannot substitute for traditional export markets (such as sugar and coffee). The vegetable export market is not large enough, and the high degree of volatility and risk and the nature of competition make it unrealistic for CBI countries to invest large amounts of capital into this market.

Second, the development of successful trade links depends on the market conditions and trade policies of both the importing and exporting countries. Although the United States and EC claim to want to remove trade barriers in the General Agreement on Tariffs and Trade (GATT) negotiations, this is not what is actually proposed by these countries.

Finally, one way to overcome the obstacles to trade links is for CBI countries to develop physical and especially human resources to take advantage of the complex market opportunities presented by the fresh vegetable market.

# VEGETABLE TRADE LINKAGES IN THE WESTERN HEMISPHERE: DISCUSSION

Timothy G. Taylor
*University of Florida*

Although issues involving international trade in fresh and processed vegetables are important to some, in the broad context of international trade in general and agricultural commodities in particular, they remain "small potatoes" to many. Thus, for those of us who have a vested interest in all aspects of the vegetable industry, the papers in this session presented some very valuable information and insight into a dimension of the fresh vegetable industry that has not received much attention by economists. The papers presented in this session were to address the issue of linkages in fresh vegetable trade in the Western Hemisphere. This, I believe, was accomplished in an interesting and stimulating manner reflecting the backgrounds and experiences of the authors.

One can group the papers in this session into two distinct categories. The papers by Dr. Sparks and Drs. Lopez and Pagoulatos analyzed vegetable trade at a very aggregate level and from the perspective of academic researchers. In contrast, the papers by Dr. Cook and Dr. Quiros were based more on the perspective of those involved in the day-to-day functioning of the vegetable industry. Thus, we have an interesting contrast between academic and real-world perspectives.

The paper by Dr. Sparks viewed trade in fresh vegetables at a very aggregate level. Fresh vegetables were treated as a single aggregate commodity (SITC 054) with countries being aggregated into nine importing and exporting regions (Latin America, United States, Canada, EEC, Middle East, Far East, Africa, and non-EEC Western Europe). In addition to providing a comparison of trade flows of vegetables between 1962 and 1982, the paper presents some results obtained from an econometric model of world vegetable trade based on the Armington model.

Perhaps the most significant contribution of this paper is the resulting data set which provides an indication of the direction of trade flows and the substantial amount of growth in fresh vegetable trade that has been witnessed over the 1962 to 1982 period. These data make apparent that vegetable trade, while still a minor component of agricultural trade, is becoming increasingly more important. Further, it gives a good general indication of who trades with whom and in what amounts.

In contrast to the descriptive value of the data in capturing the general tenor of world trade in fresh vegetables, the econometric model and attendant empirical results must, I believe, be viewed with some caution. The major problem with the model rests in the degree of aggregation. Unlike aggregates such as feed grains which are similar in their end use and storable, individual fresh vegetables are highly perishable and differ greatly as regards grade and size standards, transportability, and container specifications. Thus, while the model may explain aggregate trade flows, it is not clear that any meaningful information as regards policy formulation can be obtained since many, if not most, of the important determinants of trade in fresh vegetables between countries (as opposed to regions) are necessarily lost in aggregation.

A far better understanding of the economic (and political) forces driving trade in fresh vegetables can be derived by analyzing these issues between specific countries and for individual commodities or small groups of commodities. An excellent example of this type of analysis may be found in Bredahl, Schmitz, and Hillman who used the theory of rent-seeking behavior to analyze trade in fresh vegetables (primarily tomatoes) between the U.S. and Mexico. By considering the economic and noneconomic forces that shape trade between specific countries and for specific commodities, as done in this type of study, a much richer and meaningful body of knowledge can be obtained.

The paper by Drs. Lopez and Pagoulatos (LP) provides a rather generic and theoretical view of the economic and noneconomic forces that tend to shape trade flows in fresh and processed vegetables. While much of what is presented in the paper is hardly new and is perhaps applicable to almost any commodity, the constraints and opportunities to trade flows delineated by LP are on target and very important.

From a macroeconomic perspective, LP note that the world (especially Latin American) debt crisis and exchange rates are significant factors in shaping the direction of trade flows. While this is no doubt true, especially in the long run, the impact of these factors on vegetable trade in general should not be overstated, as I suspect the direction and magnitude of trade flows are dictated as much, if not more so, by political and noneconomic forces than by macroeconomic forces in the short run.

It must be remembered that in contrast to commodities that are both storable and very standardized, fresh vegetables are highly perishable and can be of varied quality. Hence, working relationships between importers and exporters which have been based on long-standing trust and performance may not easily be broken due to macroeconomic fluctuations.

As I noted, LP delineated a number of economic and noneconomic opportunities/barriers to vegetable trade on both the supply and demand side.

All of these are very significant. However, rather than discuss all at length, I would like to further discuss and embellish what I consider to be two of the most crucial noneconomic barriers to trade.

The issue of quality (e.g., grade and size standards) is an extremely complicated and crucial element in vegetable trade. Many countries have well defined size and quality standards. Hence, foreign producers seeking to export into such countries must be willing and able to meet these quality standards. While this seems a simple matter on the surface, it should be remembered that many countries viewed as being potentially significant exporters of vegetables, such as those in Latin America, do not necessarily have well-defined domestic quality standards and may have difficulty in consistently producing high quality produce. Furthermore, the necessary infrastructure to accomplish grading/sizing, in many cases, may be poor or nonexistent.

Quality issues can also be significant in trade between countries with well-defined internal quality standards. This is because quality standards may differ substantially between countries. Thus, domestic producers must often be willing to dedicate themselves to produce for export markets that may be somewhat different than the domestic market with which they are accustomed.

As an example, at a recent international trade forum sponsored by the United Fruit and Vegetable Association, it was reported that one of the primary constraints that U.S. vegetable producers faced in attempting to export to the European market was their unwillingness to pack their product to European specifications and supply their product on a consistent basis. European importers were generally unwilling to take U.S. produce on a sporadic basis or in container sizes other than those typical in the European market. Thus, it may not be possible for producers to view export markets as alternative sources of demand when domestic prices are low and ignore these markets when domestic prices are acceptable.

On the demand side, a noneconomic barrier to trade that merits additional comment is that of food safety. Many countries have strict pesticide labeling laws, while others may be somewhat more lax. Furthermore, there is likely to be a disparity in approved chemicals across countries. As consumer awareness and concern about chemical residues increase, significant barriers to trade may arise. Indeed, food safety issues are one of the motivating factors behind the country of origin labeling laws being pushed by some segments of the U.S. vegetable industry.

As a case in point, Florida tomato growers, as is well known, have generally been unsuccessful in obtaining protection from Mexican import competition. As such, the industry has been very vocal in claiming that Mexican producers utilize chemicals that are not labeled for use on tomatoes in the

United States. Thus, they argue that not only do Mexican producers enjoy an unfair trade advantage, but, also, their tomatoes contain harmful chemical residues. To this point, these claims (which have not been conclusively substantiated) have largely fallen on deaf ears. However, as consumer awareness concerning food safety increases, such allegations may result in significant trade barriers.

The paper by Dr. Cook covers some interesting aspects to the determinants of trade flows in fresh vegetables not directly considered by Sparks and LP. The first issue she raised relates to the role of multinational businesses. As an example, she points out that while Mexico is an exporter of vegetables to the United States, many, if not most, of the farming operations in Mexico are financed completely or in part by U.S. firms. Indeed, all Mexican vegetables are distributed by U.S. distributors. In fact, the Southwest Mexico Vegetable Distributors Association, an association of U.S. vegetable distributors located in Nogales, Arizona, is the primary advocate of the Mexican vegetable producers in the United States.

The role of multinationals in vegetable trade is important for two reasons. First, if multinationals are a dominant force in determining trade flows, many traditional trade theories may not be particularly relevant for analyzing trade flows. Theoretical models and resultant empirical models must recognize the role of multinational companies and incorporate the implications of their presence into these models.

Secondly, I think it is safe to say that markets for fresh vegetables are often very difficult to open for foreign entrants. Differences in quality standards, container specifications, quarantine restrictions and other market peculiarities specific to any given country may necessitate the creation of multinational business arrangements, if trade in vegetables is to be successfully accomplished. This possibility must be recognized and carefully studied as research on trade in vegetables continues.

Another significant comment made by Dr. Cook relates to the fact that much trade may well be retail driven. LP also alluded to this. There seems to have been a substantial increase in the demand for variety by consumers of fresh vegetables. That is, consumers are demanding more and varied types of vegetables. In a sense, one can argue that imported produce may, in some cases, be viewed as luxury items by consumers. For example, although Florida is the largest producer of winter tomatoes in the United States, the Divine Ripe tomato imported from Israel has found a market in Florida due to the perception of high quality.

The increasing consumption of vegetables in concert with the increasing demand for specialty types can have a major impact on trade flows in vegetables. The extent of this impact will largely, I believe, rest on the ability of foreign producers or their marketing agents to develop an identification of their products with unique characteristics or superior quality.

The remarks by Dr. Quiros, in a sense, summarized and synthesized many, if not all, of the elements of the previous papers. Given that his perspective comes from a Latin American country and that he has worked in government, I found his comments quite interesting.

Perhaps the most significant element of Dr. Quiros's presentation relates to that of perspectives. As researchers in the United States, it is quite easy for us to always view things from an American perspective. In the arena of international trade, be it vegetables or other commodities, it is extremely important that we understand that the perspectives, institutional arrangements, infrastructures, business ethics and practices, etc., in other countries may differ substantially from those with which we are accustomed. If we are ever to get a complete understanding of the economic and noneconomic forces that shape trade in vegetables, we must remember that these differences exist and seek to fully understand them and incorporate them into our analyses to the greatest extent possible.

## REFERENCES

Armington, P.S. "A Theory of Demand for Products Distinguished by Place of Production." *IMF Staff Papers.* 16(1969):159-177.

Bredahl, M.E., A. Schmitz, and J.S. Hillman. "Rent Seeking in International Trade: The Great Tomato War." *American Journal of Agricultural Economics.* 69(1987):1-10.

# VEGETABLE TRADE LINKAGES IN THE WESTERN HEMISPHERE: DISCUSSION

Daniel A. Sumner
*U.S. Department of Agriculture*
*North Carolina State University*

The international markets for vegetables have been studied much less intensively than those for heavily traded agricultural commodities such as grains. Even less traded commodities like meats or dairy products have drawn more academic attention. Recent efforts to examine the impact of changes of trade policies have spurred many efforts to model and estimate trade flows for many commodities as indicated by the widely cited efforts of Tyers and Anderson, the U.S. Department of Agriculture (USDA), or the recent symposium of the International Agricultural Trade Research Consortium. While these recent publications differ in many ways, they share a neglect of vegetable trade.

The preceding papers address a large gap in the literature on international trade of agricultural commodities. As a partial result of the lack of previous work, these papers are quite disparate and no attempt is made here to critique each individually. Instead, I attempt to focus on a few issues that seem important to further progress in modeling and measuring in a useful way the trade linkages in vegetable markets.

These comments concentrate on how to develop information about the positions and elasticities of the supply and demand functions that apply in analyzing trade in vegetables. I should note explicitly that the supply and demand elasticities are central in several specific issues of public policy and industry analysis. These issues include:

1. the payoff to investments in technological improvements,
2. the effects of national marketing orders or international cartelization,
3. the impact of international standards for pesticide residue, and
4. the impacts of expanding access for imports into a market such as the United States.

Thus, we care about modeling and measuring supply and demand conditions in order to better answer serious and important practical questions.

The demand for vegetables traded internationally may be considered a derived demand in the sense that when households buy the retail product, the farm produce has been combined with a number of other inputs (labor, transportation, packaging and retail services) that equal or more than equal the value at the farm gate or even at the export or import dock. In recent years the ratio of farm value to retail cost of fresh vegetables (in the United States) has been in the range of 30% and for processed fruits and vegetables it has been somewhat lower.

It may be useful to put a discussion of the demand for vegetables in the framework of Marshall's rules for derived demand. Marshall's rules would suggest that the derived demand for vegetables at the export or farm gate level is more *elastic* whenever: the retail demand for vegetables is more elastic, there is closer substitutability between vegetables and other inputs used in the marketing chain, the supply functions of these other inputs are more elastic, and the cost share of the farm produce in the retail product is larger. (Of course, this last rule is true only if the final product demand elasticity is larger than the substitution between inputs.) Each of these rules is discussed in turn.

The demand for vegetables by retail consumers has expanded in the United States and has shifted more toward fresh produce. As papers in this volume indicate, the variety of products has expanded and the convenience built into the products has increased. These changes may have caused the price elasticity facing any specific vegetable product to have increased while, treating vegetables as a composite commodity, the price elasticity has moved closer to zero.

The seasonality of vegetable markets has long been important. Recently, seasonal availability of fresh produce has expanded. Econometrics based on annual data treat broccoli sold in January as a perfect substitute for broccoli sold in July. However, it may be more appropriate to treat fresh vegetables available in different seasons of the year as distinct products. In that case, broccoli or cauliflower, both available in January, may be closer substitutes for one another than are broccoli in January and July. The paper by Cook concerning Mexican and California tomatoes suggests that the seasonality of the two growing areas may imply that the products are complements not substitutes. The tomatoes from Mexico allow a consumer to continue use of a fresh product until the California produce is available again later in the year. Florida and Mexico, with harvests at the same time of the year, are clearly substitutes in the same market. Such seasonality issues cannot be examined with annual aggregate time series.

Trade *policy* already recognizes the degree to which seasonality affects the substitutability of fresh vegetables at the final demand level. For example,

Canadian tariffs and quotas for fresh vegetables vary by season, and the Free Trade Agreement has left some seasonal restrictions in place. Econometric analysis that is to be useful for policy discussion must be based on data that take these considerations into account.

Vegetables made available in a retail market have been graded, shipped, ripened and cleaned before they are finally purchased by consumers. This process involves considerable cost and loss of raw produce along the way. Cook argues that recent changes in the marketing chain involve a substitution for labor at the household and retail levels by labor at the wholesale level and earlier. Some value added now provided on the farm includes sizing, cleaning, and packaging, that replaces labor used later in the marketing chain. One may view labor used in an early stage of chain as a substitute for labor later in the chain. Labor or capital may also be a substitute for raw produce itself in the sense that more care and effort in grading, handling, and shipping will reduce the proportion of loss through spoilage. Therefore, the same number of retail units can be achieved with fewer units purchased at the farm or export level. In general, however, it is reasonable to expect relatively low but not zero substitution elasticities between inputs in the vegetable marketing process.

The supply elasticity of nonproduce inputs to the vegetable marketing industry was included in the list of Marshall's rules for completeness. For most long or intermediate run questions, we may generally treat these supply functions as perfectly elastic. However, this may not be true of retail or wholesale space especially in the short run. Certainly, individual market operators treat the space available for display and storage as a relatively fixed resource. They may therefore focus on goods with rapid turnover to increase profits per cubic foot of display or storage area. This is one of the factors that causes demand to be more inelastic in the short run.

Marshall's rule of the "importance of being unimportant" would seem to apply to trade in vegetables. The substitution between fresh vegetables and the other inputs in the marketing chain is likely to be smaller than the final demand elasticity for the final product (retail vegetables). This is particularly true if the demand function is specified for a particular vegetable, such as tomatoes or potatoes. For these cases, the final product demand is more elastic and the elasticity of substitution will remain low. Therefore, as the share of the farm level or export level cost of the commodity has become a lower share of final product costs, the derived demand elasticity would be expected to become closer to zero.

The long-term trend for the cost share of farm produce in the retail product to fall may be expected to continue. This implies an increasing inelastic demand for produce at the farm or FOB level.

The discussion on the demand function for vegetables has not yet focused on the substitution between produce from different locations. This, of course, is the more traditional issue for international trade. When the share of one country's exports into a market of another country is small, the elasticity of demand will be high. But, it is crucial that the market be defined carefully for the analysis of market shares. Here again, the specific product and season may be vital to understanding when goods are close, if not perfect substitutes. I am not aware of empirical analysis that examines vegetable markets in this detail.

Data are generally available in USDA and Census reports on a monthly basis and, for some markets, on a weekly basis. Of course, putting these data in a usable form is not trivial, nor are the host of other econometric or practical problems of applied economic analysis that always arise. However, the potential payoff in increased understanding seems to be worth the work (especially since I'm not likely to be the one doing the work).

Information about the supply function for vegetables in international trade is also quite limited. We do know that compared to products like coffee or bananas in some Latin American countries or grains in regions of the United States, the vegetable industry uses a relatively small share of the total agricultural resources. This implies that, generally, the industry is more likely to be facing elastic supplies for the inputs it uses so that the vegetable supply elasticity will be large. Compared to, say, wheat in Kansas or coffee in Colombia, expansion of the acreage devoted to broccoli in most areas could be achieved with relatively small increases in marginal costs.

Certainly for most vegetable crops, land is not the key limiting resource. Instead, perhaps hired seasonal labor, irrigation water or access to technology or marketing services are the vital ingredients that limit expansion of the industry. The costs of these inputs and the potential for expansion determine the position and elasticity of the vegetable supply function.

Labor issues are discussed later in this volume, so may be put aside here. It is important instead to focus on nontraditional inputs that are vital in the production of vegetables that are actually exported. Comments at this workshop have emphasized the importance of insurance, packaging, transportation, and storage as well as provision of financial services and competent brokers to facilitate international trade in perishable products. Therefore, to appropriately consider international trade in new or expanding commodity markets, the idea of production or supply should be broadened to include significant parts of the marketing chain. If the product is considered to be the imported vegetables at the wholesale level, then the production includes all the value added during the farm and exporting process. Comments from those in the industry have stressed the limited resources available after the produce leaves the farm gate.

The major point on the supply side is that, for international trade in the emerging vegetable markets, the key to the supply function may lie well past the farm gate. Further, public policy that enhances farm production but inhibits the marketing process will certainly fail to encourage exports.

The papers by Cook; Sparks; Lopez and Pagoulatos; and Quiros provide a useful point of reference but mainly emphasize how far we have to go to develop a quantitative understanding of these markets. The issues are complex but important, so one may hope that these papers will encourage additional effort.

## REFERENCES

Carter, Colin A., and Walter H. Gardiner, ed., *Elasticities in International Agricultural Trade.* Westview Press, 1988.

International Agricultural Trade Research Consortium, *Bringing Agriculture into the GATT*, Symposium in Annapolis, Maryland, August 1988.

Tyers, Rodney, and Kym Anderson, *Global Effects of Liberalizing Trade in Agriculture*, draft monograph, August 1987.

# SECTION IV: ISSUES IN VEGETABLE TRADE

# 10

# THE URUGUAY ROUND OF TRADE NEGOTIATIONS: IMPLICATIONS FOR TRADE IN HORTICULTURAL PRODUCTS

James Vertrees and Leo Mayer
*U.S. Department of Agriculture*

## INTRODUCTION

The United States and its trading partners are now engaged in the eighth round of multilateral trade negotiations since the General Agreement on Tariffs and Trade (GATT) was established in 1947. This round, the Uruguay Round, was launched in September 1986 in Punta del Este, Uruguay. It represents yet another opportunity to make further progress in liberalizing trade and restoring international confidence in the GATT.

Agriculture has been given unprecedented attention in the Uruguay Round of trade negotiations. Compared to past rounds where relatively little progress was made in removing impediments to trade in agricultural products, the prominent position of agriculture in this round of multilateral trade negotiations is indicative of the increased visibility given barriers to agricultural trade in recent years. The United States and the other contracting parties to the GATT face both an opportunity and a challenge in their effort to bring agricultural trade more effectively under the GATT.

The GATT is both a multilateral agreement–the General Agreement–and an international organization–the GATT Secretariat. Currently, 95 countries accounting for over 80% of world trade are members of GATT. Another 29 countries abide by its rules.

The GATT was created in 1947 following the Second World War as one of three international organizations intended to oversee postwar economic relations. The other two organizations are the International Monetary Fund and the World Bank. The General Agreement has remained the internationally accepted standard for the conduct of international trade relations.

Four key principles underlie the General Agreement (a detailed legal document that defines the responsibilities and operating rules of member governments). First, trade policies among member countries should be applied on a nondiscriminatory basis (most-favored-nation treatment). Second, member countries should work to lower trade barriers in general and to eliminate the use of quotas in particular. If border restraints are necessary temporarily, the General Agreement favors tariffs over time. Third, a tariff concession, once made, cannot be rescinded without compensation being offered to affected trading partners. The Agreement also specifies that other forms of protection cannot be used to circumvent the effects of tariff concessions. Fourth, trade conflicts should be settled by consultation whenever possible, using a set of mutually accepted rules for conduct of the negotiations.

The principles are not inviolate, and exceptions to them have always been tolerated. Many of GATT's current problems stem from both old and new evasions of these principles. Examples of current exceptions include the Multifiber Agreement governing trade in textiles and apparel; voluntary exports restraints such as the recent limits on automobile imports from Japan; escape-clause actions such as the recent protection given the U.S. motorcycle industry; agricultural import quotas and export subsidies; barriers to trade in services and the failure to protect intellectual property rights; free trade areas such as the European Community; preferential treatment for developing countries; nontariff barriers to trade; and retaliatory trade actions.

These exceptions to the GATT's general principles make up much of the agenda of the Uruguay Round. In essence, the agenda aims to strengthen GATT discipline and expand it to cover all trade in goods and services. Procedurally, there are 15 negotiating groups. The list is as follows: (1) Tariffs; (2) Nontariff Measures; (3) Natural Resource Based Products; (4) Textiles and Clothing; (5) Agriculture; (6) Tropical Products; (7) GATT Articles; (8) MTN Agreements and Arrangements; (9) Safeguards; (10) Subsidies and Countervailing Measures; (11) Intellectual Property Rights; (12) Trade-Related Investment Measures; (13) Dispute Settlement; (14) Functioning of the GATT System; and (15) Services.

The Agriculture Negotiating Group has focused on several issues to date, including export subsidies, health and sanitary issues, the role of developing countries in agricultural trade, and the importance of food security. A technical working group has concentrated on developing a means of measuring the level of subsidies–the so-called Producer Subsidy Equivalent (PSE) approach. Still to come is a formal working group to negotiate harmonization of health and sanitary standards.

In a broader context, a distinguishing feature of the Uruguay Round is its concentration on trade barriers, especially nontariff barriers, that are integrally linked to national economic policies. This underscores the point that international trade can no longer be dealt with apart from other domestic economic policy concerns such as farm price and income support programs. Progress on trade liberalization means changing these national programs, and for this reason domestic policies will increasingly become the focus of trade negotiations.

The value of GATT lies not only in its rules, but in the fact that it also provides a forum where countries can resolve disputes over national policies. It is one of the few policy forums where long-run goals guide the resolution of short-term conflicts. The GATT Secretariat has little independent power; it merely reflects the will of its members. GATT plays a passive enforcement role, relying mainly on the good fairy of its members to abide by its rules. It doesn't actively police compliance, but responds to complaints by its members.[1] The dispute settlement procedures are slow, often taking several years for a final, nonbinding, ruling. In essence, the General Agreement lacks a set of strong, substantive rules and workable enforcement procedures.

Despite these limitations and problems, the GATT has worked. It can be argued that the strongest achievements of the GATT have been what it has prevented rather than its explicit accomplishments. The GATT was created mainly to reduce the possibility of another debilitating trade war similar to that which followed implementation of the Smoot-Hawley Tariffs at the beginning of the Great Depression. It also was intended to undo much of the damage caused by those tariffs. By this test, the GATT can be judged successful. Certainly, trade relations have suffered many crises over the past 40 years, but there has been no setback to world economic growth similar to the Great Depression. Moreover, GATT-sponsored MTNs have helped lower the Smoot-Hawley-era tariffs by over 90%: the average tariff rate for most developed countries is now less than 5%.

The history of significant reductions in tariff levels was started with the first GATT-sponsored MTN–called the Geneva Round–in 1947. Over the next 15 years the GATT sponsored four more rounds of MTNS–the Annecy (France) Round; the Torquay (England) Round; the second Geneva Round; and the Dillon Round–but little additional tariff reduction was accomplished. Partly, the lack of progress resulted from pressure in the United States against further tariff cuts, but also because much energy was spent on forming the EC and integrating it into the world trade system. In the sixth GATT-sponsored MTN–the Kennedy Round, which lasted from 1964 to 1967–significant progress was made in lowering tariffs. Duties were cut by an average of 36% and the cuts were spread over a broad set of products with some cuts in tariffs being made on almost 80% of dutiable imports.

The Kennedy Round was also important because for the first time an agreement was reached to resolve conflicts over nontariff barriers in the form of an Antidumping Code which the United States never signed. The Tokyo Round–1973 to 1979–succeeded in further lowering tariff rates for many goods and in producing a number of agreements on codes of conduct, such as the Subsidies Code, the Government Procurement Code, the Countervailing Duty and Antidumping Code, and a Safeguard Code.

Past GATT negotiations have been more successful in freeing up industrial trade than agricultural trade. This is not to say that agricultural trade has not been on the agenda. Rather, there has been a relative lack of success in removing agricultural trade barriers due largely to the strong links between domestic agricultural policies and international trade, the special provisions for agriculture in the GATT, the prevalence of nontariff barriers for agriculture, and the difficulties in negotiating their removal.

Most of the progress in agriculture was achieved in the last three MTN rounds. In the Dillon Round (1960-61) some concessions on agricultural products were offered and received by the United States. The most important was the duty-free binding for soybeans and corn gluten feed and near duty-free binding for soybean meal, other oilseeds, and cotton into the EC. In the Kennedy Round, little progress was made in bringing domestic agricultural policies under GATT rules but significant agricultural trade concessions were offered and received by participants. In the Tokyo Round, agriculture was a specific agenda item for the first time. The United States received agricultural tariff and quota concessions from Japan and the EC and granted import concessions mainly on cheese and livestock products.

The attention given to agriculture in the MTNs has increased over time as has the frustration among trading partners over the trade distortions that originate with domestic farm programs. International trade tensions have elevated agriculture to the highest levels of government as indicated by the 1986, 1987, and 1988 OECD Ministerial Communiques and by the communiques of the Venice, Tokyo, and Toronto Economic Summits.

Underscoring the concerns about agricultural trade barriers, the contracting parties to the GATT have agreed to "achieve greater liberalization of trade in agriculture and bring all measures affecting import access and export competition under strengthened and more operationally effective GATT rules and disciplines." Specific agricultural objectives of the Uruguay Round are to: (1) improve market access; (2) improve the competitive environment by increasing discipline on the use of all direct and indirect subsidies and other measures affecting trade; and (3) minimize the adverse trade effects of sanitary and phytosanitary regulations and barriers. In essence, the contracting parties have put their domestic agricultural subsidy programs on the negotiating table.

On July 6, 1987, the United States proposed to the GATT negotiating Committee on Agriculture that all agricultural subsidies that affect trade be completely phased out over a 10-year period. Specifically, the U.S. proposal would:

- completely phase out all agricultural subsidies which directly or indirectly affect trade;
- freeze and phase out the quantities of commodities exported with the aid of export subsidies;
- phase out all import barriers; and
- harmonize all animal and plant health and sanitary regulations.

The U.S. proposal centers on reducing the aggregate level of support given to agricultural producers. The proposal is encompassing, covering all agricultural commodities, food, beverages, forest products, and fish and fish products. During the time period designated as the First Tier by the U.S. proposal, contracting parties would agree to a means of measuring the aggregate level of support. Included in the aggregate measure of support are all forms of market price support, including import quotas, variable levies, tariffs, and minimum import prices, income support such as deficiency and storage payments, and other support such as subsidized crop insurance and input and processing subsidies. Permitted support includes only direct income payments decoupled from production and marketing and bona fide foreign and domestic food aid programs.

In the follow-up time period known as the Second Tier, countries would agree to the specific policy changes that each country would take to achieve its commitments to reduce overall government support for agriculture. Each country's implementation plan would have the character of a GATT binding. Annual reviews during the transition period would determine whether additional modifications were needed. Additionally, changes in GATT rules would be negotiated that would be consistent with a new trading environment at the end of the transition period.

Horticultural products including vegetables are covered by the U.S. proposal although no commodity-by-commodity coverage is anticipated. Negotiations for vegetables would likely come under the headings of access and phytosanitary issues.

There are barriers to vegetable trade around the world. In the United States, most imports of vegetables are subject to both phytosanitary regulations and tariffs. Lettuce, for example, is subject to a seasonal tariff of 0.4 to

2.0 cents per pound and tomatoes by a tariff of 2.1 to 3.0 cents per pound. Countervailing or antidumping duties may be imposed when the Commerce Department finds that an exporting country has an unfair advantage. Additionally, marketing orders regulate the quality, quantity, and pack standards for domestic and imported vegetables.

Nor is the United States alone in protecting its horticultural industries. Canada provides seasonal tariff protection against imports of fresh fruits and vegetables although year-round tariffs have been lowered in recent years. The seasonal tariff for fresh-market snap beans, green peas, green peppers, and radishes are a minimum of 10%. Tariffs on broccoli, snap beans, cucumbers, and peas for processing are a minimum of 10% year-round, and the year-round tariff on frozen broccoli is 20%. The duty on potatoes is $0.35 per cwt year-round.

The European Community has separate support systems for fresh and processed vegetables, both of which are subject to import duties. Some products also are exported with subsidies. A few fresh vegetables have comprehensive support coverage including tomatoes, eggplant, cauliflower, and zucchini. The EC, a net importer of fresh vegetables, uses a reference price system to protect import-sensitive fresh vegetable markets. This price, a minimum import price, is based on past market prices adjusted for production costs. In addition to tariffs, some EC processed vegetable imports are subject to import certification (tomato products, canned peas, etc.) and processing subsidies (tomatoes). Japan supports the production of several vegetables through price stabilization funds and imposes phytosanitary restrictions at the border. Imports of many fresh vegetables, including fresh tomatoes, potatoes, and peppers, are prohibited because of insects and disease which occur in the United States.

There are many other countries with barriers to vegetable trade. In Korea, for example, barriers to trade in vegetables remain as a legacy from an earlier day. The effect is visible in the early spring months when the countryside around the major cities is covered with expensive plastic green houses. Without the border protection offered these producers, vegetable imports would limit price protection and discourage the high cost of domestic production. For a nation like Korea, with its rapid rate of industrialization and extremely low level of unemployment, the release of labor from intensive, high-cost agricultural production could be beneficial both internally and to vegetable-exporting nations.

There are a few examples of countries where imports of vegetables are unrestricted. Hong Kong, for example, admits imports of fresh and frozen vegetables duty-free with no restrictions. This is one of the few cases in the world where this is true.

For most countries, there are many reasons for imposing barriers to vegetable trade, including protection of domestic producers and encouragement of national self-sufficiency. Besides year-round tariffs, the methods used include seasonal and ad valorem tariffs, import quotas, restrictive licensing systems, and phytosanitary regulations that restrict imports. It is practices like these that led the United States to put forth its proposal for freeing up global agricultural trade. It is not an overstatement to say that the U.S. proposal is unprecedented in scope, program coverage, and potential structural impact. It is also important to note that U.S. agricultural trade objectives are supported by the Congress as evidenced by Section 1101 of the Omnibus Trade and Competitiveness Act of 1988.

Other major trading countries have also submitted agriculture proposals to the GATT, including the European Community, the Cairns Group (Argentina, Australia, Brazil, Canada, Chile, Colombia, Hungary, Indonesia, Malaysia, New Zealand, Philippines, Thailand, and Uruguay), Canada, Japan, and the Nordic countries (Finland, Iceland, Norway, and Sweden). While none are as far-reaching as the U.S. proposal, nearly all call for reductions in agricultural subsidies that distort trade.

The United States maintains that long-term reform is the fundamental objective that GATT partners should commit to. In contrast, the EC and others, are more interested in short-term measures that freeze or reduce agricultural subsidies. In December 1988, a midterm review by trade ministers will be held in Montreal to assess progress of the Uruguay Round.

Whether the contracting parties will succeed in substantially improving the competitiveness of the world trading system for agricultural products cannot be predicted. It is clear, however, that we are at an unprecedented state in our understanding of the trade distortions and costs of agricultural subsidies and in emphasis given to agriculture in the MTN. This is especially the case for major agricultural commodities directly supported by governments. It remains for nations to take the difficult steps of changing domestic agricultural programs and associated border measures in order to liberalize agriculture trade. It is generally accepted that this is best done on a multilateral, coordinated basis within the GATT framework. Yet at the heart of the issue is the fact that countries are reluctant to change policies, especially if they feel any threat to their national sovereignty.

Overall, the prospects are for continued improvement in the international flow of agricultural commodities and products. No one should be overly optimistic, however, that all barriers to agricultural trade will disappear overnight. That is an unlikely prospect. More likely is a slow evolution toward a world of freer trade in all products, agricultural and industrial.

For American farmers, that is good news. Despite the recent setback in farm production in this country, the capacity is still large to satisfy domestic and foreign markets. The need for overseas markets will increase as production and exportable supplies grow.

## NOTES

[1] An example of its lack of enforcement power was pointed out at the meeting of trade ministers in Geneva in 1982, where the idea for the Uruguay Round of trade negotiations began. At that meeting, the United States focused attention on the problems that the EC was causing with its farm export subsidies and called for the GATT to limit the use of these types of subsidies. The meetings went on for a full week, with daily news conferences each afternoon to report on progress. The fourth day into the news conferences, the EC spokesman curtly reminded the news reporters who pressed him that "the GATT has no sheriffs, no courts, and no jails." It was his way of reminding those present that U.S. support for more discipline on agricultural subsidies was going nowhere, and that the EC had no intention of changing its policies.

# 11

# VEGETABLE TRADE AND THE CARIBBEAN BASIN INITIATIVE

James L. Seale, Jr.
*University of Florida*

## INTRODUCTION

The Caribbean Basin Economic Recovery Act (CBERA, PL 98-67 of the U.S. Congress) is the primary policy mechanism of the Reagan Administration's Caribbean Basin Initiative (CBI). The CBI is intended to generate regional political stability and economic growth via trade, economic assistance, and tax incentives to private sector investments. This legislation is one of four that allows eligible commodities to enter the United States duty-free from the Caribbean Basin. Under Section 212b of CBERA, countries are either "designated" or "nondesignated" by the President as beneficiaries of the Act. At the present time, 22 of 28 Caribbean Basin countries, referred to as the CBERA group, are designated as beneficiaries. (See Table 11.1, column (1)). The six nondesignated countries (Anguilla, Cayman Islands, Guyana, Nicaragua, Suriname, and Turks and Caicos Islands) are eligible by geographic criteria but have been excluded by the President.

The purpose of this paper is to discuss U.S. trade policy with the CBERA nations and relate these policies to vegetable exports to the United States from selected CBERA countries. The first section gives an overview of the economic structure of the 22 designated CBERA countries and is followed by a section on U.S.-Caribbean agricultural trade. Next is a section on U.S. trade policy towards the Caribbean Basin and its impact on CBERA vegetable exports to the United States. Finally, proposals for improving trade policies with these countries are discussed.

## STRUCTURE OF CBERA COUNTRY ECONOMICS

To better understand vegetable trade between Caribbean Basin countries and the United States, it is important to be aware of basic characteristics and the economic structures of all 22 designated CBERA countries. Table 11.1 reports each of the 22 countries' populations in 1985 (column 2), arable land (column 3), agriculture's contribution to gross domestic product (GDP) in 1980 (column 4); real GDP (columns 5-7); and real per capita GDP in 1975, 1980, and 1985 (columns 8-10). For this paper, the 22 are divided into three groupings: Commonwealth countries (including Belize); non-Commonwealth islands; and Central American countries. Clearly the Commonwealth countries are small, with Jamaica and Trinidad and Tobago being the largest in terms of population and arable land. The Dominican Republic and Haiti are relatively large in terms of both population and arable land while countries

Table 11.1 Selected Characteristics of Designated CBERA Countries, Selected Periods, 1975-85

| Designated countries | Population 1985 (1,000) | Arable land 1983 (1,000 ha.) | Agriculture's share of GDP in 1980 | Gross domestic product constant 1980 U.S. million dollars | | |
|---|---|---|---|---|---|---|
| | | | | 1975 | 1980 | 1985 |
| (1) | (2) | (3) | (4) | (5) | (6) | (7) |
| **Commonwealth** | | | | | | |
| Antigua-Barbuda | 80 | 8 | 6 | 107 | 107 | 134 |
| Bahamas | 230 | 7 | 4[c] | 1,155 | 1,475 | 1,725 |
| Barbados | 250 | 33 | 9 | 616 | 861 | 940 |
| Belize | 170 | 53 | 27 | 159 | 171 | 149 |
| British Virgin Islands | 12 | 3 | 9[c] | 32 | 52 | 73 |
| Dominica | 80 | 7 | 28 | 44 | 59 | 70 |
| Grenada | 110 | 5 | 24 | 52 | 63 | 73 |
| Jamaica | 2,340 | 207 | 8 | 4,381 | 2,667 | 1,548 |
| Montserrat | 10 | 2 | 3 | 18 | 24 | 28 |
| St. Christopher-Nevis | 40 | 8 | 13 | 52 | 48 | 50 |
| St. Lucia | 130 | 5 | 10 | 87 | 113 | 127 |
| St. Vincent-Grenadines | 120 | 13 | 13 | 55 | 58 | 76 |
| Trinidad-Tobago | 1,180 | 70 | 2 | 3,740 | 6,233 | 5,774 |
| **Non-Commonwealth** | | | | | | |
| Dominican Republic | 6,240 | 1,110 | 20 | 5,511 | 6,631 | 3,553 |
| Haiti | 5,270 | 552 | 33 | 1,043 | 1,437 | 1,535 |
| Netherlands Antilles-Aruba[d] | 260 | 8 | 1 | 933 | 1,152 | 1,063 |
| **Central American** | | | | | | |
| Costa Rica | 2,490 | 283 | 18 | 3,003 | 4,832 | 2,914 |
| El Salvador | 4,820 | 560 | 28 | 2,743 | 3,567 | 4,379 |
| Guatemala | 7,960 | 1,330 | 25 | 5,583 | 7,879 | 8,503 |
| Honduras | 4,370 | 1,570 | 22 | 1,717 | 2,544 | 2,659 |
| Panama | 2,180 | 462 | 9 | 2,819 | 3,559 | 3,729 |

(cont. next page)

Table 11.1. (continued)

| | Real per capita gross domestic product (1980 $U.S.) | | | Agricultural trade[a] | | | | |
|---|---|---|---|---|---|---|---|---|
| | | | | Latest avail- able | Agr.exports | | Agr. imports | |
| | 1975 (8) | 1980 (9) | 1985 (10) | (11) | value ($mil.)[b] (12) | % of exports (13) | value ($mil.) (14) | % of imports (15) |
| **Commonwealth** | | | | | | | | |
| Antigua-Barbuda | 1,510 | 1,427 | 1,672 | 1984 | 1.1 | 6 | 32.4 | 25 |
| Bahamas | 5,660 | 7,024 | 7,500 | 1984 | 32.0 | 8 | 157.1 | 3 |
| Barbados | 2,502 | 3,458 | 3,714 | 1985 | 43.8 | 12 | 102.9 | 17 |
| Belize | 1,215 | 1,179 | 914 | 1985 | 56.8 | 63 | 35.0 | 27 |
| British Virgin Islands | 3,216 | 4,333 | 5,642 | 1982 | 1.0 | 78 | 16.4 | 28 |
| Dominica | 617 | 808 | 925 | 1985 | 17.0 | 60 | 15.5 | 28 |
| Grenada | 521 | 589 | 655 | 1982 | 14.0 | 76 | 20.0 | 35 |
| Jamaica | 2,144 | 1,227 | 662 | 1984 | 145.9 | 20 | 251.6 | 22 |
| Montserrat | 1,531 | 2,000 | 2,355 | 1978 | 0.1 | 20 | 3.2 | 70 |
| St. Christopher-Nevis | 1,021 | 923 | 937 | 1982 | 12.9 | 69 | 11.5 | 26 |
| St. Lucia | 787 | 942 | 976 | 1985 | 35.4 | 68 | 34.1 | 27 |
| St. Vincent-Grenadines | 593 | 586 | 749 | 1980 | 13.0 | 82 | 21.8 | 38 |
| Trinidad-Tobago | 3,706 | 5,692 | 4,872 | 1985 | 46.4 | 2 | 361.3 | 24 |
| **Non-Commonwealth** | | | | | | | | |
| Dominican Republic | 1,115 | 1,193 | 569 | 1983 | 489.8 | 76 | 215.1 | 17 |
| Haiti | 202 | 247 | 233 | 1982 | 50.1 | 30 | 126.6 | 34 |
| Netherlands Antilles-Aruba[d] | 3,902 | 4,571 | 4,028 | 1984 | 0.5 | < 1 | 162.8 | 4 |
| **Central America** | | | | | | | | |
| Costa Rica | 1,528 | 2,120 | 1,121 | 1982 | 618.0 | 70 | 100.2 | 11 |
| El Salvador | 662 | 744 | 788 | 1982 | 233.5 | 55 | 186.8 | 20 |
| Guatemala | 926 | 1,139 | 1,068 | 1983 | 771.7 | 69 | 143.4 | 10 |
| Honduras | 554 | 689 | 608 | 1984 | 613.5 | 87 | 95.6 | 12 |
| Panama | 816 | 1,819 | 1,710 | 1985 | 236.4 | 79 | 175.8 | 13 |

SOURCE: Seale et al.

[a]Agriculture was defined as SITC codes 0, 1, 2 (excluding 27 and 28), and 4.

[b]$mil. = million dollars U.S.

[c]Share in 1978.

[d]Aruba was designated as the 22nd CBI country in 1986 but prior to that time was included as part of the Netherlands Antilles.

in the Central American group have, on average, the largest population and amounts of arable land among the three groups.

The importance of agriculture as a contributor to GDP in the Commonwealth countries is diverse ranging from 2% for Trinidad and Tobago to more than 30% for Dominica. Agriculture's relative share of GDP is generally larger for the Eastern Caribbean Islands than the others in this group.

In the Dominican Republic, Haiti, and the Central American group (except for Panama), agriculture plays an important role as a contributor to GDP.

The performance of the Commonwealth countries in terms of real GDP, particularly real GDP per capita, has in most cases been better than that of the other two groups. Most of the smaller islands had low, but positive growth between 1980 and 1985. Belize, Jamaica, and Trinidad and Tobago, however, had negative real per capita income growth with Jamaica having a particularly large decrease; Jamaica's real per capita income in 1985 was less than one-third of that in 1975. All countries in the other groups except El Salvador had negative real per capita income growth between 1980 and 1985; the Dominican Republic and Costa Rica had the largest declines. Haiti, the poorest CBERA nation, also had negative growth in real per capita income between 1980 and 1985.

Table 11.1 also reports the value of agricultural exports (column 12) and its share of total exports (column 13) for the latest years that United Nations trade data are available (column 11). Agriculture's share of total exports of the Commonwealth countries has a wider range than those of the other two groups. Agriculture's share of total exports for the four largest Commonwealth island economies (Bahamas, Barbados, Jamaica, and Trinidad and Tobago) was relatively small (ranging from 20% for Jamaica [1984] to less than 3% for the Bahamas [1984] and Trinidad and Tobago [1985]), while it was generally much larger for the smaller Commonwealth economies, Antigua and Barbuda being the exception. For Montserrat, agriculture's share was 20%; all the others had a share of 60% or more. Haiti and the Dominican Republic had shares of 30 and 76%, respectively; the Netherlands Antilles and Aruba had shares of less than 1%. The Central American countries all had shares greater than 50%.

All Commonwealth countries except Belize imported a greater value of agricultural products than they exported. Agricultural imports for this group (except for the Bahamas) constituted a large proportion of total imports. For the non-Commonwealth islands, Haiti and the Netherlands Antilles imported more agricultural products than they exported while the Dominican Republic did the opposite. The Central American group all imported more agricultural products than they exported.

Total value of agricultural exports from the region over the period 1975-85 generally increased until 1979 or 1980 and then declined (Seale et al. n.d.). The major agricultural exports from the region were sugar, coffee, cocoa, bananas, and meat products excluding poultry (especially for the Central American group) (Goodloe n.d.; Seale et al. n.d.).

Recently, Seale et al. chose eight representative CBERA countries (Barbados, Jamaica, St. Lucia [Leeward-Windward Islands], and Trinidad and

Tobago from the Commonwealth; the Dominican Republic from the non-Commonwealth islands; Costa Rica, Guatemala, and Honduras from the Central American group) to illustrate composition and trends of major CBERA agricultural exports, 1975-85. The five leading agricultural exports from the eight were ranked in descending order by export value in 1985. Sugar was ranked in the top five for every country except St. Lucia (primarily a banana and cocoa producer). Other important agricultural exports were bananas (St. Lucia and the three Central American countries), coffee (Jamaica, Trinidad and Tobago, and the Dominican Republic), and fresh chilled or frozen meat (Costa Rica). Vegetables, fresh or simply preserved, were ranked third in Jamaica and fifth in the Dominican Republic.

## U.S.-CARIBBEAN AGRICULTURAL TRADE

The United States is the major exporter of agricultural products to the eight CBERA nations listed above plus Haiti and is also an important importer of their agricultural products (Seale et al. n.d.). Major agricultural exports to the United States from these nine are reported in Table 11.2 and are ranked by total value in 1987. These rankings have changed little over the 1975-87 period except for Haiti and Jamaica. Sugar was first in all years for Barbados, the Dominican Republic, and Trinidad and Tobago (except during 1980-83 for Trinidad and Tobago). For St. Lucia, cocoa was first in all years for which data were available.

For the three Central American countries, bananas and plantains and coffee and products were the two largest exports to the United States during this period; for Costa Rica and Honduras, bananas and plantains were first except for 1976 (coffee in Costa Rica) and 1978 (coffee in Honduras), while for Guatemala coffee was always first. For Haiti, fruits and preparations, ranked last of the five in 1975, surpassed coffee to be ranked first in 1987.

Vegetables and preparations replaced sugar as Jamaica's number one agricultural export to the United States in 1986 and 1987. Vegetables and preparations are also important agricultural exports to the United States for other countries in this group; in 1987, vegetables and preparations ranked third in Barbados and St. Lucia and fourth in the Dominican Republic, Costa Rica, and Guatemala.

## U.S. TRADE POLICY WITH CBERA COUNTRIES

The United States is a major trading partner with CBERA countries for both nonagricultural (Pelzman and Schoepfle 1988) and agricultural products

Table 11.2. Major Agricultural Exports to the U.S. from Selected CBERA Countries, 1975-87, $1,000 U.S.[a]

| Country/Commodity | Years | | | | | | |
|---|---|---|---|---|---|---|---|
| | 1975 | 1976 | 1977 | 1978 | 1979 | 1980 | 1981 |
| **Barbados** | | | | | | | |
| Sugar & rel. prods. | 17,875 | 13,810 | 8,719 | 5,982 | 11,928 | 37,443 | 13,679 |
| Tobacco, unmfg. | n.a.[b] | n.a. | n.a. | n.a. | n.a. | n.a. | n.a. |
| Veg. & prep. | 0 | 0 | 0 | 0 | 11 | 58 | n.a. |
| **Jamaica** | | | | | | | |
| Veg.& prep. | 154 | 125 | 166 | 509 | 994 | 1,531 | n.a. |
| Sugar & rel. prods. | 35,019 | 22,645 | 7,085 | 3,617 | 9,604 | 27,814 | 188 |
| Bev., ex fruit juices | n.a. | n.a. | n.a. | n.a. | n.a. | n.a. | n.a. |
| Nursery stock, cut flowers | 340 | 690 | 766 | 761 | 883 | 832 | 983 |
| Coffee & substitutes | n.a. | 40 | 0 | n.a. | n.a. | n.a. | 153 |
| **St. Lucia (Leeward-Windward Is.)** | | | | | | | |
| Cocoa & prods. | 3,723[c] | 1,759[c] | n.a. | n.a. | n.a. | n.a. | 44[d] |
| Essential oils | 150[c] | 98[c] | 137[c] | 198[c] | 319[c] | 38[c] | n.a. |
| Veg. & prep. | n.a. | n.a. | n.a. | n.a. | 362[c] | 189[c] | n.a. |
| Bananas, plantains | n.a. | n.a. | n.a. | n.a. | n.a. | n.a. | n.a. |
| **Trinidad and Tobago** | | | | | | | |
| Sugar & rel. prods. | 11,830 | 25,646 | 11,452 | 14,360 | 9,940 | 1,671 | 2,221[d] |
| Cocoa & prods. | 3,723 | 1,759 | 5,098 | 5,144 | 4,198 | 2,017 | 3,674 |
| Oilcake & meal | n.a. | n.a. | n.a. | n.a. | n.a. | n.a. | n.a. |
| **Dominican Republic** | | | | | | | |
| Sugar & rel. prods. | 448,775 | 226,103 | 171,231 | 116,596 | 164,382 | 262,494 | 355,827 |
| Cocoa & prods. | 27,685 | 46,876 | 90,671 | 85,726 | 80,964 | 56,264 | 50,023 |
| Coffee | 35,541 | 84,924 | 171,037 | 113,018 | 124,704 | 62,280 | 65,581 |
| Veg. & prep. | 12,873 | 13,178 | 13,635 | 16,243 | 14,460 | 17,074 | 17,617 |
| Meats, exc. poultry | 4,770 | 9,015 | 3,285 | n.a. | n.a. | n.a. | 13,316 |
| **Haiti** | | | | | | | |
| Fruits & prep. | 399 | 476 | 454 | 853 | 1,322 | 1,983 | 2,707 |
| Essential oils | 3,600 | 5,663 | 7,982 | 9,591 | 5,035 | 5,036 | 3,431 |
| Sugar & rel. prods. | 5,794 | 2,096 | 631 | 1,800 | 3,165 | 6,483 | n.a. |
| Coffee & prods. | 5,422 | 15,875 | 23,376 | 13,158 | 6,192 | 9,723 | 4,618 |
| Cocoa & prods. | 2,407 | 2,707 | 4,864 | 8,176 | 5,341 | 3,197 | 2,605 |
| **Costa Rica** | | | | | | | |
| Bananas, plantains | 79,494 | 94,948 | 83,761 | 77,689 | 82,900 | 98,837 | 120,629 |
| Coffee & prods. | 17,209 | 30,165 | 87,249 | 68,921 | 110,126 | 60,593 | 35,047 |
| Meats, exc. poultry | 32,007 | 36,813 | 37,298 | 52,926 | 85,905 | 59,923 | 70,389 |
| Fruits & prep. | n.a. | n.a. | n.a. | 786 | 404 | 586 | n.a. |
| Nursery stock, cut flowers | 389 | 719 | 1,915 | 3,362 | 3,902 | 5,411 | 3,298 |
| **Guatemala** | | | | | | | |
| Coffee & prods. | 64,308 | 106,170 | 210,979 | 204,968 | 253,960 | 196,111 | 106,204 |
| Bananas, plantains | 18,851 | 22,767 | 22,412 | 18,617 | 18,114 | 31,434 | 36,896 |
| Sugar & rel. prods. | 32,779 | 87,954 | 69,714 | 26,855 | 33,313 | 98,763 | 96,092 |
| Veg. & prep. | 157 | 830 | 1,834 | 2,562 | 3,814 | 4,596 | 5,978 |
| Meats, exc. poultry | 22,475 | 24,192 | 23,994 | 27,163 | 40,808 | 23,739 | 12,916 |
| **Honduras** | | | | | | | |
| Bananas, plantains | 34,305 | 68,997 | 81,010 | 90,164 | 108,341 | 121,055 | 141,395 |
| Coffee & prods. | 26,823 | 37,339 | 55,247 | 120,314 | 102,694 | 73,618 | 52,624 |
| Meats, exc. poultry | 19,376 | 26,740 | 27,633 | 36,777 | 63,293 | 63,648 | 49,620 |
| Fruits & prep. | 1,948 | 4,474 | 4,352 | 4,806 | 4,637 | 6,160 | 6,421 |
| Sugar & rel. prods. | 3,286 | 2,370 | 5,942 | 7,903 | 17,941 | 43,764 | 50,141 |

(cont. next page)

Table 11.2. (continued)

| Country/Commodity | Years 1982 | 1983 | 1984 | 1985 | 1986 | 1987 |
|---|---|---|---|---|---|---|
| **Barbados** | | | | | | |
| Sugar & rel. prods. | 12,230 | 9,048 | 7,259 | 10,642 | 1,480 | 6,200 |
| Tobacco, unmfg. | n.a. | n.a. | n.a. | n.a. | 0 | 442 |
| Veg. & prep. | 33 | 13 | n.a. | 0 | 30 | 32 |
| **Jamaica** | | | | | | |
| Veg. & prep. | 2,735 | 3,982 | 4,846 | 8,490 | 8,479 | 7,354 |
| Sugar & rel. prods. | 3,526 | 15,119 | 13,797 | 9,300 | 3,037 | 4,362 |
| Bev., ex fruit juices | 265 | 515 | 1,126 | 1,235 | 2,155 | 2,672 |
| Nursery stock, cut flowers | 1,018 | 1,038 | 1,147 | 1,060 | 1,467 | 1,681 |
| Coffee & substitutes | 501 | 771 | n.a. | n.a. | 1,029 | 1,543 |
| **St. Lucia (Leeward-Windward Is.)** | | | | | | |
| Cocoa & prods. | 0 | 44 | 89[d] | 136[d] | 72 | 129 |
| Essential oils | n.a. | n.a. | n.a. | n.a. | 0 | 52 |
| Veg. & prep. | n.a. | n.a. | n.a. | n.a. | 3 | 47 |
| Bananas, plantains | n.a. | n.a. | n.a. | n.a. | 22 | 23 |
| **Trinidad and Tobago** | | | | | | |
| Sugar & rel. prods. | 53 | 247 | 9,167 | 4,173 | 4,954 | 3,010 |
| Cocoa & prods. | 1,679 | 1,505 | 1,603 | 646 | 880 | 1,173 |
| Oilcake & meal | n.a. | n.a. | n.a. | n.a. | 0 | 504 |
| **Dominican Republic** | | | | | | |
| Sugar & rel. prods. | 123,472 | 178,562 | 217,430 | 153,137 | 119,857 | 76,637 |
| Cocoa & prods. | 56,725 | 55,843 | 80,877 | 68,008 | 66,331 | 68,960 |
| Coffee | 82,643 | 67,485 | 78,097 | 75,476 | 113,021 | 57,343 |
| Veg. & prep. | 18,613 | 22,436 | 25,592 | 25,571 | 27,464 | 24,223 |
| Meats, exc. poultry | 13,175 | 9,400 | 2,206 | 17,469 | 25,909 | 23,520 |
| **Haiti** | | | | | | |
| Fruits & prep. | 2,944 | 3,964 | 4,068 | 4,215 | 3,878 | 4,722 |
| Essential oils | 3,803 | 5,254 | n.a. | n.a. | 4,025 | 4,083 |
| Sugar & rel. prods. | 2,958 | 49,945 | 7,723 | 0 | 1,555 | 3,370 |
| Coffee & prods. | 17,937 | 18,384 | 17,433 | 11.016 | 5,523 | 1,233 |
| Cocoa & prods. | 1,525 | 1,305 | 696 | 482 | 895 | 0 |
| **Costa Rica** | | | | | | |
| Bananas, plantains | 125,606 | 151,681 | 152,731 | 139,316 | 153,770 | 144,393 |
| Coffee & prods. | 46,855 | 36,672 | 48,319 | 63,317 | 95,898 | 84,312 |
| Meats, exc. poultry | 53,378 | 36,980 | 44,765 | 51,059 | 73,079 | 64,921 |
| Fruits & prep. | 1,499 | 2,065 | 4,364 | 4,379 | 11,872 | 15,362 |
| Nursery stock, cut flowers | 3,075 | 3,366 | 6,671 | 7,318 | 9,853 | 11,761 |
| **Guatemala** | | | | | | |
| Coffee & prods. | 141,503 | 144,685 | 197,155 | 187,063 | 384,527 | 217,598 |
| Bananas, plantains | 35,710 | 29,369 | 24,111 | 39,015 | 43,027 | 56,470 |
| Sugar & rel. prods. | 21,963 | 63,570 | 68,107 | 42,545 | 56,849 | 22,098 |
| Veg. & prep. | 9,075 | 8,678 | 11,091 | 11,632 | 13,540 | 20,255 |
| Meats, exc. poultry | 6,931 | 17,058 | 16,411 | 22,367 | 8,352 | 14,975 |
| **Honduras** | | | | | | |
| Bananas, plantains | 145,441 | 129,051 | 146,707 | 158,269 | 148,645 | 209,865 |
| Coffee & prods. | 37,267 | 40,656 | 47,866 | 44,632 | 97,299 | 69,217 |
| Meats, exc. poultry | 35,513 | 35,610 | 21,942 | 11,818 | 20,871 | 18,577 |
| Fruits & prep. | 6,720 | 7,432 | 8,303 | 10,991 | 8,265 | 15,058 |
| Sugar & rel. prods. | 24,650 | 30,069 | 33,118 | 11,502 | 8,898 | 5,408 |

SOURCE: Data from *Foreign Agriucltural Trade of the United States (FATUS* various issues except where noted.

[a]Agricultural products are defined in FATUS as "(i) nonmarine food products and (ii) other products of agriculture, such as fibers, raw hides and skins, fats and oils, beer, and wine, that have not passed through complex processes of manufacture." Not included are "such manufactured products as textiles, leather boots and shoes, cigarettes, naval stores, forestry products, and distilled alcohol."

[b]n.a. = data not available from **FATUS**.

[c]Data for Leeward-Windward Islands.

[d]Compiled from official statistics of the U.S. Department of Commerce.

(Seale et al. n.d.). Accordingly, U.S. trade policy has important economic and social implications for the region. Certain products may enter the United States duty-free under the following: most favored nation (MFN) duty rates as specified by the General Agreement on Tariffs and Trade (GATT); Trade Schedule of the United States (TSUS), items 806.30/807.00; the Generalized System of Preferences (GSP) under GATT; and CBERA. The first two essentially apply to all nations while the latter two are preferential programs for eligible developing countries and CBERA countries, respectively. Of the four, CBERA, the foundation of the CBI, is the only one specifically for Caribbean Basin countries.

The central objective of CBERA is to increase economic growth and political stability in the region by allowing preferential access for eligible products from designated CBERA countries into the U.S. market for 12 years starting January 1, 1984. Eligible goods must meet the following rules-of-origin requirements: the article must be imported directly from a beneficiary country; not less than 35% of the appraised costs of value of an article must be performed in a beneficiary or group of beneficiary countries (includes Puerto Rico and the U.S. Virgin Islands) with allowances up to 15% of the cost (value) to be from U.S.-made components; and for items produced from non-CBERA components, substantial transformation must be met according to U.S. Customs Service standards. Products excluded from duty-free entry include textiles and apparel, canned tuna, petroleum and its products, footwear and shoes, certain leather and leather apparel, rubber and plastic gloves, luggage, handbags, leather flat goods, watches and watch parts containing materials from communist nations (U.S. International Trade Commission 1987).

Eligibility for duty-free status does not exempt products from other types of restrictions. Although duty-free under CBERA, sugar quantities are restricted by U.S. import quotas and, along with beef and veal products, by need to file an *acceptable* Staple Food Production Plan insuring that the present level of food production will not be affected by land use for producing sugar and beef products. To date, Antigua and Barbuda, Montserrat, the Netherlands Antilles, St. Lucia, and St. Vincent and the Grenadines have not met this requirement (U.S. International Trade Commission 1987). Imports of ethanol were originally designated as duty-free under CBERA; this was later amended by section 423 of the Tax Reform Act of 1986 which limits duty-free entry of ethanol from CBERA nations beginning January 1, 1987, unless wholly fermented and distilled in the beneficiary country or having local content used in dehydration increasing to 75% within a 3-year period (U.S. Congress, House 1987). This will restrict ethanol imports into the U.S. from CBERA countries as the fermenting and distilling processes are not cost-competitive in the CBERA nations.

Duty-free entry for products under CBERA is further limited by U.S. antidumping and countervailing laws. In 1986, the Commerce Department ruled against Costa Rica's cut-flower industry in a countervailing investigation. Accordingly, Costa Rica was forced to withdraw all subsidies to cut-flower producers or face substantial U.S. import duties for its cut-flower exports to the United States. This ruling could affect cut-flower industries in Jamaica and other Caribbean countries.

## IMPACT OF CBERA ON VEGETABLE TRADE TO THE UNITED STATES

Essentially, all agricultural exports to the United States including vegetables are duty-free under CBERA if a country meets certain requirements. However, many major traditional agricultural CBERA exports (e.g., coffee, cocoa, and fresh bananas) to the United States are duty-free under MFN while many competitive fruits and vegetables are duty-free under GSP. Table 11.3 groups fresh vegetables into three categories: those duty-free year-round under both GSP and CBERA; those duty-free part of the year under GSP, all year under CBERA; and those not duty-free part or all year under GSP, but duty-free under CBERA. Many of the major vegetable crops grown in the Caribbean were already duty-free prior to CBERA (e.g., peppers, dasheens, okra, onions, peas, and eggplants). Other crops such as tomatoes and cucumbers were duty-free during their major growing season. It is only those items listed under the last grouping that one would expect to gain significantly from CBERA trade liberalization; however, most of the vegetables under this last category are not suitable for cultivation in the Caribbean.

Table 11.3. Duty-free Status of Selected Competitive Fresh Vegetables under GSP and CBERA

| Duty-free under GSP and CBERA |
|---|
| Onion sets, pearl onions (small), garlic, cauliflower, broccoli, brussels sprouts, cabbage, lettuce, chicory, carrots (not reduced), radishes, beets, horseradish, peas, lima beans, cowpeas, chickpeas, lentils, pidgeon peas, eggplants, celery (not reduced), peppers, jicamas, pumpkins, chayote, okra, squash, sweet potatoes, dasheens, yams, turnips |
| **Duty-free during growing season under GSP, all year under CBERA** |
| Tomatoes (11/15-2/28 or 29), cucumbers (12/1-4/31), celery (not reduced, 4/15-7/31) |
| **Not duty-free under GSP, duty-free under CBERA** |
| Potatoes, certain onions, leeks, carrots (reduced size and over 10 cm. length), certain beans, globe artichokes, celery (reduced size), spinach, fiddlehead greens, sweet corn, cassava |

SOURCE: U.S. International Trade Commission, no date.

Although under CBERA, additional vegetable crops have received duty-free status, CBERA does not provide special exemption for several nontariff barriers to trade. Those that affect vegetable trade are health, sanitary, and phylosanitary standards; marketing standards; and trade-remedy provisions which can be limited to perishable vegetables (U.S. Congress, House 1987).

Trends in the value of selected vegetable exports to the United States for selected Caribbean Island and Central American countries and for the aggregate values of these two subregions are reported in Table 11.4. For

Table 11.4. U.S. Imports of Vegetables and Preparations from Selected Caribbean Countries, U.S. $1,000, 1982-87

| | Caribbean Islands | | | | | |
|---|---|---|---|---|---|---|
| | 1982 | 1983 | 1984 | 1985 | 1986 | 1987 |
| Antigua | | | | | | |
| Cucumbers | 0 | 0 | n.a. | n.a. | 34 | 30 |
| Total | 5 | 1 | n.a. | n.a. | 34 | 37 |
| Bahamas | | | | | | |
| Cucumbers | 735 | 803 | 611 | 549 | 207 | 12 |
| Peppers | 8 | 25 | n.a. | 10 | 66 | 0 |
| Total | 855 | 827 | 684 | 643 | 276 | 30 |
| Barbados | | | | | | |
| Preparations | 33 | 13 | n.a. | n.a. | 30 | 27 |
| Total | 33 | 13 | n.a. | n.a. | 30 | 32 |
| Caribbean | | | | | | |
| Tomatoes | 263 | 573 | 748 | 907 | 2721 | 1463 |
| Beans | 195 | 227 | 285 | 373 | 92 | 93 |
| Cucumbers | 786 | 919 | 875 | 1851 | 1175 | 536 |
| Eggplant | 65 | 140 | 258 | 90 | 231 | 71 |
| Garlic | 2 | 5 | 32 | 11 | 30 | 1 |
| Onions | 1 | 0 | 35 | 44 | 3 | 22 |
| Peas | 1681 | 2742 | 2790 | 3119 | 3087 | 3113 |
| Peppers | 1040 | 1343 | 2016 | 3366 | 3300 | 1651 |
| Potatoes | 0 | 11 | 430 | 178 | 6 | 147 |
| Squash | 35 | 43 | 786 | 687 | 518 | 302 |
| Preparations | 5080 | 7618 | 9615 | 7511 | 8324 | 9542 |
| Total | 22518 | 27840 | 31567 | 35571 | 36611 | 32357 |
| Dominica | | | | | | |
| Eggplant | 0 | 0 | 0 | 109 | 19 | 0 |
| Preparations | 0 | 0 | n.a. | n.a. | 6 | 0 |
| Total | 0 | 0 | n.a. | n.a. | 77 | 4 |
| Dominican Rep. | | | | | | |
| Tomatoes | 77 | 162 | 287 | 594 | 2701 | 1460 |
| Beans | 195 | 227 | 277 | 41 | 54 | 75 |
| Cucumbers | 17 | 71 | 48 | 64 | 6 | 13 |

Table 11.4. (continued)

| | Caribbean Islands | | | | | |
|---|---|---|---|---|---|---|
| | 1982 | 1983 | 1984 | 1985 | 1986 | 1987 |
| Eggplant | 65 | 140 | 256 | 80 | 64 | 68 |
| Garlic | 0 | 5 | 32 | 10 | 30 | 1 |
| Onions | 1 | 0 | 35 | 44 | 3 | 22 |
| Peas | 1672 | 2740 | 2787 | 3007 | 3087 | 3105 |
| Peppers | 888 | 1005 | 1558 | 1635 | 1632 | 1112 |
| Potatoes | 0 | 11 | 429 | 178 | 6 | 148 |
| Squash | 31 | 32 | 691 | 361 | 148 | 96 |
| Preparations | 3910 | 6146 | 8201 | 5657 | 7128 | 7905 |
| Total | 18598 | 22436 | 33269 | 37555 | 27464 | 24223 |
| Haiti | | | | | | |
| Cucumbers | n.a. | n.a. | n.a. | n.a. | 25 | 40 |
| Preparations | 90 | 101 | n.a. | n.a. | 55 | 0 |
| Total | 120 | 140 | n.a. | n.a. | 103 | 57 |
| Jamaica | | | | | | |
| Tomatoes | 74 | 411 | 424 | 252 | 7 | 0 |
| Beans | n.a. | n.a. | 7 | 319 | 30 | 14 |
| Cucumbers | 34 | 45 | 152 | 1092 | 887 | 437 |
| Eggplant | n.a. | n.a. | 3 | 11 | 144 | 2 |
| Peppers | 120 | 289 | 425 | 1703 | 1548 | 519 |
| Squash | 3 | 11 | 94 | 324 | 337 | 198 |
| Preparations | 890 | 929 | 1049 | 1200 | 963 | 1146 |
| Total | 2735 | 3982 | 4846 | 8490 | 8479 | 7354 |
| Montserrat | | | | | | |
| Tomatoes | 0 | 0 | n.a. | n.a. | 13 | 0 |
| Squash | 0 | 0 | n.a. | n.a. | 9 | 4 |
| Preparations | 0 | 0 | n.a. | n.a. | 0 | 14 |
| Total | 1 | 0 | n.a. | n.a. | 27 | 30 |
| St. Lucia | | | | | | |
| Peppers | n.a. | n.a. | n.a. | n.a. | 0 | 10 |
| Total | n.a. | n.a. | n.a. | n.a. | 3 | 47 |
| St. Vincent | | | | | | |
| Cucumbers | 0 | 0 | n.a. | n.a. | 16 | 3 |
| Preparations | 0 | 151 | n.a. | n.a. | 59 | 158 |
| Total | 0 | 151 | n.a. | n.a. | 150 | 180 |
| Trinidad-Tobago | | | | | | |
| Peppers | 12 | 3 | n.a. | n.a. | 48 | 6 |
| Squash | 0 | 0 | n.a. | n.a. | 6 | 5 |
| Preparations | 157 | 203 | n.a. | n.a. | 71 | 282 |
| Total | 170 | 208 | n.a. | n.a. | 152 | 356 |

SOURCE: FATUS

both subregions, total value of vegetables and preparations exports to the U.S. were greater in 1987 than the year prior to CBERA (1983); while the Central American aggregate value has risen each year since 1983, that of the Caribbean Islands rose until 1986 and then declined in 1987. This trend is continuing for 1988 (U.S. Department of Agriculture May-June 1988).

Individually, all designated Central American countries had more vegetable preparations exported to the United States in 1987 than in 1983. Costa Rica and Guatemala had particularly good growth. For the Caribbean Islands, the results are less positive. Vegetables and preparations exports from the Dominican Republic and Jamaica increased from 1983 to 1985 but decreased thereafter. Those of several smaller islands (Antigua, Barbados, Montserrat, St. Lucia, and St. Vincent) increased consistently from 1983 to 1987, but in value terms were small; those from the Bahamas and Haiti actually were less in 1987 than in 1983.

Peas, vegetable preparations, and dasheens (not listed) all performed well since CBERA's enactment. Exports of cucumbers from the Central American countries in the aggregate have risen steadily but not for any one individual country. Cucumber exports from the Caribbean Islands have declined dramatically since 1985 and were less in 1987 than in 1983. Countries that have done particularly well for the above vegetables are Costa Rica (preparations), the Dominican Republic (dasheens and peas), and Guatemala (peas and preparations).

Success with tomato exports has been particularly poor. Both the Dominican Republic and Jamaica invested heavily in export tomato production which resulted in large increases in exports followed by sharp declines due to the inability to compete effectively in the U.S. winter tomato market. (Jamaica's tomato exports peaked in 1984 and were down to zero by 1987.) Other crops from the Caribbean Islands have shown similar patterns; cucumbers, peppers, and squash exports all increased in the early years of CBERA followed by declines.

## IMPLICATIONS FOR AGRICULTURAL DEVELOPMENT AND VEGETABLE EXPORTS

Although CBERA allowed additional duty-free status for certain agricultural products, major crops such as fresh bananas, coffee, cocoa, and sugar were already duty-free under MFN or GSP. Additionally, CBERA did not exempt imports of beneficiary countries from other nontariff barriers. As such, agricultural trade liberation has been limited in scope and effect.

There have been some success stories. Both the Dominican Republic and Guatemala have significantly increased vegetables and preparations exports to the United States. Jamaica has also been successful to some extent but has failed dismally in exporting fresh tomatoes to the United States. Banana and coffee exports have been reasonably robust (Seale et al. n.d.)

One of the most harmful U.S. agricultural policies towards the Caribbean

Table 11.5. U.S. Imports of Vegetables and Preparations from Central America, U.S. $1,000, 1982-87

| | Central America | | | | | |
|---|---|---|---|---|---|---|
| | 1982 | 1983 | 1984 | 1985 | 1986 | 1987 |
| Central America | | | | | | |
| Tomatoes | 0 | 1 | n.a. | n.a. | 37 | 24 |
| Asparagus | 9 | 7 | n.a. | n.a. | 51 | 28 |
| Beans | 17 | 9 | 4 | 23 | 39 | 48 |
| Cucumbers | 34 | 108 | 219 | 364 | 303 | 1009 |
| Garlic | 444 | 1 | 6 | 154 | 105 | 50 |
| Onions | 15 | 6 | 37 | 0 | 112 | 185 |
| Peas | 1791 | 2040 | 3050 | 2661 | 3621 | 4930 |
| Peppers | 3 | 6 | n.a. | n.a. | 0 | 95 |
| Squash | 2 | 11 | 43 | 99 | 191 | 457 |
| Preparations | 1391 | 1723 | 1395 | 2285 | 1866 | 3817 |
| Total | 15531 | 14888 | 17831 | 21761 | 24015 | 34081 |
| Belize | | | | | | |
| Tomatoes | 0 | n.a. | n.a. | n.a. | 37 | 13 |
| Cucumbers | 0 | n.a. | n.a. | n.a. | 37 | 666 |
| Squash | 0 | n.a. | n.a. | n.a. | 69 | 41 |
| Preparations | 0 | 3 | n.a. | n.a. | 38 | 9 |
| Total | 7 | 8 | n.a. | n.a. | 196 | 767 |
| Costa Rica | | | | | | |
| Asparagus | n.a. | n.a. | n.a. | n.a. | 3 | 0 |
| Cucumbers | 5 | 5 | n.a. | n.a. | 16 | 1 |
| Garlic | 7 | 7 | n.a. | n.a. | 2 | 0 |
| Onions | n.a. | n.a. | n.a. | n.a. | 0 | 1 |
| Peas | n.a. | n.a. | 1 | 35 | 6 | 16 |
| Peppers | 3 | 1 | n.a. | n.a. | 0 | 83 |
| Squash | 2 | 10 | 29 | 91 | 103 | 128 |
| Preparations | 216 | 409 | 624 | 669 | 798 | 1707 |
| Total | 3721 | 4117 | 4380 | 5137 | 5943 | 7439 |
| El Salvador | | | | | | |
| Asparagus | n.a. | 0 | n.a. | n.a. | 29 | 0 |
| Cucumbers | n.a. | 0 | n.a. | n.a. | 0 | 91 |

(continued, next page)

Table 11.5. (continued)

| | Central America | | | | | |
|---|---|---|---|---|---|---|
| | 1982 | 1983 | 1984 | 1985 | 1986 | 1987 |
| Peas | 0 | 20 | 24 | 29 | 95 | 113 |
| Preparations | 11 | 46 | n.a. | n.a. | 20 | 3 |
| Total | 1262 | 1065 | 1471 | 2069 | 2356 | 3000 |
| Guatemala | | | | | | |
| Asparagus | 9 | 7 | n.a. | n.a. | 19 | 20 |
| Beans | 17 | 9 | 4 | 15 | 39 | 48 |
| Cucumbers | 2 | 3 | 73 | 44 | 62 | 48 |
| Garlic | 437 | 1 | 6 | 154 | 104 | 50 |
| Onions | 15 | 5 | n.a. | n.a. | 112 | 184 |
| Peas | 1589 | 2002 | 2962 | 2584 | 3463 | 4636 |
| Peppers | 0 | 5 | n.a. | n.a. | 0 | 10 |
| Squash | 0 | 1 | 14 | 0 | 0 | 51 |
| Preparations | 235 | 451 | 296 | 609 | 501 | 1447 |
| Total | 9075 | 8678 | 11091 | 11632 | 13540 | 20255 |
| Honduras | | | | | | |
| Tomatoes | n.a. | n.a. | n.a. | n.a. | 0 | 12 |
| Cucumbers | 28 | 99 | 143 | 263 | 189 | 201 |
| Peas | 0 | 1 | 61 | 13 | 57 | 164 |
| Squash | n.a. | n.a. | n.a. | n.a. | 2 | 9 |
| Preparations | 916 | 815 | 446 | 905 | 462 | 491 |
| Total | 983 | 932 | 706 | 1798 | 1852 | 2214 |
| Panama | | | | | | |
| Asparagus | 0 | 0 | n.a. | n.a. | 3 | 0 |
| Cucumbers | 0 | 0 | n.a. | n.a. | 0 | 2 |
| Peas | 0 | 5 | n.a. | n.a. | 0 | 1 |
| Squash | 0 | 0 | n.a. | n.a. | 18 | 228 |
| Preparations | 14 | 0 | n.a. | n.a. | 47 | 154 |
| Total | 17 | 5 | 156 | 1027 | 126 | 398 |

SOURCE: FATUS, various issues.
NOTE: n.a. = data not available.

(and many other countries) is its sugar policy. Due to artificially high producer and consumer prices for sugar in the United States, U.S. sugar production has increased at the same time demand for sugar in the United States has fallen. The U.S. price of sugar since 1982 has been kept high by adjusting imports through quotas. The sugar quota for the Dominican Republic, Guatemala, and Honduras in 1987 was less than 25% what its sugar imports were in 1981. In 1987 alone, sugar quotas for the Dominican Republic and Guatemala were reduced by 43 million and 34 million U.S. dollars, respectively. This reduction was greater than the total vegetable and preparations exports to the United States in that year. To make up the difference in sugar export value for the years 1981 and 1987, the Dominican Republic's vegetables and preparations exports would have had to increase 21-fold; during that period it increased about 80%. For Guatemala's vegetable exports to make up the difference, it would have had to increase over 12 times, but actually increased only one-fifth that amount.

The development and marketing of new and hardier nontraditional agricultural crops is a necessary ingredient to development for many of the CBERA countries. However, to entertain the hope of converting huge areas devoted to sugar production into profitable vegetable or fruit production for export is not realistic. It is similar to the idea of diversifying Oklahoma away from wheat into broccoli production. Economically, it will not happen. The Caribbean region is important to the United States for a variety of reasons. Although the intent of CBERA is commendable, without further concessions and preferential trade arrangements, it will not promote quick and sustained economic growth. The really important CBERA exports are exempt from duty-free status under CBERA or are constrained by other measures. True liberalization of sugar and textile imports entering the United States from the Caribbean would probably do more for economic growth and political stability than anything CBERA at present has to offer.

Investments by U.S. firms have also lagged behind expectations. This is due in part to poor infrastructure in the region, poor education, and corrupt or unstable governments. Lack of guarantees by our government has also discouraged investment. Often our government is unwilling or unable to give assurances that once a U.S. firm invests in producing in the region that the products can enter duty-free into the United States. What little investment has occurred has been recently discouraged. Ethanol exports as explained above will no longer be exempt from duty as was originally legislated in CBERA. Costa Rica's success in exporting cut flowers resulted in threats of duty.

## REFERENCES

Goodloe, C.A. "Interrelationships of Pacific Basin, Caribbean Basin, and World Markets for Agricultural Products." *Alternative Agricultural Enterprises for the Caribbean and Pacific Basins.* Edited by Dewayne Ingram, Gainesville, Fla.: Caribbean and Pacific Basin Advisory Groups, forthcoming.

Pelzman, J., and G.K. Schoepfle. "The Impact of the Caribbean Basin Economic Recovery Act on Caribbean Nations' Exports and Development." *Economic Development and Cultural Change* 36(1988):753-96.

Seale, J.L., Jr., C.G. Davis, and W.D. Mulkey. "Agricultural Imports and Exports in Selected Caribbean Basin Countries, 1975-1985." *Alternative Agricultural Enterprises for the Caribbean and Pacific Basins.* Edited by Dewayne Ingram, Gainesville, Fla.: Caribbean and Pacific Basin Advisory Groups, forthcoming.

U.S. Congress, House. Committee on Ways and Means. Subcommittee on Oversight. *Report on the Committee Delegation Mission to the Caribbean Basin and Recommendations to Improve the Effectiveness of the Caribbean Basin Initiative.* Washington, D.C.: U.S. Government Printing Office, 1987.

U.S. Department of Agriculture. Economic Research Service. *Foreign Agricultural Trade of the United States.* Various issues. Washington, D.C.: U.S. Government Printing Office, 1975-88.

U.S. International Trade Commission. *Annual Report of the Impact of the Caribbean Basin Economic Recovery Act on U.S. Industries and Consumers Second Report 1986.* USITC Publication 2024. Washington, D.C.: U.S. Government Printing Office, 1987.

U.S. International Trade Commission. *Harmonized Tariff Schedule of the United States.* USITC Publication 2030. Washington, D.C.: U.S. Government Printing Office, n.d.

# 12

# LABOR AND INTERNATIONAL TRADE IN VEGETABLES

Philip L. Martin and Gary Thompson
*University of California and University of Arizona*

## INTRODUCTION

There are two ways to think about labor and international trade in vegetables. The first is to ask how the availability of immigrant farmworkers to U.S. agriculture helps U.S. producers to compete with foreign producers, thus reducing U.S. imports of vegetables and increasing U.S. exports. The second approach is to ask how many jobs would be created abroad if foreign vegetable production expanded in response to liberalized U.S. trade policies or more expensive farm labor. This second approach usually asks how much expanded employment abroad would reduce illegal migration to the United States. This paper deals with both issues.

Most U.S. vegetable production is labor-intensive, meaning that 30 to 50% of the cost of producing lettuce, fresh tomatoes, and broccoli is the cost of hiring labor for planting, harvesting, and packing. Lettuce provides a typical example: the cost of production in the Salinas area of California is about $5 per carton of 24 heads, or 21 cents each, and labor represents about 40% or $2 of this cost, about 8 cents per head. Most vegetable harvest workers are paid piece-rate wages, so producer labor costs are constant and worker earnings fluctuate with yields and crop conditions; these piece rates enable most workers to earn $5 to $7 hourly in California.

Fresh vegetables are increasingly being produced and marketed like manufactured goods, that is, vegetable producers and marketers scour the world for the lowest-cost production area and then grow for the affluent consumers who are mostly in industrial societies. Affluence and consumer preferences have created a year-round demand for fresh vegetables, and improvements in production and transportation systems have enabled producers to satisfy this demand. The major labor questions are how U.S. and foreign producers will share the expanding market for U.S. fresh vegetables and what implications relative U.S. and foreign market shares have for the employment and wages of U.S. and foreign farmworkers and immigration patterns.

Historically, the United States encouraged the immigration of farmworkers and discouraged imports of fresh vegetables, or in more colorful language, the United States preferred Mexican tomato pickers to Mexican tomatoes. For a variety of reasons, off-season imports of fresh vegetables have been increasing, especially from Mexico, and net imports of fresh fruits and vegetables now account for about 10% of total U.S. consumption (Brown and Suarez, 1988, p. 13). The major issue addressed in this paper is how expanded fresh vegetable imports will affect U.S. and foreign farmworkers and the migration of farmworkers to the United States.

This paper has two parts. The first reviews briefly the U.S. farm labor market to explain why the availability and cost of labor was not an impediment to the recent expansion of the U.S. vegetable industry. The paper then turns to recently enacted immigration reforms, which should reduce the availability and increase the cost of immigrant farmworkers; however, fraud in the farmworkers legalization program has instead generated a harvest of confusion about the future farm workforce.

The second part of the paper discusses the relationship between trade in vegetables and labor migration. This question is normally posed as a trade-off between trade and migration, but the Mexican tomato example demonstrates that creating seasonal jobs in Mexico is not enough to keep potential U.S. migrants at home.

## THE U.S. FARM LABOR MARKET

There is no typical or average U.S. farm labor market; instead, there are thousands of microfarm labor markets which are obscured in published employment and wage data. For example, a quarterly U.S. Department of Agriculture (USDA) survey reported that the hourly wages of California workers who were paid under piece-rate systems averaged $6.77 in July 1988, but this wage is not that typically earned by workers in California's major vegetable, lettuce, or its second-ranked vegetable, tomatoes. Piece-rate lettuce workers in Salinas, on the average usually earn more than $7, while San Diego tomato pickers average the minimum wage or less. Despite the assumption that most U.S. vegetable workers are migrants whose migratory behavior should reduce or eliminate wage differences, such wage differences are common.

One reason why U.S. farm wages vary so much from commodity to commodity and region to region is because most U.S. farm labor market activity includes some type of unlawful behavior. In theory, the U.S. farm labor market is one of the country's most tightly regulated labor markets. Labor laws require, inter alia, the disclosure of wages and working conditions at the time of recruitment. If such a disclosure rule were applied to companies recruiting on college campuses, companies interviewing students would be prepared to discuss office sizes and parking spaces. However, in agriculture there are numerous gaps between theory and reality which make it hard to paint an average or overall picture of the farm labor market.

The central figure in farm labor markets is the first-level supervisor or labor contractor. These bilingual intermediaries match most vegetable workers with seasonal jobs; each intermediary creates his or her microfarm labor market. Generally, the number of duties assumed by the foreman or FLC intermediary is the best summary indicator of workforce characteristics and labor market structure. A foreman who must recruit in the United States and Mexico may also have to transport the workers to the farm, arrange for their housing and meals, supervise and pay them, and handle any work-related or personal emergencies. Such "patron" intermediaries usually have crews of vulnerable immigrant workers who accept whatever wages are offered, who do not question housing and transportation charges, and who do not know their rights under U.S. labor laws.

Intermediaries with fewer responsibilities tend to hire settled workers, i.e., workers who already have U.S. housing and who can arrange their own transportation. In these more formal labor markets, hiring is sometimes done at a central location on the basis of written applications, employees may be given handbooks which outline their rights and responsibilities, and in a few instances there is a union or other grievance mechanism to deal with inevitable workplace disputes. Labor markets to fit every stereotype can be found, from the abusive foreman who takes half of a worker's daily wages for substandard housing to relatively honest foremen who favor their friends and relatives to foremen who are required to follow well-established personnel practices and who supervise workers who know and exercise their rights.

Farm labor markets are believed to have deteriorated or become more unsatisfactory in the 1980s because the system of foremen and FLC's supervising vulnerable workers expanded. This expansion coincided with the surge in illegal immigration to the United States and a decline in union contracts. It is hard to determine cause and effect in this triangle of the expansion of intermediaries, more illegal workers, and fewer union contracts, but this triangle stabilized farm labor costs and encouraged labor-intensive agriculture to expand. For example, strawberries are one of the most labor-intensive commodities grown in California: in 1980 there were 11,000 acres; in 1988, there were about 17,000 acres, or 55% more.

There are three hallmarks of the 1980s farm labor market. First, farmworkers' employment is concentrated on a handful of large farms; there are 20,000 California crop farm employers, but in 1985 the largest 350 paid 43% of total crop wages. Second, an immigrant and vulnerable workforce sets the tone of the labor market; the availability of vulnerable immigrants determines whether wages will rise or whether foremen can charge for jobs, housing, or work equipment. Third, intermediaries are the glue which holds the farm labor market together. The labor market hallmarks of employment concentration, immigrant workers, and intermediaries are not new; they were identified in the 1880s as the features which permitted California to have large labor-intensive farms whose often absentee owners paid minimal attention to the workers who harvested their crops.

Farm labor's hallmarks are 100 years old, but there have been cyclical changes in farm labor market. Extreme worker surpluses in the 1930s prompted reforms, as did "labor shortages" after the bracero program was terminated in the mid-1960s. Union activity in the 1970s, new farm labor laws, and the extension of benefits such as unemployment insurance to farmworkers encouraged more domestic workers to stop migrating and more immigrant workers to settle in the United States, setting in motion events which led to more aggressive farmworkers and a second generation which did not do farmwork.

The irony of recent history is that farmworkers' settlement, which should have made fewer and more professional settled farmworkers available for seasonal jobs, instead encouraged the revival of the foreman/FLC and immigrant worker system to reverse the wage gains achieved by settled workers and to combat unions, pushing settled workers and their children out of agriculture. This influx of immigrants, an unchanged minimum wage, and stagnant unions lowered inflation-adjusted or real farm wages in the 1980s.

Looking ahead, there are several plausible farm labor market scenarios for the 1990s. Newly legalized farmworkers could settle in the United States and demand wage and benefit improvements, repeating the labor market patterns of the early 1970s in which settled workers were able to press for wage increases. Alternatively, temporary worker programs such as the H-2A or Replenishment Agricultural Workers programs could expand, setting the stage for a repeat of the 1950s when U.S. workers were driven by braceros into nonfarm jobs. Third, an end to illegal immigration might push up farm wages enough to encourage another 1960s wave of labor-saving mechanization. Finally, if immigration and labor laws are not enforced, the 1980s foreman/FLC and illegal immigrant worker system could continue into the 1990s.

The four scenarios–worker settlement and unions, temporary foreign workers driving U.S. workers into urban jobs, mechanization, and a continuation of the intermediary-illegal alien system–have recent historical precedents. No scenario is preordained; the scenario which unfolds in the 1980s depends primarily on governmental actions. Governmental decisions were the single most important determinant of past farm labor market evolution, and they will shape the trajectory of the 1990s farm labor market.

The reason government plays such a key role in the farm labor market is because government actions regulate the size and characteristics of the farm workforce, and the size and characteristics of the farm workforce affect the structure of agriculture, the importance of intermediaries and unions, and the nature of the farm labor market. It appears that California agriculture will have largely an immigrant and vulnerable workforce for the foreseeable future. These immigrants might be newly legalized Special Agricultural Workers, contractual temporary workers such as H-2As who are obliged to leave the United States after their contracts expire, RAWs who must do a certain amount of farmwork before they can become U.S. residents free to live and work where they wish or illegal alien workers.

The number and type of immigrant workers depends on government decisions. If the number of immigrant workers to do handwork is reduced, most observers do not expect U.S. agriculture to turn to American workers; instead, they predict a wave of mechanization and a sharp increase in fruit and vegetable imports. In this sense, the U.S. farm labor market has been pushed past the point of no return; a century of immigrant farmworkers has made most observers pessimistic about the prospects for reattracting U.S.-born workers into the seasonal farm workforce.

## IMMIGRATION REFORM

The Immigration Reform and Control Act of 1986 (IRCA) has spotlighted the 1985 farm workforce because workers who did 90 days of qualifying work in the 12 months ending May 1, 1986, may apply to become legal U.S. residents under the Special Agricultural Worker or SAW program. Immigration reform was expected to reduce the availability and increase the cost of immigrant farmworkers; however, widespread fraud in the SAW program has generated only a harvest of confusion about the future farm workforce.

In 1985, California farm employers reported 906,000 workers to Unemployment Insurance authorities. An analysis of a 5% sample of these workers indicates a 1985 farm payroll of $2.8 billion and 10.5 million weeks of farmwork. The "average" worker earned $3,100 for 12 weeks of work on a California farm, and three-fourths of all workers had just one farm job in

Table 12.1. Workers Employed on California Farms in 1985

| Characteristic | All Workers | SAS Workers |
|---|---|---|
| Workers | 905,860 | 806,000 |
| Farm Earnings ($) | 2.8 billion | 2.2 billion |
| Average ($) | 3,088 | 2,756 |
| Farm Weeks | 10.5 million | 8.7 million |
| Average | 11.6 | 10.8 |
| Less than $1,000 Workers | 373,780 (40%)[a] | 349,760(43%)[a] |
| Average Farm Earnings ($) | 255 | 250 |
| Average Farm Weeks | 2.3 | 2.2 |
| Migrant Workers[b] | 112,640 (12%) | 110,680 (14%) |
| Average Farm Earnings ($) | 3,408 | 3,346 |
| Average Farm Weeks | 17.2 | 17.1 |
| Seasonal Workers[b] | 252,400 (28%) | 224,660 (28%) |
| Average Farm Earnings ($) | 3,259 | 3,221 |
| Average Farm Weeks | 15.4 | 15.4 |
| $12,500 to $19,999 Workers | 108,700 (12%) | 45,540 (6%) |
| Average Farm Earnings ($) | 9,868 | 9,145 |
| Average Farm Weeks | 28.6 | 25.3 |
| $20,000 or More Workers | 50,620 (6%) | 41,780 (5%) |
| Average Farm Earnings ($) | 13,600 | 11,956 |
| Average Farm Weeks | 22.4 | 20.5 |

SOURCE: Special Tabulation of 1985 Quarterly Employer Reports to the California Employment Development Department, 1987.

[a]Percent of all farm or SAS workers; percentages do not sum to 100 percent because not all of the $1,000 to $12,500 workers satisfied the definitions of migrant (at least two farm jobs in two counties) or seasonal ($1,000 to $12,500 and 5 to 30 weeks of farmwork).

[b]There were 301,560 migrant and seasonal workers employed on California farms and 272,600 on SAS farms.

1986. About one-eighth of all workers were migrants, and one-quarter were seasonal workers. The UI data include all workers employed on California farms, including farmworkers, supervisors, clerks, and accountants; in UI claimant data, about two-thirds of all persons applying for UI benefits on the basis of work done on a California farm have farmworkers' occupations.

The UI data permit workers to be assigned to the primary commodities of their employers (an employer's primary commodity is that which generates 50% or more of farm sales). IRCA permits only illegal alien workers who did fieldwork in "seasonal agricultural services" (SAS) to apply for SAW legal status, and SAS have been defined to include most edible crops such as fruits and nuts, vegetables, mushrooms, grains, and a few nonedibles such as Christmas trees and flowers.

SAS employers reported 806,000 workers to UI authorities in 1985, and the characteristics of workers employed on SAS farms were very similar to those of all workers employed on California farms. SAS workers include a substantial fraction of low earners, and about one-eighth of the SAS workers

Table 12.2. California Workers Employed in Seasonal Agricultural Services in 1985

| Distribution by SAS Earnings | SAS Workers (1000) | % | SAS Earnings ($1000) | % | SAS Weeks (1000) | % | Avg. Earnings | Avg. Weeks |
|---|---|---|---|---|---|---|---|---|
| Less than $1,000 | 467 | 58 | 124,726 | 6 | 1,098 | 13 | 267 | 2.3 |
| 1,000 to 3,999 | 188 | 23 | 406,023 | 19 | 2,330 | 28 | 2,163 | 12.4 |
| 4,000 to 7,499 | 73 | 9 | 400,415 | 19 | 1,832 | 22 | 5,517 | 25.2 |
| 7,500 to 12,499 | 43 | 5 | 412,440 | 19 | 1,553 | 19 | 9,691 | 36.5 |
| 12,500 to 19,999 | 24 | 3 | 365,334 | 17 | 984 | 12 | 15,454 | 41.6 |
| More than 20,000 | 12 | 2 | 414,160 | 20 | 595 | 7 | 33,729 | 48.5 |
| Total | 806 | 100 | 2,123,137 | 100 | 8,392 | 100 | 2,634 | 10.4 |
| Distribution by SAS Weeks | | | | | | | | |
| 18 to 40 SAS Weeks | 115 | 14 | 706,179 | 33 | 3,103 | 37 | 6,142 | 27.0 |
| 3 to 40 SAS Weeks | 409 | 51 | 1,178,852 | 56 | 5,419 | 65 | 2,885 | 13.3 |
| 3 to 17 SAS Weeks | 294 | 36 | 472,673 | 22 | 2,315 | 28 | 1,610 | 7.9 |

SOURCE: Special tabulation of 1985 Quarterly Employer Reports to the California Employment Development Department, 1987. This table is based on a 5% random sample of the 1,199,920 workers (social security numbers) reported at least once by a California farm employer in 1985. Farm employers have SIC codes for crops (01), livestock (02), and selected ag services (071,072), and SAS workers had at least one job whose employer had an SIC code of 011, 0132, 0133, 0134, 016, 017, 018, 0191, 071, 0721, 0722, 0729.

are migrants, and one-quarter are seasonal workers.

There is a great deal of interest in how many of these SAS workers may qualify for the SAW legalization program, which requires illegal alien workers to have done at least 90 days of fieldwork in SAS commodities between May 1, 1985, and May 1, 1986. The UI data do not permit a direct translation of these qualifying requirements to estimate the number of qualifying workers. However, these requirements can be approximated with 1985 UI earnings and weeks data by assuming that January through April employment patterns were similar in 1985 and 1986.

One conversion is from the SAW 90-day work requirement to UI data on weeks worked. Since IRCA requires at least 90 days of qualifying work, the UI data can isolate persons who had at least 18 weeks of work with an SAS employer in 1985 (18 5-day weeks is 90 days). However, to avoid the inclusion of managers, clerks, and other nonfield workers, an upper limit on weeks worked should be established. USDA defines persons employed 150 or more days on one farm as regular or year-round workers; this analysis used 40 weeks as the upper limit because few fieldworkers are likely to find employment 5 days each week over extended periods. Most SAW applicants reportedly need to find employment during at least 25 weeks to obtain 90 days of SAS employment.

The workers employed 18 to 40 weeks by SAS employers are one universe

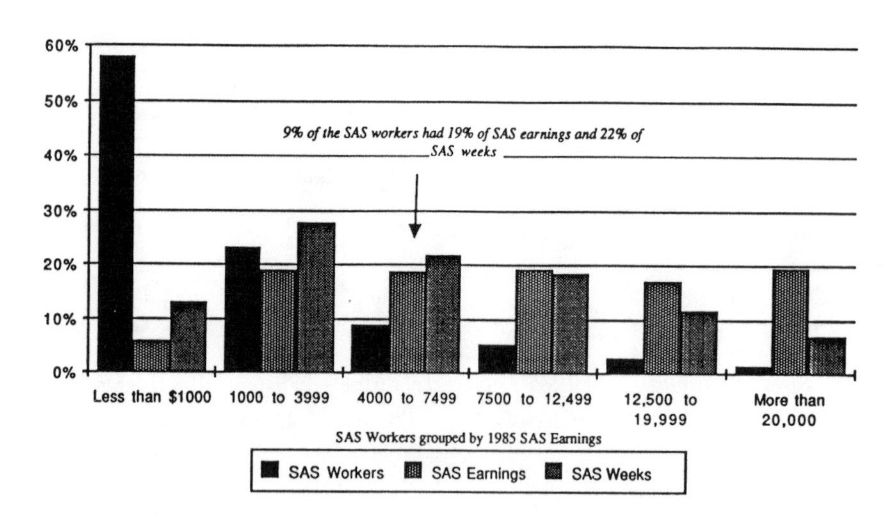


Figure 12.1. California SAS Workers Distributed by Their 1985 SAS Earnings

from which California SAW applicants can be drawn. About 115,000 workers were employed in SAS commodities for 18 to 40 weeks in 1985; they averaged $6,100 for 27 weeks of SAS work. Most of these 18- to 40-week SAS workers satisfy the seasonal farmworkers stereotype: three-quarters earned $1,000 to $7,500, and this subgroup averaged $4,400 for 25 weeks of SAS work. Only half of the 18- to 40-week SAS workers had more than one farm employer in 1985, suggesting that many SAW applicants will need to list just one employer to satisfy the 90-day work requirement. About two-thirds of these SAS workers satisfy the definition of seasonal workers, but only one-quarter satisfy the migrant definition.

Alternatively, the universe of SAW applicants can be approximated by isolating the workers who had qualifying earnings from SAS employers in 1985. It is hard to translate SAS earnings into days of farm work, especially because a day of farm work for the SAW program is defined as one hour or more. However, the SAW program permits applicants to estimate their days worked on the basis of earnings, e.g., some SAW applications state that the claimed 100 days of qualifying work was based on 1985 earnings of $4,000, an hourly wage of $5, and an average 8 hours of work per day.

Farmworkers are paid hourly and piece-rate wages. Hourly wages in California average $4 to $5, and piece-rate earnings are $5 to $7 per hour. Hourly workers usually work 8 or more hours daily, while piece-rate workers average 6 to 7 hours of work. Assuming a minimum $40 daily wage, SAS workers would have to earn at least $2,700 from SAS employers to qualify for SAW status. A rough approximation of the SAW universe based on earnings data might include one-half of the workers who earned $1,000-$3,999 from SAS employers in 1985 (93,840 workers), all of the $4,000-$7,499 (72,580), and one-half of the $7,500-$12,500 group (21,280), or a total of 187,700 potentially SAW-eligible workers.

The data reported by SAS employers to UI authorities in 1985 indicate that California's potential SAW universe ranges from 115,000 to 188,000 workers. Of course, not all of these SAW-eligible workers were illegal aliens: a September 1987 survey of farm employers found that employers believed 42% of their seasonal workers were illegal aliens who would apply for the SAW program (Martin and Luce). Applying this percentage to the UI data yields 48,000 to 78,000 SAW-eligible workers. A 1983 survey of field workers reported even fewer illegals; about 25% of the workers interviewed were clearly illegal aliens, 50% had green cards or permanent resident alien status (the validity of these green cards was not established), and 25% were U.S. citizens (Mines and Martin).

These UI and survey data indicate that the SAW program has been too successful. As of August 1988, about 433,000 SAW applications had been filed in California, 54% of all SAW applications. The SAW program is not expected to generate one million applicants nationwide before it ends on November 30, 1988. INS completed its reviews of about 267,000 SAW applications, and approved 80% of them; however, INS suspects fraud in about half of the pending open cases, so this approval rate may fall as more fraudulent applications are identified. However, even a 70% approval rate applied to one million SAW applications yields 700,000 SAWs, including 350,000 in California, more than most observers anticipated and more than would be expected if fewer than half of the 188,000 workers in the California UI data were illegal aliens. The number of SAWs is also surprisingly high because about 50,000 illegal alien farmworkers became legal U.S. residents under the general legalization program.

UI and survey data conflict with the SAW data; that is, either California farm employers reported only one-third of their 1985 employees, or two-thirds of the SAW applications are fraudulent. There may also be a combination of employer underreporting and SAW fraud. It should be emphasized that this conclusion is only suggestive because the UI data may underestimate the SAW-eligible universe if workers used several social security numbers (SSNs) in 1985 to accumulate SAS weeks and earnings, making the $1,000 earnings cutoff too strict. In one sample, about 20% of the SAW applicants had more than one SSN in 1985-86 (Martin, Luce, and Newsom). The SAW-eligible universe may also be larger than suggested by the UI data if SAW applications filed in California included qualifying work done in other states such as Oregon and Washington, although only 2% of the California SAW applications in one sample included any work done outside of California (ibid).

Persons who qualify for SAW status can become temporary and eventually permanent resident aliens who are free to live and work anywhere in the United States. Farm employers argued that many SAWs would quit doing farmwork as soon as they obtained legal status, so a Replenishment Agricultural Worker (RAW) program was included in IRCA which permits the entry of foreign workers who must do at least 90 days of farmwork annually. If a RAW worker does at least 90 days of farmwork for three years, the RAW worker may become a permanent resident alien in the United States free to live and work anywhere.

RAW workers can be admitted after October 1, 1989, if the Secretaries of Labor and Agriculture agree that there will be a shortage of workers available to work in "seasonal agricultural services." There are two alternative ways to calculate the maximum number of RAW workers which can be admitted. The simplest ceiling is 95% of the number of SAWs legalized minus the number of SAWs who did at least 15 days of SAS work in FY 1989 plus or minus the change in the number of H-2A workers in SAS crops.

The more complex method for determining the maximum number of RAWs to be admitted in FY 1989 requires solving a shortage equation which yields the number of additional man-days that SAS employers will need to do their FY 1990 farmwork, i.e., the projected gap between labor needs and labor availability in 1990. Solving this equation requires the USDA to determine the demand or need for workers, to determine how many man-days were worked by all workers in SAS in FY 1989, and then to project whether more or fewer man-days will be needed in FY 1990 because of changes in acreage, to avoid any crop losses which occurred in 1989, or to account for mechanization or changing personnel practices. DOL has the responsibility to determine the supply or availability of workers, that is, how many man-days are lost to SAS agriculture by worker exits, how many workers normally enter SAS each year, and how many more days of work would be available to SAS if employers improved wages, working conditions, or their recruitment efforts. The USDA and DOL make these calculations in man-days, and, if the USDA man-day need estimate exceeds the DOL availability estimate, this difference in man-days is divided by the average days worked in SAS and then becomes the ceiling for the RAW program.

An example might illustrate these calculations. Under the first alternative, 95% of 800,000 approved SAWs is 760,000; this number is then reduced by say, 600,000 SAWs who each did 15 or more days of SAS work in FY 1989 and by, say, a 10,000-worker increase in the H-2A program for a ceiling of 150,000 RAWs. Under the second procedure, calculations are in man-days. If the need-availability gap is 9 million man-days and the average days worked is 90, then the RAW ceiling is 100 thousand. In this example, the second calculation is controlling, that is, up to 100,000 RAWs could be admitted.

These calculations have heightened interest in farmworkers' turnover. Once again, employer-reported data to UI authorities can provide an indication of the retention of workers, earnings, and weeks worked from one year to the next. Beginning with the 806,000 workers (social security numbers) reported by California SAS employers in 1985, only 43% were also reported in 1986 and only 31% in 1984, 1985, and 1986. However, most of the workers who exited had low earnings and did relatively few weeks of work: the 43% of SAS workers reported in 1985 and 1986 earned 81% of SAS earnings in 1986 and did 77% of the weeks worked in 1986. This suggests a turnover rate in man-days of about 20%; that is, DOL might be expected to find that about 20% of the man-days worked in SAS in FY 1988 were performed by workers who did not do SAS work in FY 1989. Questions attached to the December Current Population Survey in the mid-1970s also indicate a 20% turnover rate.

Turnover rates do not vary greatly among the major subgroups of workers.

For example, the 1985-86 retention rate for workers earning $4,000 to $7,500 is 81%, but the earnings retention rate remains at 81%, suggesting that most of the exiting workers were very low earners. Similarly, migrant workers have a high earnings retention rate, although the earnings retention rate for seasonal and mixed farm and nonfarm workers was lower than average. SAWs should be similar to the $4,000 to $7,500 earnings group, reinforcing the suggestion that about 80% of them should remain working on farms.

UI data indicate that 906,000 individuals were employed on California farms sometime in 1985, but most of these workers did very few weeks of work on farms and had low farm earnings. This substantial group of low-earning workers and a much smaller group of high-earning workers affect farmworkers' averages, so that relatively few workers resemble the seasonal farmworker's stereotype of a worker employed about half the year who earns $4,000 to $6,000. The UI data do not identify the personal characteristics of different groups of workers, but they do suggest that it may be most useful to divide the workers employed on California farms into three major groups: very casual low earners (40% ), migrant, seasonal, and other middle-earning farmworkers (42% ), and regular or year-round workers (18%).

Employer-reported wages and weeks-worked data can also be used to estimate the number of workers eligible for the SAW legalization program. According to the 1985 UI data, from 115,000 to 188,000 California workers roughly satisfied SAW program requirements. However, not all of these workers were illegal aliens. The August 1988 number of SAW applications in California (433,000) exceeds the maximum estimate of eligible workers (188,000), suggesting that farmers underreported workers to UI authorities or that many SAW applications are fraudulent.

The RAW program may admit foreign workers after October 1, 1989 to replenish or replace newly legalized SAWs who quit doing farmwork. A complex two-part formula establishes the maximum number of RAW workers who can be admitted, but California UI data suggest that about 80% of all man-days are performed by workers who remained working on farms in 1985-86. If this retention rate remains stable in 1988-89, the maximum number of RAWs will be about 150,000.

## VEGETABLE TRADE AND LABOR MIGRATION

The 1980s surge in legal and illegal migration to the United States prompted immigration reforms to reduce illegal immigration in order to maintain public acceptance of legal immigrants. The Immigration Reform and Control Act of 1986 should reduce the flow of workers across the U.S. border and have its greatest effects abroad in Latin America, which is home to an estimated 50 to 70% of the legal and illegal immigrants who arrive in the United States each year. Several Latin American nations have argued that they prefer to export goods instead of people, and this section evaluates the emigration-reducing potential of expanded vegetable production in Mexico and Central America.

Despite decades of recruitment by U.S. employers and an emigration tradition, most citizens of Latin American nations never leave their country of birth. The emigrants from these nations in the United States include: legal immigrants who have obtained a green card that permits them to live and work in the United States; nonimmigrant aliens in the United States for a particular purpose such as tourism or education; and illegal aliens or undocumented workers who entered the United States illegally or who violated the terms of their legal entry. Mexicans loom large in all three categories, and Mexico frequently asserts that the United States increases migration incentives by employing undocumented Mexican workers and denying Mexican products ready access to U.S. markets.

Mexico already exports vegetables to the United States, and undocumented Mexicans are an important part of the American vegetable industry's work force, so vegetable agriculture is a sector that can illustrate how expanded trade might reduce illegal migration. Agriculture is an important employer throughout Latin America, but land policies; shortages of water, credit, and other critical inputs; and governmental pricing and marketing strategies have helped to keep many farmers small, inefficient, and poor. Most Latin American nations export noncompetitive agricultural products to the United States, such as bananas and coffee, but Mexico argues that it would export more competitive products such as tomatoes, peppers, and strawberries if U.S. farmers did not have easy access to Mexican workers and if the U.S. government did not erect trade barriers to such products.

The United States considers itself the world's free trader, and U.S. agriculture has traditionally been a prime beneficiary of attempts to reduce trade barriers. However, the recession and strong dollar of the early 1980s shifted more vegetable producers from the free trade grain sector toward the protectionist dairy and sugar sector. Labor-intensive U.S. agriculture in concentrated in Florida and California, and vegetable producers in these states argue that they cannot simultaneously mechanize, reform their labor markets, and fend off low-wage competition. Instead, most U.S. vegetable commodity groups advocate formal programs to admit temporary alien farmworkers for agricultural jobs.

One test of the trade versus migration debate is the fresh market tomato, a vegetable that has been the subject of debate for over 30 years. Tomatoes are Mexico's most valuable labor-intensive commodity export, and since 1970

Mexico has supplied one-third to two-thirds of the winter tomatoes consumed in the United States. Winter fresh tomatoes are produced by a handful of commercial farms in Southern Florida and Sinaloa in northwestern Mexico, and the Mexican producers allege that a U.S. tariff and "harassment" by Florida producers through a federal marketing order that sets size and quality standards reduce their production and hence employment.

Most cost-of-production studies conclude that Mexico can produce tomatoes cheaper than Florida, but the Mexican production cost advantage is reduced because of higher Mexican marketing costs. After a five-year tomato war in the late 1970s, Mexican producers began to act as Cournot duopolists: the Mexicans estimate total U.S. demand and Florida production, and then assume that the gap is theirs to fill. The Mexican tomato industry employs about 170,000 seasonal workers to produce and pack tomatoes for the U.S. market. If the Florida tomato industry shrank, would the illegal migration of workers to the United States be reduced? At first glance, it appears that Mexican producers would employ more workers to satisfy the U.S. winter tomato market, and this additional employment of workers might represent up to one-fourth of the 600,000 persons Mexico believed to be in the United States illegally on a seasonal basis in the mid-1980s. However, it must be remembered that Mexican tomato jobs are seasonal, that some of the Florida workers are (illegal) Haitians, and that rising production costs might raise tomato prices and reduce U.S. demand for tomatoes.

A more important caution reflects the composition of the Mexican tomato work force. According to the Mexican producers' organization, over 80% of the seasonal tomato workers are migrants from other areas of Mexico. Anecdotal evidence suggests that some of these workers migrate to Sinaloa for January through April tomato harvest and then continue northward for summer farmwork in the United States (Thompson, Anson, and Martin). An induced expansion of the Mexican tomato industry could increase internal Mexican migration and illegal border crossings. Such a result is not unprecedented: the "twin plants" or maquiladoras created in Mexico by U.S. companies in the mid-1960s to provide border area employment for ex-braceros drew Mexicans to the border. The maquiladoras employed young women–not the men who had been braceros–so men and older women in border areas searched for jobs in the United States. The lesson from these maquiladoras might also apply to an induced expansion of the tomato industry; an expansion might increase, rather than reduce, the illegal migration of workers.

Trade in commodities is a theoretical substitute for migration. However, after recruitment forges migration networks that link families and villages on two sides of an international border, the employer-recruiting pull of jobs becomes less important and the push of family ties and wage differences looms larger in migration decisions. It appears that four decades of recruitment and illegal immigration have forged such migration networks between the United States and Mexico, and it seems probable that similar migration networks are evolving to link the United States and Central American labor markets in the 1980s.

## THE TOMATO CASE

The most contentious agricultural imports from Mexico and Central America are fruits and vegetables that compete with U.S. production. Most of this trade competition occurs during the winter fresh vegetable season, when Florida and Mexico are producing tomatoes, cucumbers, and peppers for the U.S. market. In 1980, Mexico exported $303 million in fresh vegetables, supplying 20% of the fresh winter tomatoes and 30% of the tomatoes and 49% of the cucumbers.

Mexican fresh winter vegetables are a special case of considerable interest because Mexicans are more than half of the illegal aliens in the United States. These Mexicans are disproportionately from rural and agricultural areas, and the Mexican government has been most adamant in asserting that the United States must accept "either Mexican tomatoes or Mexican tomato pickers." Unlike non-Mexican illegal aliens, studies of undocumented workers who are or have been in the United States report that up to two-thirds of Mexican *indocumentados* have been farmworkers in Mexico, and that almost three-fourths came from the eight central Mexican states in which braceros were recruited for U.S. agriculture from 1942 through 1964. If the Mexican vegetable industry expands and the U.S. industry contracts, more of these undocumented workers should find jobs in Mexico and not migrate to the United States. Since tomatoes are the most important vegetable grown and exported from Mexico, this discussion centers on Mexican tomatoes.

The tomato has been at the center of the trade-versus-migration debate throughout the 1970s. The tomato is a fruit that was classified as a vegetable in 1893, when the U.S. Supreme Court ruled that "in the common language of the people" tomatoes are a vegetable and thus imported tomatoes were subject to the 10% tariff on fresh vegetables (but not fresh fruit) levied by the Tariff Act of 1883. Tomatoes are the most valuable vegetable grown in the United States, worth $1.1 billion in 1983. There are two types of tomatoes: the fresh market or salad tomato worth $600 million and produced primarily in Florida and the mechanically harvested processing tomato used to make ketchup and produced in California.

During the December through May winter season, Americans consume fresh tomatoes with a farm value of $165 million. The two major production areas are southern Florida and Sinaloa in northwestern Mexico. In both areas, tomato production is dominated by a handful of large farms that rely on hired managers and workers to produce and harvest the crop. These commercial producers often own their own packing sheds and transportation equipment. In Florida, 209 farms produced tomatoes in 1978, with the largest 13 farms accounting for 25% of Florida production and the largest 60 farms 67%. A 1980 study reported that the 10 largest vegetable farms in Mexico ranged from 700 to 3,500 acres each and accounted for half of Sinaloa's winter vegetable exports (Bredahl et al.).

In 1981-82, Florida producers shipped 12.6 million pounds of tomatoes and the United States imported 4.7 million pounds from Mexico. Tomatoes are 95% water, so transportation costs mean that Florida tomatoes dominate east of the Mississippi and Mexican tomatoes in the West.

Since 1966-67, the Mexican share of the U.S. tomato market twice peaked at over 65% in 1970 and again in 1977-78. The battle behind these roller coaster market shares helps to illustrate the complexity of untangling trade and migration linkages. It is hard to analyze comparative advantage precisely, and it is even more difficult to show that increasing tomato production in Mexico will diminish emigration pressures quickly.

The simplest way to analyze comparative advantage is to establish the cost of production in Mexico and Florida (Buckley et al.). Although cost-of-production studies have come to different conclusions, a typical review of production costs shows that Mexico can produce tomatoes cheaper than Florida, but this cost advantage is eroded by higher marketing costs and unit tariff of 1.5 to 2.1 cents per pounds. However, this tariff has remained fixed while the price of tomatoes rose, so the *ad valorem* equivalent was only 8% of the value of imported tomatoes in 1984.

Mexican wages averaged $5.65 daily in 1978-79, versus $26.88 in Florida, so Mexican producers rationally use more labor to produce each carton of tomatoes. Indeed, most Mexican tomato plants are individually staked and most Mexican tomatoes are not picked until they begin to change from green to red. Most Florida tomatoes are not staked and are picked green. In 1979, Mexican tomatoes required more than twice the labor to produce a 30-pound carton: 27 minutes in Mexico and 13 minutes per carton in Florida.

Wages and other input costs have risen faster in Mexico than in Florida, and rising Mexican production costs have been only partially offset by successive peso devaluations. Mexican wages (in peso terms) increased 400% between 1977 and 1984, versus 35% (in dollar terms) in Florida, but the dollar-equivalent daily wage in Mexico is about the same as the hourly wage in Florida. Wages are 53% of production costs in Mexico and 40% of production costs in Florida.

The Mexican government alleges that Florida producers manipulate the federal marketing order to discourage Mexican imports, thus restricting the size of the Mexican industry and its employment opportunities. In 1968, Florida growers successfully petitioned the USDA to increase the minimum size of vine-ripened tomatoes. This "tomato war" raged for five years, until U.S. importers of Mexican tomatoes persuaded the USDA to drop dual size standards for (Florida) green and (Mexican) vine-ripened tomatoes. In 1975, Florida producers petitioned unsuccessfully to substitute a 25-pound carton for the 30-pound carton in use, a change that would have forced adaptations in Mexican packing and transportation arrangements.

In 1978, Florida growers lodged a dumping complaint with the U.S. Treasury alleging that Mexican producers were offering tomatoes in the United States at prices below their production costs. The Florida producers eventually lost when the U.S. Court of International Trade ruled in 1984 that perishable commodities could sometimes be offered at below-production-cost prices, but Florida "harassment" encouraged the Mexican UNPH (Union Nacional de Productores de Hortalizas) to continue to "voluntarily" limit tomato acreage. Each Mexican producer in the state of Sinaloa must submit a tomato planting request to a regional growers association (CAADES), which coordinates tomato plantings and shipments through UNPH.

Producing more winter tomatoes exclusively in Mexico appears at first glance to promise significant new employment. However, several caveats are in order. First, tomato prices would probably rise (and U.S. consumption fall) as Sinaloa producers utilized additional land and water to triple production. Second, illegal Mexicans are an unknown but substantial fraction of the Florida tomato work force, so shifting production to Mexico could force the return of workers currently employed in the United States, reducing job opportunities for un- and underemployed Mexicans who have not yet emigrated. Third, most of the new jobs created in Mexico are low-wage and seasonal, and the characteristics of Mexican migration and wage differences might still encourage substantial illegal immigration. Finally, there may not be much increased employment in Mexico (and less employment for Mexicans in Florida) if Mexican tomato producers simply diverted production that now goes to domestic markets to the United States.

Most of the seasonal workers currently employed in the Mexican tomato industry are migrants from outside Sinaloa. According to CAADES, 80% of the seasonal tomato workers are from Oaxaca, Guerrero, Durango, and Guanajuato, and anecdotal evidence suggests that at least some of these internal Mexican migrants arrive in Sinaloa in January, work for three to four months, and then slip across the U.S. border in April and May. Although relatively few tomato workers can save enough in four months to pay coyote border-crossing fees of $300 to $600, the Mexican tomato industry does promote internal migration and bring at least some Mexicans closer to the border.

Instead of creating additional jobs and reducing emigrating pressures, a larger winter vegetable industry in Mexico may actually increase labor migration to the United States, much as the 1965 Border Industrialization Program (BIP). The BIP program began modestly, with 12 plants employing 3,000 workers before the end of 1965 (Grunwald). However, the Mexican government wanted the BIP program to expand, so in 1971 the constitutional ban on the foreign ownership of Mexican production facilities was subverted with a trusteeship law that permitted 100% foreign ownership and bonding costs were reduced for BIP plants in 1973. Border cities such as Juarez, Tijuana, and Mexicali developed industrial parks to attract BIP plants, known as Maquiladoras in Spanish. Mexico also permitted the Maquiladoras to move farther away from the border, where wages were lower; and by 1974 these mostly U.S.-owned twin plants employed 76,000 Mexican workers.

Lopez Portillo encouraged the further expansion of Maquiladoras despite the unemployment that followed layoffs and plant closings during the 1975 recession. In 1984, an estimated 130,000 Mexicans were employed in 600 Maquiladoras, an average 217 employees per plant. Most employees are young unmarried women who sew garments and assemble electronic components and collectively earn about $1 billion annually. Maquiladora wages must exceed local minimum wages by at least 50%, and this wage premium has helped to make border wages among the highest in Mexico.[1]

The BIP program generated jobs and earnings relatively quickly in Mexico, but did it reduce emigration pressures? The evidence suggests that BIP pulled more Mexicans from the interior to the border areas than could be employed in the Maquiladoras, and that the Maquiladora preference for young women did little to increase jobs for ex-braceros, who were mostly men. Maquiladora workforces are 60 to 90% young women, an employment pattern that generates cultural clashes when young women support their unemployed families. Mexican border cities have grown enough so that their populations and underemployment rates will increase without further internal immigration, even though some internal Mexican migration to the U.S. border area continues.

BIP plants did not generate their hoped for secondary employment multipliers because almost 99% of the inputs for BIP products are imported into Mexico and 30 to 75% of BIP wages are spent in the United States (this spending explains why mayors of U.S. border towns and cities are strong supporters of the BIP program despite U.S. unemployment rates of 30 and 40%). Despite the small job multipliers of BIP plants, the Mexican government's official policy is to further expand BIP employment. Indeed, the Banco de Mexico noted recently that BIP expansion in 1983 was hampered by labor shortages caused by Mexicans who were "attracted by higher wages in the U.S. [who] sought and found temporary jobs north of the border."

Such labor shortage complaints along the border weakens the argument that expanded vegetable production in northern Mexico will greatly diminish emigration pressures. Maquiladoras can or must pay higher wages to attract internal migrants who remain jobless but closer to the border. Even migrants who find jobs in Mexico may migrate across the U.S. border because their friends and relatives in the United States make them aware of wage differences of 8:1 for similar work.

Decades of Mexican migration to the United States have forged migration networks that transmit job and wage information from the United States to Mexico, making migration to the United States a family or community tradition (Mines). This migration tradition and the persisting wage differences suggest that job creation without wage increases may *not* automatically stop the flow of workers across the U.S. border and may paradoxically increase emigration. Such family and wage difference motivation for migration suggests that the U.S. and Mexican labor markets are already (partially) integrated, and only sharp reduction in wage differences will reduce migration incentives.

A final complication in this trade versus migration trade-off is that both Florida and Mexican producers have been adopting mechanical harvesters to pick green tomatoes that then ripen in storage and transit. Improvements in tomato varieties and mechanical harvesting may soon reduce the tomato harvest work force in both areas by 60 to 80% as growers fend off nascent union-organizing efforts. If vegetable production is mechanized in the United States and Mexico, the job-creating potential of expanded production diminishes.

Policymakers in the United States have preferred to import farmworkers rather than labor-intensive agricultural commodities from Mexico and other migrant sending countries. Although the effects of the most recent U.S. immigration reform have yet to be entirely felt, the agricultural guestworker provisions may provide producers of labor-intensive vegetables an ample supply of low wage labor. Other plausible scenarios resulting from the immigration reform include: (i) newly legalized farmworkers demanding higher wages and improved working conditions; (ii) a reduction of illegal immigration which may raise farm wages enough to encourage labor-saving mechanization; and (iii) the further expansion of farm labor contractor intermediaries if immigration and labor laws are not enforced. The actual scenario which unfolds will depend on the U.S. government's willingness to enforce the new immigration reform law.

Policies designed to promote job creation in migrant countries of origin through trade liberalization in labor-intensive commodity markets may be one alternative to guestworker programs which allow those same labor-intensive commodities to be produced in the United States. However, trade liberalization may not have such effects on migration. The tomato case demonstrates that if a substantial fraction of the newly employed workers in Mexico are internal migrants, some of whom continue migrating to the United States after their seasonal jobs end, then a trade-induced expansion of the Mexican tomato industry might increase illegal migration to the United States. Such an unintended increase in illegal migration brought about by the induced creation of jobs in Mexico has precedent in the Border Industrialization Program, which created jobs for young women but not for the former bracero workers who were the intended job recipients.

A drastic reduction in the current wage gap may be required to limit illegal migration from Mexico to the United States. Simply creating more jobs may not provide enough of an incentive to keep Mexican workers in Mexico when the U.S. wage is about eight times the Mexican wage for comparable work. Freer trade in labor-intensive agricultural commodities can provide seasonal jobs in Mexico and decrease the demand for illegal farmworkers for producing the same commodities in the United States but job creation does not close wage gaps. Instead of referring to trade versus migration in vegetable production, the relationship may be characterized more aptly as trade *and* migration.

## NOTES

[1] In August 1988, an Imperial Valley carrot grower sought approval to ship California-grown carrots to Mexico, have them packed in Mexico, and then reimport them into the United States Grimmway Farms, based in Lamont, CA, reported that other California growers are also exploring the possibility of packing California-grown produce in Mexico.

## REFERENCES

Bredahl, M.E., J.S. Hillman, R.A. Rothenberg, and N. Gutierrez. "Technical Change, Protectionism, and Market Structure: The Case of International Trade in Fresh Winter Vegetables," Univ. of Arizona, Agri. Experiment Station Tech. Bul. 249, August 1983.

Brown, Richard N., Jr., and Nydia R. Suarez. "Fresh Fruits and Vegetables:

Some Characteristics of the U.S. Market for Nine Selected Imports, 1975-85," Agriculture & Trade Analysis Division, USDA, ERS, 20005-4788, June 1988, p. 13.

Buckley, K.C., J.J. VanSickle, M.E. Bredahl, E. Belibasis, and N. Gutierrez. "Florida and Mexico Competition for the Winter Fresh Vegetable Market," USDA, ERS, Agri. Econ. Rpt. No. 556, June 1986.

Grunwald, J. "The Assembly Industry in Mexico," in *The Global Factory: Foreign Assembly in International Trade*, eds. J. Grunwald and K. Flamm, Washington, D.C.: The Brookings Institution, 1985.

Martin, Philip, and Stephanie Luce. "IRCA's Effects on Large Farms," *California Agriculture*, Vol. 42, No. 3, May-June 1988, pp. 26-28.

Martin, Philip, Stephanie Luce, and Nancy Newsom. "Researchers Present Mid-Term Review of SAW Program," *Ag Alert*, April 20, 1988, pp. AA8-9.

Mines, Richard. *The Evolution of Mexican Migration to the U.S.: A Case Study* (Berkeley: Giannini Foundation Information Report 82-1, 1982).

Mines, Richard, and Philip Martin. *A Profile of California Farmworkers* (Berkeley: Giannini Foundation Report 86-2, 1986).

Thompson, Gary. "Tariffs and Non-Tariff Barrier Impacts on Illegal Immigration: The U.S. Fresh Winter Tomato Market," *International Association of Agricultural Economists Occasional Paper No. 5.* Forthcoming.

Thompson, Gary, Ricardo Amon, and Philip Martin. "Agricultural Development and Emigration: Rhetoric and Reality," *International Migration Review*, Vol. 20, No. 3, Fall 1986, pp. 575-97.

Velez, M. "Estudio Socio-Economico de los Trabajadores Estacionales del Campo en el Valle de Culiacan: La Vivienda un Problem Especifico," *Analysis de la Situacion Agricola de Sinaloa*, Boletin Bimestral No. 93, Enero-Febrero:48-59.

# VEGETABLE TRADE ISSUES: DISCUSSION

Emilio Pagoulatos
*University of Connecticut*

This discussion includes comments on the three fine, preceding papers on issues in the vegetable trade.

The first set of comments, discussed by Vertrees and Mayer, focuses on GATT and the effect these negotiations have had on international trade. First, GATT has had several successes since its inception. For example, nominal tariffs have been reduced substantially from about 40% to 5% for most members of GATT. As a result, industrial trade has increased about 20 times over the life of GATT. In addition, the number of countries participating in the rounds has quadrupled from its original 23 members.

However, GATT has also had some failures, evidenced in the fact that some forms of protectionism are growing. For example, the United States, the European Community, and Japan are, together, spending almost $70 billion per year on farm subsidies. Many types of transparent and nontransparent non-tariff instruments of protection are increasing. One type of barrier that is rapidly growing is voluntary export restraints and other forms of voluntary import and export arrangements. Actually, these are not "voluntary" at all and have the same negative effects on international trade as other barriers; they, therefore, cannot be ignored in a discussion of international trade. In addition, GATT does not cover trade of services (which constitutes 30% of all trade), foreign direct investment, or intellectual property.

One encouraging note in international trade is the growth in multinational corporations. In the United States, over 50% of imports are handled by multinationals within their own subsidiaries. This is *not* trade in the textbook sense; i.e., it must be analyzed within the imperfect competition framework, but it contains the promise that the multinationals themselves may be the advocates for reducing trade barriers between countries, and that could be a positive trend in international trade.

One issue of concern related to the current Uruguay Round is that it is scheduled to end in 1990, but the United States will be implementing a new farm bill during the same year, and the two sets of policies may be out of phase. Domestic negotiations for the farm bill may have to be made before the international negotiations are completed.

The second set of comments is directed to the trade issues confronting the Caribbean Basin Initiative (CBI) discussed in the paper by Seale. When sugar imports began to decline, Caribbean countries joined in support of the CBI as a way to enhance international trade and open new export markets. However, the CBI faced problems from its inception. First, the CBI excluded many products, such as textiles, leather, and shoes, that had the potential for developing a significant export market and instead concentrated its efforts on products with little export potential, such as fresh vegetables. Second, and more importantly, at the time the CBI was introduced, the participating countries were already severely handicapped by a foreign debt problem. The implication of the debt crisis is that the CBI made few meaningful provisions for providing capital that would spur investment initiatives. The Foreign Development Insurance Corporation is one of the few instruments for providing investment initiatives but has not met its goal because it has also pursued protectionist objectives. Thus, no investment support has been given to any commodity that has the potential to be a competitive product in the U.S. marketplace.

The final set of comments is related to labor issues within the context of international trade discussed in the Martin and Thompson paper. First, the effects of the immigration law reforms have not been seen yet due to this year's drought. There was less work available for migrant workers resulting in a short-term surplus in farm labor. Second, labor migration and trade are generally considered to be substitutes, but they could also potentially be complements. The liberalization of trade could be enhanced by a concurrent liberalization in the movements of factors of production, including capital and labor movements. A true integration of the world economy could be achieved by this liberalization process and so, perhaps, it is worthwhile to consider including negotiations in labor migration in future GATT rounds.

# ISSUES IN VEGETABLE TRADE: DISCUSSION

Daniel A. Sumner
*U.S. Department of Agriculture*
*North Carolina State University*

The papers in this section illustrate the wide variety of policies and economic conditions that affect international trade in the vegetable industry. The papers deal with current international trade negotiations, the U.S. efforts for trade and aid in the Caribbean, and domestic hired farm labor issues in the United States.

## URUGUAY ROUND AND VEGETABLE TRADE

The Uruguay Round of multilateral trade negotiations is proceeding at the deliberate pace that characterizes a group with over 90 sovereign members. However, the Round has had a promising first 2 years and there remains a good chance that substantial liberalization of trade in farm commodities will result when this round is concluded in 1990.

Bringing agricultural trade policy under international rules is not an easy task nor a foregone conclusion. Over the last 40 years most agricultural trade has operated outside the rules of the General Agreement on Tariffs and Trade (GATT). This Uruguay Round will be a historic success if this pattern is reversed and countries agree to reduce or eliminate the use of the variety of barriers and subsidies now employed.

Achieving such an agreement is difficult but possible and to the clear benefit of all trading nations. However, for many commodity groups, domestic production subsidies are a major indirect trade barrier, and these subsidies are supplemented with import restrictions and explicit, international subsidized dumping. Powerful interests have and will resist reform. Vegetable trade has fewer of these sorts of barriers but is restricted nonetheless.

Among the most promising features of the Uruguay Round is the focus on harmonizing phytosanitary rules so that health and safety concerns are not used as backdoor trade barriers. There is a relatively high probability that countries will agree to use an international panel of experts to develop a harmonized set of standards for pesticide residue and related issues. This would go a long way towards reducing one of the significant bothersome problems for exporters.

A major potential benefit of regularizing the rules for agricultural trade is that this will help avoid the spread of *ad hoc* bilateral disputes. Under antidumping provisions, Section 22 procedures and Section 301 of the Trade Act of 1974 (and its amendments) the United States has often attacked trade practices of other countries. Other nations have their own mechanisms for attacking the policies of their own trade partners. These disputes disrupt normal patterns and reduce long-term investments because they make trade less secure. The U.S.-Mexico "Tomato War" and U.S.-Mexico/Canada potato conflicts are just two examples of the kind of disputes that might be avoided by clearer international trading rules for agriculture.

A useful innovation in the Uruguay Round has been the inclusion of LDC's in the GATT negotiation process and, especially, the emergence of the Cairnes group, which includes a number of Latin American agricultural exporters. The LDC participants in the GATT include a number of major vegetable traders and their interests are important for real multilateral liberalization. However, a key to furthering LDC interests in the GATT is for LDC importers to be willing to lower their own access barriers.

## THE CARIBBEAN BASIN INITIATIVE

The analysis of the CBI and vegetable trade suggests that this U.S. policy move was of mostly symbolic value. One may question why such an initiative was taken in the first place and why other nations supported it. The inclusion of countries seemed to be arbitrary and overall the benefits seem too small to be measurable, in aggregate, or for specific industries such as vegetables.

Relative to real multilateral liberalization, measures like the CBI are futile. For example, the United States has left the sugar program in place and has maintained the textile trade barriers. These trade barriers are much more significant than the CBI. The CBI should not have been expected to do much and that seems to have been its result; not much.

## FARM LABOR

Farm labor is important in the vegetable industry and, together with weather and technology, is a key to comparative advantage in vegetable trade. The U.S. policy for hired farm labor hinges on immigration policy as well as domestic rules. The 1986 changes in immigration rules are too recent to allow full evaluation, but they seem to have had relatively little impact so far. In this context, import of labor has been considered as a substitute for the import of farm commodities in the fruit and vegetable industries.

In their description of current conditions, Martin and Thompson suggest that, contrary to the worries of some in the industry, hired farm labor has not been a constraint to U.S. fruit and vegetable output in the year since the 1986 immigration reform was implemented. However, thinking of the supply and demand for hired farm labor in terms of shortages and constraints misses the point, especially for an industry that over a longer run faces a relatively elastic supply of hired labor. The significant issue for the comparative advantage of the U.S. vegetable industry is the wage at which U.S. growers can attract workers who are willing to perform demanding seasonal work with a minimum of supervision.

A completely open U.S. border for hired labor might lower labor input cost somewhat. However, costs of living in the United States, at basic standards considered socially acceptable, place a floor under farm labor costs even without competition from other sectors. Most labor *is* relatively mobile between sectors and wages in the rest of the U.S. economy. This means that hired farm labor costs in the Uunited States will be well above those in Latin America. U.S. growers have relied on technology and management to compete with imports.

A further response of U.S. firms to international competition is to move some of their most labor intensive operations to other nations. This is a long established practice in the electronics industry and we have heard significant evidence that it is a growing practice in the vegetable industry. Whether through joint ventures or other forms of investment, there seems to be significant potential gain for both U.S. firms and Latin American economies from expanding such activities. Shipping of vegetables may be an attractive alternative to the emigration of the labor force for a number of countries. U.S. firms can provide some investment and also facilitate successful marketing of produce in the United States.

## SUMMARY

Overall, with trade liberalization for agricultural commodities and for investments and services, the integration of the economies of the United States and its neighbors offers real opportunities for the vegetable industry.

APPENDIX

# SUMMARY AND SYNTHESIS OF A WORKSHOP ON VEGETABLE MARKETS IN THE WESTERN HEMISPHERE

Leo C. Polopolus
*University of Florida*

## INTRODUCTION

This book grew out of a workshop held on September 6-7, 1988 at Rutgers University. The purpose of this appendix is to summarize the core of ideas and issues that transpired then. Note that the institutional affiliation of some authors has changed since then.

The Rutgers University Workshop, "Markets for Vegetables in the Western Hemisphere: Trends, Policies, and Linkages," was somewhat extraordinary on several counts. First, it had a balanced group of experts representing academia, government, and private industry. Secondly, even though the number of participants was relatively small, there was broad geographic representation from the Western Hemisphere, with registrants from the Western, Southern, Midwestern, and Northeastern parts of the United States as well as representatives from Mexico, Central America, and South America. Thirdly, and most importantly, each participant brought forth a specialized component of information regarding vegetable production, marketing, and trade that resulted in a useful final product of information. The only possible criticism of the composition of the work group was a scarcity of U.S. vegetable producers.

The two-day meeting on the Rutgers University campus was organized into five plenary sessions, plus introductory remarks by the New Jersey Secretary of Agriculture and the Coorganizer of the Workshop. The major sessions dealt with the United States Vegetable Market, Policies and Institutions, Trade Linkages in the Western Hemisphere, Issues in Vegetable Trade, and a Policy and Research Forum in Vegetable Trade.

New Jersey Secretary of Agriculture Arthur Brown opened the workshop with a brief yet interesting narration of the very successful "Jersey Fresh" program to promote perishable agricultural products marketed in the Northeast region from New Jersey. Secretary Brown also discussed some of the future problems for agriculture in New Jersey, including problems of water supply and urban/rural conflicts. He noted the opportunities in the area of international trade for agricultural products.

Dr. Rigoberto Lopez of Rutgers University, Coorganizer of the Workshop, provided the charge for the two-day meeting. Dr. Lopez stated that the two challenges of the workshop were to: (1) increase the level of understanding on trade policies and linkages involving vegetables; and (2) assess potential benefits and strategies for trade in fresh and processed vegetables in the Western Hemisphere.

## THE U.S. VEGETABLE MARKET

The U.S. vegetable market was analyzed from both the demand and supply aspects. Shannon Hamm, Agricultural Economist with the Economic Research Service, United States Department of Agriculture, outlined the factors affecting the supply of vegetables in the U.S. market. Shifts are continually occurring, with allocations of supplies to the fresh and processing outlets increasing over time, while the allocation to the canning outlet decreased in recent years. California now accounts for a dominant share of processed vegetable production. There has been a dramatic recent growth in supplies of specialty vegetables, particularly specialty lettuce and ethnic vegetables. The value of imported vegetables has increased in recent years. There is considerable competitive pressure in traditional vegetable supply areas in the United States, particularly for frozen vegetables, because of problems with wage costs, free trade, and other factors.

Dr. Vickie McCracken of Washington State University presented an overview of the demand for vegetables in the United States. The dramatic increase in per capita vegetable consumption was analyzed from the perspective of changes internal *and* external to the industry. The away-from-home food market has contributed to the increased demand. The increased per capita consumption has been particularly noticeable for fresh and frozen vegetables at fast-food restaurants. Fresh broccoli and fresh cauliflower consumption have increased dramatically, as has the per capita consumption of frozen potatoes. Empirical regression analyses of household consumption suggest that the vegetable industry will benefit from an aging population. Consumption patterns also reveal increased interest in variety of vegetables consumed.

Empirical investigations are hampered by a lack of timely data. There is also need for more consistent data, data for the increasing number of vegetables marketed, and data regarding consumer attitudes regarding various vegetable products.

Discussants for the two papers on the U.S. vegetable market were Dr. Glenn Zepp, Agricultural Economist with ERS/USDA, and Dr. John Brooker of the University of Tennessee. Dr. Zepp noted that vegetable supplies are affected by changes in transportation, storage, production, and harvesting technologies. Supplies are also affected by changing price relationships and government subsidies. Vegetable demand can be changed from processing technologies as well as shifts in external factors such as income, household size, and age of vegetable consumers. Dr. Brooker raised the issue of who is in control of our diet? Is it influenced more by advertising or by product availability? He noted that costs of production studies are generally lacking to determine a region's competitive position in vegetables. Also, there is a lack of data for minor vegetable crops.

## POLICIES AND INSTITUTIONS

Drs. Thomas Pierson and John Allen of Michigan State University started off this session with an exciting multimedia presentation focused on the marketing dimensions of changes in the produce industry in the United States and Canada. The following market segments were identified and explained: appearance, consistency, convenience, freshness, excitement, nutrition, quality, safety, taste, understanding, uniqueness, variety, and price/value. A key point was that produce purchases are based on overall *value* rather than price alone. The marketing challenge is to heighten consumer value from perceptions of fresh fruits and vegetables. Consumer value perceptions are defined as perceived benefits in relation to price of product. Market participants need to move away from a commodity approach to a marketing orientation. For the marketing approach, the key is to determine the wants, needs, and perceptions of consumers. Firms then need to develop and position products and services to match consumer wants and needs.

Dr. Leo Polopolus of the University of Florida provided a comprehensive outline of the role of public policies in vegetable production and marketing. Public intervention is called upon because voluntary approaches to problems with market competition, health hazards, safety violations, disorderly marketing, and environmental pollution break down. The following public policies affecting the vegetable sector were briefly discussed: orderly marketing (market information and marketing orders), fair trade and competition (general economic regulations and specialized regulations for agricultural industries), food safety and health, international trade, agricultural labor, transportation, environmental quality, and nonfederal or state and local policies. The high priority public policy concerns for vegetables in the Western Hemisphere include food safety, minimum quality standards, and improved market information.

Dr. Ken Shwedel of Estudios Economicos Banamex in Mexico presented a paper on the policies and institutions in vegetable marketing from the Mexican perspective. Two introductory points are that vegetables are not considered basic food items in Mexico and that the institutional environment is important to systems behavior. Food policy in Mexico favors consumers relative to producers. Price controls, for example, are imposed on processed vegetables, but not on fresh vegetables. Some of Mexico's problems regarding vegetables include the following:

- Unfair marketing practices (e.g., brokers take advantage of growers)
- Producer organizations
- Quality control
- Volume of output too large or market windows too small
- Tax policy
- U.S. policies, including nontariff barriers

The discussants of the papers on policies and institutions were Dr. Enrique Figueroa of Cornell University and Charles Brader of the Agricultural Marketing Service of USDA. Dr. Figueroa noted that farm level demand elasticities were different from elasticities at the retail level. Maybe an elasticity of convenience could be computed. Another point was that market regulations of the processing sector have impacts on fresh vegetable markets. The list of public policies for vegetables should also include educational policies. Research and teaching resources dealing with vegetables at Land Grant universities are inadequate in relation to their economic importance in the American food system. Mr. Brader elaborated upon the marketing information and grading systems for vegetables by AMS/USDA. An important source of market support for potatoes, peas, tomatoes, beans, and sweet corn comes from Section 32 funds. Section 32 funds are derived from import duties and up to 30% of these funds are made available for government purchases of nonbasic commodities, such as vegetable products. Western European countries in the Organization for Economic Cooperation and Development (OECD) have developed minimum quality standards for their fruits and vegetables sold for import and export. The United States does *not* have similar standards.

## TRADE LINKAGES IN THE WESTERN HEMISPHERE

Four major papers were presented at this session dealing with various aspects of international trade in vegetables. An interesting paper by Dr. Roberta Cook of the University of California at Davis revealed the recent switch from competition to coordination in vegetable trade between California and Mexico. This has been due in part to the flight of many California growers into Mexico. Also, many California growers have extended their operations into Mexico so as to lengthen their marketing season and broaden their product mix. New vegetable production areas in Mexico have also been developed, such as Baja, California, and a region south of Yuma, Arizona.

Dr. Amy Sparks of the Economic Research Service of the USDA presented a summary of her research on a simultaneous econometric model of world vegetable trade with emphasis on trade flows and barriers to trade. A key point is that international trade of fresh vegetables more than quadrupled between 1962 and 1982. The primary trading regions are Latin America, the United States, the European Economic Community (EEC), the Middle East, the Far East, Africa, and the non-EEC Western European nations. One of the data limitations of the study involved the problem of excessive product aggregation.

The paper by Drs. Rigoberto Lopez of Rutgers University and Emilio Pagoulatos of the University of Connecticut attempted to develop a conceptual analysis of vegetable trade. Actually, the growth in international trade in fresh vegetables has been twice the growth in vegetable production in recent years. The European Economic Community is the largest market for fresh vegetables and the Community is also the largest importer of processed vegetables. Lopez and Pagoulatos calculated export propensities, import penetration, and net trade positions. In the Western Hemisphere, natural resources are *not* constraints to vegetable supplies, although credit availability and technology may be constraints. Tariffs are not really a major barrier to vegetable trade in the Hemisphere. Nontariff barriers, particularly related to pesticides, are considerably more significant deterrents to vegetable trade. A diagram was developed to analyze the impact of pesticides on trade.

Rodolfo Quiros of IICA in Central America discussed some of the knotty policy and research issues involved with strengthening trade linkages in fresh horticultural product markets in the Caribbean Basin. Historically, these markets were developed for off-season trade into the United States. The vegetable market is not, however, deemed to be a big enough market to significantly increase the gross national products of Central American countries. Six major issues were identified that influence the vegetable market:

Macroeconomic policies

- Institutional support or lack thereof (bureaucracy and rigidities of legal/operational framework)
- Implications of the debt crises
- Lack of comparative advantage
- Market windows not stable for fresh horticultural markets
- Tariff and nontariff barriers

While horticultural crops are an option in Latin America, they do not appear to be a substitute for domestic crops or traditional export crops.

Comments to the papers on trade linkages were presented by Dr. Daniel Sumner of the U.S. Council of Economic Advisers and Dr. Timothy Taylor of the University of Florida. Dr. Sumner indicated the need to better understand demand and supply elasticities. The derived demand for vegetables at the farm and wholesale levels may differ substantially from the demand at retail level because of the increased role of service and convenience factors at the retail level. In contrast with highly aggregative trade models, Dr. Taylor suggested that the economic and political forces driving fresh vegetable trade can be more clearly discerned with analyses of individual commodities for specific countries. Dr. Taylor also identified quality (grade and size) standards and food safety issues as the two most crucial noneconomic barriers to vegetable trade. Dr. Taylor also suggested that foreign producers may need to develop close business relationships with multinational corporations to penetrate foreign markets because of country-to-country differences in quality standards, container specifications, quarantine restrictions, and other market peculiarities.

## ISSUES IN VEGETABLE TRADE

This session of the workshop delved into three special topics of considerable importance to future vegetable trade in the Hemisphere–GATT negotiations, the CBI, and labor migration. The paper by Dr. Leo Mayer, Assistant Secretary, and Dr. James Vertrees, Economist with the USDA, updated the status of the Uruguay Round of GATT negotiations, with implications for horticultural products. The Uruguay Round is expected to concentrate upon trade and nontariff barriers that are linked to domestic policies and programs. For vegetables, the GATT negotiations are expected to focus upon problems of market access and phytosanitary issues. Both of these areas contribute to substantial barriers to international trade in vegetable products.

Dr. James Seale of the University of Florida discussed vegetable trade and the Caribbean Basin Initiative. Dr. Seale concluded that among the various CBI countries, those in Central America have benefited most from the program (compared with the Caribbean Island nations). Vegetable imports from CBI countries into the United States have increased from Guatemala (peas), Costa Rica (processed vegetables), Jamaica (tomatoes), and for a short time cucumbers from several CBI countries. The success for the Dominican Republic and Guatemala in increasing vegetable sales in the U.S. market *has not* been offset with the tremendous loss in sugar sales to the U.S. market because of sharply reduced sugar quotas.

The paper by Dr. Philip Martin of the University of California at Davis on labor and international trade in vegetables concentrated upon the immigration issue. Dr. Martin concluded that the availability of immigrant farm workers into the United States, mostly from this Hemisphere, permitted the vegetable industry to expand at relatively constant cost, particularly for California and the Southwest. The recently enacted Immigration Reform Act was discussed in terms of legalizing large numbers of previously illegal farm workers. Many of the immigrant workers given Seasonal Agricultural Worker (SAW) protection for eventual U.S. citizenship were fraudulent applicants and never bona fide agricultural workers. Overall, labor has not been a constraint to the growth of the U.S. vegetable industry.

According to Dr. Emilio Pagoulatos of the University of Connecticut, the GATT rounds have provided both successes and failures. U.S. trade legislation and U.S. farm laws both tend to run counter to trade liberalization. Multinationals now account for 50% of U.S. imports. It is unclear just how labor migration patterns will be affected by GATT negotiations. Dr. Sumner of the U.S. Council of Economic Advisers noted that U.S. farmers were not adequately represented at the workshop. He noted that the CBI is somewhat irrelevant and certainly no panacea. However, Dr. Sumner views the U.S.-Canadian trade agreement as being a more significant program for mutual benefit. GATT has not really examined vegetable markets to any degree.

## FORUM ON VEGETABLE TRADE

The final session of the workshop included panel members from various locations and organizations in the Western Hemisphere. Panelists included New Jersey Secretary of Agriculture Arthur Brown, Economist Rodolfo Quiros of IICA of Costa Rica, Dr. Andrew Schmitz of the University of California at Berkeley, James Vertrees of the U.S. Department of Agriculture, Benjamin Ghitis, Director General of Ritecsa, grower-shipper from Peru, and John Brealey, President of a farm firm in Costa Rica.

Benjamin Ghitis discussed problems of a grower-shipper of vegetables seeking marketing outlets in the United States and other foreign markets.

His firm has developed the production technology for asparagus and other products but is having problems with transportation services. He recommends having an American adviser and developing a joint venture with a foreign firm for penetration of foreign markets.

John Brealey, a grower-shipper in Costa Rica, reported that it was relatively easy to export melons to the U.S. market but found it difficult to collect the revenue from goods sold in the United States. He questioned the promotion by USAID of similar vegetable products (strawberries) for many countries. Mr. Brealey also stressed the need to tie his operations to U.S. firms via joint ventures, plus the need for research aimed at local conditions. There is also no substitute for dealing with reliable suppliers, buyers, and distributors. The multiplicity of small farms in Central America creates additional problems for export marketing. Finally, there is a serious need to determine market windows for vegetables in non-U.S. markets.

Secretary Brown discussed the potential importance of developing agricultural markets with increased value added. Niche marketing is also important. Auction markets have been developed in New Jersey for parsley. Research investments are crucial for future growth and development of horticultural industries. Harvesting and postharvest handling technologies loom as serious impediments to future success. Grading and packing quality must also be improved.

Dr. Andrew Schmitz challenged the agricultural economics profession to develop a better understanding of how products are really marketed. The roles of people and institutions require closer examination. There is a need to increase the number of case studies of marketing agricultural products, as well as to analyze international capital flows and labor migration across national boundaries.

# INDEX